THE DISAPPEARING RUSSIAN FOREST

A Dilemma in Soviet Resource Management

BRENTON M. BARR
University of Calgary

&

KATHLEEN E. BRADEN
Seattle Pacific University

ROWMAN & LITTLEFIELD

HUTCHINSON
LONDON

ROWMAN & LITTLEFIELD

Published in the United States of America in 1988
by Rowman & Littlefield, Publishers
(a division of Littlefield, Adams & Company)
81 Adams Drive, Totowa, New Jersey 07512

First published in Great Britain 1988
by Hutchinson Education
An imprint of Century Hutchinson Ltd
62-65 Chandos Place, London WC2N 4NW
ISBN 0 09 182267 X

Library of Congress Cataloging-in-Publication Data

Barr, Brenton M.
   The disappearing Russian forest.

   1. Forests and forestry—Soviet Union.
2. Forest management⸌—Soviet Union.   3. Forest
products industry—Soviet Union.   I. Braden, Kathleen E.
II. Title.
SD207.B37   1987   333.75′0947   87-16565
ISBN 0-8476-7402-9

90 89 88
5 4 3 2 1

Printed in the United States of America

This book is dedicated to Carol Ann Braden, who was a small flower in the forest, and to Peggy Melane Barr, who facilitated the project's completion

Contents

Illustrations

Tables

Preface

We undertook this book as our contribution to the continuing attempt by scholars outside the USSR to understand the resources of that vast and fascinating land. The forest industries have tended to be the "poor cousin" of the USSR, both in terms of attention from Western researchers and in levels of investment allocated by decision makers. The dearth of material outside the Russian language on the topic of forest industries, however, creates a gap in our understanding of how the Soviet Union makes use of a very important resource.

We specifically sought to provide (1) an economic-geographic analysis which we hope will be of value to those in academe who study the USSR, (2) information to business people about a country which makes up a very large portion of the world's forest industry, and (3) ourselves with a compendium of rather disparate material collected over the years by two people who share not only respect for what the forest can provide to the world's consumers, but also a love for the trees left in place.

Although nonRussian material has been scarce on this topic, the authors wish to acknowledge the work of others in the West, notably Jaroslavl Holowacz and Jan Solecki in Canada, Jarmo Eronen in Finland, and Peter Blandon in the United Kingdom. Subsequent to the completion of the manuscript, the authors have obtained copies of the recent study of Soviet eastern forest resources and forest-product exports to Japan by Fenton and Maplesden (1986), and of the new two-volume Soviet forestry encyclopedia edited by Anuchin *et al.* (1985). These two works are important new contributions to the literature. We also appreciate the contribution of scholars such as Leslie Dienes, Philip Pryde, Judith Thornton and the late Ted Shabad in helping us to understand the various dimensions of the overall issues that affect Soviet forest resources.

The quality of the debate over management of forest resources in the USSR bears witness to the fine array of Soviet scholars who specialize in this field. Influence of Soviet scholars with whom the authors consulted in the past should be acknowledged: V. V. Glotov in Moscow at the All-Union Institute for Raising the Qualifications of Leading Workers and Specialists of Forest and Woodworking Industries; A. P. Petrov, at the Kirov Forestry Academy in Leningrad; and I. N. Voyevoda at the Institute of Economics and Organization of Industrial Production, USSR Academy of Sciences in Novosibirsk.

The authors acknowledge the assistance of Paul Lee, Janet Johnston, Terry Seng, and Martyn Hitchcock at Rowman and Littlefield in preparation of the manuscript. While the authors share responsibility for the content of the book, Barr was primary author of Chapters 1, 3, 4, and 5, and Braden of Chapters 6, 7, 8, and 9. Chapter 2 was written jointly. Braden and Barr jointly performed editing tasks, and Barr handled the herculean job of technical production (noted gratefully by Braden!) on the Apple Macintosh and Apple Laserwriter. All errors are the sole responsibility of the authors.

Finally, we thank our families for their warm and unflagging support and patience during the preparation of this book.

Brenton Barr
Calgary, Alberta

Kathleen Braden
Seattle, Washington

May, 1987

THE DISAPPEARING RUSSIAN FOREST
A DILEMMA
IN SOVIET RESOURCE MANAGEMENT

1
Some Basic Questions

SOVIET FORESTS IN RUSSIAN PERSPECTIVE

How valuable a resource are the forests of the USSR? How efficiently are they utilized by Soviet decision makers? The USSR possesses approximately one-third of the world's coniferous forest, as well as a significant share of its deciduous species. Russians have traditionally considered their forests to be inexhaustible. Most Soviet and western analyses of this country's forests and wood-processing industries focus on problems of species, product mix, regional siting of processing plants, development of transportation systems, and costs associated with movement of raw materials and products. Processing is deemed to be moving eastward as accessible forests are exhausted. Increasingly, the vast eastern forests are assumed to be economic for harvesting with the construction of railways such as the BAM (Baykal-Amur Mainline) and the AYAM (Amur-Yakutsk Mainline), and observers continue to remark on technological progress in substituting various forms of wood waste for roundwood by the wood-processing industries.

On the other hand, many analysts observe that the Soviet wood-processing industries do not receive priority investment by the country's managers, and that the supply of processed goods (notably paper) is inadequate. Nevertheless, roundwood and relatively unprocessed timber comprise a significant share of Soviet exports, particularly to hard-currency markets. In turn, Soviet wood-processing is an important consumer of imported technology, particularly from western European countries like Finland, Sweden, Austria, and the Federal Republic of Germany. The timber and wood-processing industries of the USSR, therefore, appear to be underdeveloped in terms of the country's potential but are too important to be completely neglected in helping to meet the country's basic demand for various industrial and consumer products. Compared to all other resource-processing sectors of the Soviet economy, however, forest products are of small significance. If they did not comprise such a large extent of the Soviet ecumene and figure so significantly in extensive spatial development, particularly in peripheral regions, their interest to economic geographers would be minor.

Soviet forests, however, play a broad role in numerous aspects of Soviet society other than providing raw materials for foreign trade and domestic consumption. Comprising nearly half the country's land area, Soviet forests affect the quality of the environment in a complex series of ecological interactions with other physical phenomena and in providing life-sustaining and recreational properties for human beings.

A small but important part of the Soviet growing stock is utilized as fuel and domestic building materials by rural inhabitants, particularly on collective and state farms and in remote regions. Approximately one-quarter of the timber harvested annually from all sources is used in this manner. Although wood accounts for approximately 1 percent of the Soviet energy balance, it is vital for the personal fuel needs of at least nearly half of the country's 96 million rural inhabitants, who in 1985 lived in the RSFSR (39 million), Belorussia (3.8 million) and the Baltic republics (2.4 million), areas comprising most of the USSR's actual growing stock.

The basic interest of geographers is in the spatial variation of Soviet forests and wood-processing. Soviet forests are concentrated in the RSFSR; over three-quarters of the USSR's growing stock under central state forest management is found east of the Urals, where only 11 percent of the Soviet population resides (Figure 1.1). Two-fifths of the Soviet population live in the European-Uralian zone of the RSFSR, with nearly one-fifth of the centrally administered growing stock. The entire USSR European-Uralian zone accounts for nearly 23 percent of this growing stock but 73 percent of the country's population. When the five republics of Central Asia are added to these shares, the total area outside of Western Siberia, Eastern Siberia, and the Far East accounts for 23.1 percent of this growing stock but 89 percent of the country's population.

The spatial imbalance between the forest resource and the consumer (as represented by population size) in Figure 1.1 summarizes the basic geographical dilemma facing Soviet industrial managers in the timber and wood-processing sectors. The effect of this imbalance is magnified when foreign markets are served, particularly those of the client states in Eastern Europe and of the market economies further west. The markets of the Pacific basin, particularly Japan, in theory, should benefit from the natural locational advantages of Eastern Siberia and the Soviet Far East. These Soviet regions, however, lack some appropriate infrastructure, are short of capital and labor, have an adverse species composition in many of their forests (especially the share of larch), and face intense regional market competition from North American Pacific and Southsea forests. Furthermore, most of Eastern Siberia is as far from Moscow, for example, as from ports on the Pacific Ocean, and expensive, long-haul movement of timber and wood products is incurred before many markets are reached in either direction. Although construction of new railways such as the BAM and the AYAM will enhance the accessibility of these regions, to date they have had little impact on the timber and wood-products sectors of Eastern Siberia and the Far East.

Spatial analysts usually invoke the "Baykal Meridian" to suggest that many commodities such as grain, coal, iron ore, copper, and timber produced east of Lake Baykal incur unacceptable increases in delivered value when shipped by rail to Soviet European domestic and foreign markets. Similarly, however, we must remember that the Baykal Meridian probably also applies to goods moved to Pacific domestic and export markets by rail from west of Lake Baykal. Although the Soviet command economy is able to override basic economic restrictions on the movement of commodities, real cost penalties are incurred because scarce resources could also be allocated to reflect alternative priorities.

An examination of economic efficiency leads to a striking conclusion on spatial choices: if the criterion of cost-effectiveness were applied to the regional development of Soviet timber and wood-processing industries, most of the Siberian and Far Eastern forest resource would not be utilized in this century, and intervening opportunities in European-Uralian areas would be a stronger focus

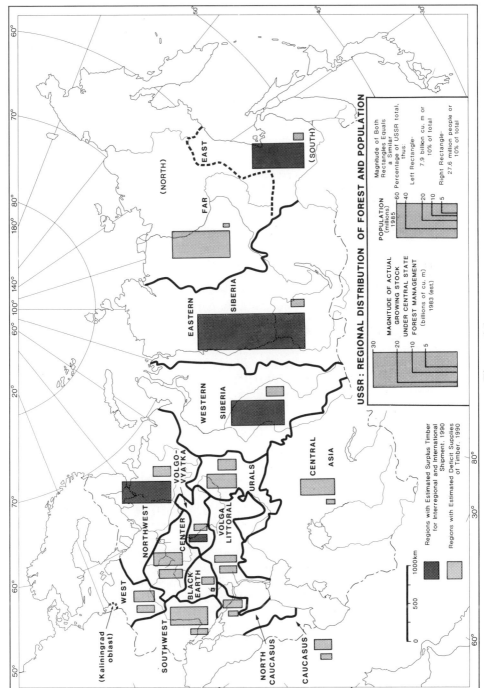

USSR: REGIONAL DISTRIBUTION OF FOREST AND POPULATION

MAGNITUDE OF BOTH RECTANGLES EQUALS A SIMILAR

Magnitude of Both Rectangles Equals a Similar Percentage of USSR total, thus:

Left Rectangle- 7.9 billion cu. m or 10% of total

Right Rectangle- 27.6 million people or 10% of total

POPULATION (millions) 1985

MAGNITUDE OF ACTUAL GROWING STOCK UNDER CENTRAL STATE FOREST MANAGEMENT (billions of cu. m) 1983 (est)

Regions with Estimated Surplus Timber for Interregional and International Shipment, 1990

Regions with Estimated Deficit Supplies of Timber, 1990

(NORTH)

(SOUTH)

FAR EAST

EASTERN SIBERIA

WESTERN SIBERIA

VOLGO-VYATKA

NORTHWEST

CENTER

VOLGA LITTORAL

URALS

CENTRAL ASIA

WEST

(Kaliningrad oblast)

SOUTHWEST

BLACK EARTH

NORTH CAUCASUS

CAUCASUS

1000km

0   500   1000km

Figure 1.1

for planners. The mature and overmature growing stock of many coniferous forests in the Northwest, Volgo-Vyatka, and Urals regions (Figure 1.2), for example, are currently underutilized.

Soviet foresters themselves are divided on the issue of whether this zone should be permitted to play an appropriate economic and locational role in major Soviet domestic and European markets. Those foresters, for example, whose analyses are based on natural criteria, including distance, heavily favor more intensive utilization of the European-Uralian forest. Others, whose analyses incorporate traditional objectives of the CPSU (Communist Party of the Soviet Union), Gosplan (State Planning Commission), and the Council of Ministers, heavily favor the development of Asian forests and the relocation of many processing facilities east of the Urals. Arguments of the former group, however, dominate much of the thinking underlying the present book and appear to be influencing new geographical approaches to raw material supply for some wood-processing sectors, particularly pulp and paper, according to statements made at the Twenty-sixth CPSU Party Congress in 1981 and repeated at the Twenty-seventh CPSU Party Congress in 1986.

AN AGENDA FOR ANALYSIS

The Soviet forest resource has enormous potential, probably as much or more than that of any other nation or major region. Why is the forest-product sector of the USSR's economy not commensurate with the size and quality of the country's resource? Why do forest products not play as important a role in that country as they do in many other industrial nations? In other words, the great natural abundance of timber has not created concomitant economic advantages despite the theoretical ability of the USSR to focus investment and managerial skill on most industrial processes. Could our Western understanding of resource potential and economic opportunity be fundamentally at odds with the agenda of Soviet industrial and political managers? What developments should we expect on the basis of the USSR's potential riches? How far do normal understandings of comparative advantage and industrial requirements facilitate our understanding of this complex, centrally administered economy without recourse to other industrial objectives or agendas? Our agenda in *The Disappearing Russian Forest* is to present these concerns initially, conduct an examination of evidence, and return to the issues in the final chapter to offer some conclusions.

One basic concern lies, for example, with goals and tools chosen by Soviet planners. Soviet five-year plans usually contain impressive, although not exaggerated, expectations for forestry and wood-processing. Planning targets, however, traditionally are underfulfilled, and goals are revised downward. The Twelfth Five-Year Plan envisions increased output over the 1986-1990 period of 15 to 18 percent for pulp, 11 to 15 percent for paper, 17 to 20 percent for paperboard, and 30 percent for particleboard (*Current Digest of the Soviet Press* [hereafter abbreviated *CDSP*], vol. 37 [47], p. 24). Certain key industries of the

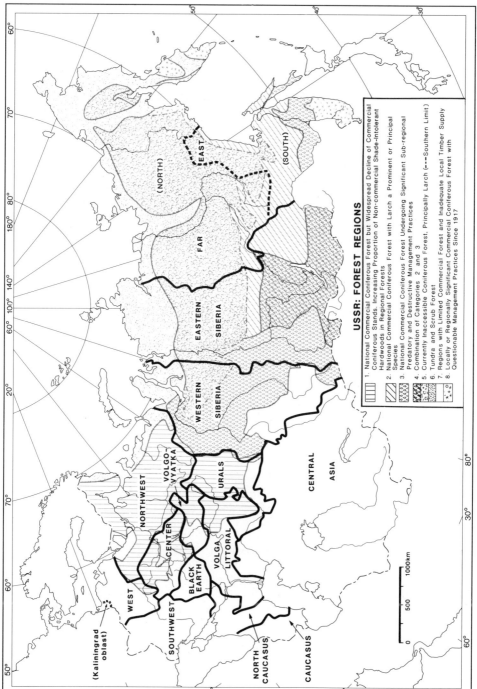

USSR: FOREST REGIONS

1. National Commercial Coniferous Forest but Widespread Decline of Commercial Coniferous Stands. Increasing Proportion of Non-commercial Shade-Intolerant Hardwoods in Regional Forests
2. National Commercial Coniferous Forest with Larch a Prominent or Principal Species
3. National Commercial Coniferous Forest Undergoing Significant Sub-regional Predatory and Destructive Management Practices
4. Combination of Categories 2 and 3
5. Currently Inaccessible Coniferous Forest, Principally Larch (---Southern Limit)
6. Tundra and Scrub Forest
7. Regions with Limited Commercial Forest and Inadequate Local Timber Supply
8. Locally or Regionally Significant Commercial Coniferous Forest with Questionable Management Practices Since 1917

Figure 1.2

sector have not performed well during the previous Tenth and Eleventh Five-Year Plans (Table 1.1).

Table 1.1
Growth in Physical Output Indicators for USSR Forest-Product Industries during the Tenth and Eleventh Five-Year Plans (%)

Industry	10th 5-YP 1976-1980		11th 5-YP 1981-1984[a]	
	Average Annual Change	Total Change	Average Annual Change	Total Change
Logs	-2	-7	-1	+3[b]
Lumber	-3	-13	-4	-1
Plywood	-2	-7	-1	+5
Particleboard	+5	+21	+9	+15
Fiberboard	+2	+8	+4	+9
Pulp	0	-1	+2	+11
Paper	0	-2	+2	+9

[a]Excludes final year of the Eleventh Five-Year Plan, 1985.

[b]Reflects jump in output between 1983 and 1984.

Source: Computed from physical output data in *Narodnoye Khozyaystvo SSSR v 1980 godu* (1981, pp. 174-177); and *Narodnoye Khozyaystvo SSSR v 1984 godu* (1985, pp. 186-89).

The Tenth plan had projected an average of 25 percent growth in forest industries for the 1976-1980 period. Shortfalls in roundwood removals (logging) especially had an adverse impact on lumber and plywood. As a result, when the indicators for the Eleventh plan were published, no specific targets were listed for logging, lumber, and plywood. Pulp and fiberboard were each scheduled to achieve 5 percent annual growth, and as of 1984, both would have had to experience a strong finish in 1985 to achieve that target. Annual output of particleboard was planned to grow by 10 percent. Although performance throughout forest industries improved during the Eleventh Five-Year Plan in comparison to that achieved during its predecessor, output targets are still not being attained for most sectors.

We wonder, therefore, what tools really are available to Soviet forest planners and how effectively these tools can be utilized before their potency is dulled by other conflicting or hidden priorities and limitations. Notions of improved efficiency in resource allocation and siting of processing facilities are hardly *terra incognita* to Soviet planners. Optimality is a watchword of most advanced economic analyses emanating from government authorities, including the Academy of Sciences. And yet, the patterns which continue to emerge in forestry and wood-processing reveal little direct optimality, but rather project a sense of conservatism, of sticking to "the tried and true." At all costs, one gathers, the plan's eventual goals must be met! But the plan seems to be a pragmatically derived device to achieve output, rather than to enhance efficiency. In turn, this pragmatism probably consumes excessive investments, thus further ensuring that planners' targets are seldom achieved. We wonder also about the true significance of freight rates, of stumpage fees, of industrial bonuses, of planning targets, and of comprehensive physical inter-industry analyses. The spatial or regional patterns of industrial processing and the continued tolerance of inefficient or even obsolete producers suggest that the vision of the planner and the reality of the "implementer" are not linked. Can we expect, therefore, to find economic rationality in a complex system which continues to operate according to a different agenda?

Perhaps as Eronen (1984) suggests, a more appropriate way to understand Soviet location patterns and industrial developments is through an understanding of planners' strategies. This represents a pragmatic, almost ad hoc, form of behavior governed by a sense of expediency, of "muddling through at any cost." The Soviet penchant for adding industrial capacity to existing facilities rather than undertaking the more risky investment at greenfield sites suggests that a convenient and continual reinterpretation of locational principles to justify the wisdom of each major investment may in fact reflect the realities of the Soviet economic and political worlds. The tried and true approach, the ability to meet targets which are laid out in a bureaucratic morass rather than an economic plane may carry with it a form of optimality far more universal than that which assumes the freedom of action purportedly available to major individual Western investors. If rough accordance with planning guidelines (even downward revisions) is the hallmark of the Soviet industrial system, we might conclude that the major political leaders, including industrial managers, perceive that the most optimal solution to industrial development is not necessarily the one that provides the greatest return on investment, but rather is the one that *works*.

Furthermore, if the key goals of Soviet industrial managers involve expediency and attempts to fulfill plan targets regardless of true or immediate "costs," should we expect economics alone to bring about significant spatial shifts of production within the USSR? Considerable attention is paid by analysts of many Soviet industrial sectors to the imbalance between the European-Uralian heartland and the great northern and Asian "resource" peripheries of the Soviet Union. Many of our models suggest that industrial relocation away from developed areas to the resource frontiers is to be expected in the USSR because of apparent savings to the entire economy. Such shifts, however, despite our myths, have not proceeded unhindered elsewhere in the world where large space economies with developed cores and scattered peripheries have emerged since the beginning of the Industrial Revolution. If the goals of the industrial system are to increase output and support key industrial, military, and social priorities, the spatial elements of the economy such as those created by past industrial investment and the natural occurrences of raw materials should probably be geared to meeting these objectives. Manipulation of these elements does not constitute a somewhat independent process involving infrastructure, industrial complexes, population, etc., even if, in the long run, cheaper unit costs of production and greater returns on investment could be achieved.

We can apply similar questioning to the realm of foreign trade. If greater economies in the domestic use of space and organization of production do not have significance for individual investors and organizations, should we expect foreign trade to reflect the fundamental influence of comparative advantage and economies of resource utilization? Foreign trade seems to reflect expediency in accomplishing planning goals and production objectives, some with short-run and some with long-term payoffs. Exports in part pay for technology and products which the USSR chooses not to produce, or is unable to acquire in an immediate operational sense. Imports facilitate development, acquisition of prototypes, and the filling of production gaps which otherwise would endanger the fulfillment of additional objectives. Does foreign trade, at least with CMEA (also called COMECON) members and Western industrial societies, have a future, or is it a somewhat temporary activity to facilitate the various five-year plans and specific industrial or military goals? Does domestic industry deeply benefit from imported technology and products, or could the USSR achieve the same ends over time if certain international priorities were not imposed by the continuing fierce economic and political competition between the East and the West? If Soviet labor and capital shortages become more severe in the future, might we expect greater imports of certain timber and wood products both from CMEA and the West, which in turn could be paid for by fuel exports or greater exports of industrial goods in those areas where the Soviet Union has a competitive advantage or superior product credibility?

Underlying all these themes and specific questions, however, is the Soviet record of reform and organizational change. Throughout the period under review in this book (1960-1984), we have seen such measures as the reintroduction of the ministerial system following Khrushchev's downfall, the growth and decline in influence of major administrative units, the division and reunification of various ministries and state committees, the creation of the amalgamation or association (*ob'edineniye*), different economic reforms, and recently the creation of "super" ministries. Do all these activities really have an economic significance, or are they merely part of a desperate attempt to *appear* to be working toward a solution in the absence of real change? The emphasis on *policy* rather than *program* suggests that a certain amount of window dressing accompanies the Soviet industrial sphere of operations. In some extreme cases, we wonder whether the achievement of an award for good window dressing is not far more important than the fulfillment of the need to supply consumers with the requisite items. In this manner, therefore, industrial decrees and resolutions, economic plans and output targets, and periodic Party congresses all may fulfill an important agenda in Soviet life. The effectiveness of Soviet industry, therefore, probably should be judged in terms of the overall success of the Soviet Party and governmental political, social, and military objectives rather than strictly in terms of economic efficiency and optimality, no matter how desirable these items may be in theory. We suggest that the performance of various industrial sectors, including forestry and wood products, can probably be assessed most meaningfully not in terms of economic criteria but in terms of the continuing ability of the Soviet Union to meet its major self-imposed domestic and international social, political, and military goals.

The authors are reluctant in this book, therefore, to undertake a strict comparative technical or economic analysis of Soviet and, for example, North American forestry and wood-processing activities, although we are aware of the relative weights which different activities comprise in each case. Rather, it seems to us more productive to interpret forests and wood-processing industries in relation to Soviet expectations for themselves and the constraints or institutional frameworks which govern their industrial decision-making, spatial activities, and patterns of economic development. We return to these themes, questions, and general concerns in the final chapter of this book and employ them to interpret many of the specific observations and analyses which comprise the intervening chapters.

STRUCTURE OF THE BOOK

The Disappearing Russian Forest examines many current spatial and developmental dilemmas affecting the Soviet timber resources and wood-processing industries. We proceed on the basis of events which have transpired during the past quarter century and offer tentative suggestions of patterns of development which might occur by the year 2000. Extensive and detailed analyses of historical data sets and particular industries lie beyond the purview of this book. The title, *The Disappearing Russian Forest*, expresses the Soviet geographical dilemma in utilization of major regional forests: should the traditional practice of high-grading European-Uralian and accessible Siberian forests be continued? Should planners permit an extensive regeneration backlog characterized by minimal silviculture and considerable natural regrowth of forests with undesirable age and species composition? Should the USSR instead undertake extensive reforestation and environmental intervention in species and site quality in the European-Uralian zone to enhance the regional economic development of the resource and to ensure the efficacious utilization of existing wood-processing facilities and infrastructure? These basic questions force choices on Soviet forest-industry planners. The status quo approach meets current developmental needs, but it is becoming increasingly expensive as more remote forests are developed. The reforestation alternative requires extensive capital expenditures, but offers increasingly attractive savings in transportation costs; in utilization of existing infrastructure such as roads, railways, processing facilities, and settlement systems; in the length of time needed for regeneration of timber; and in the expenditures associated with the harsh physical environments of Siberia and the Far East.

At present, many of the best forest lands are continuing to undergo depredation, and the resulting regrowth produces forests with inappropriate trees and a lack of commercial viability. If this environmental degradation continues, the Soviet Union will have missed an important opportunity to undertake efficient regional development and the multifaceted preservation of its forests. Although utilization of accessible eastern timber will continue regardless of regional priorities associated with regeneration - and some suggest that high-grading of Siberian forests might proceed while extensive regeneration occurred in the European-Uralian zone - the authors suggest that the USSR conceivably in the reasonably near future might be placed in a position of importing large amounts of timber or wood products as a lower-cost alternative to extensive eastern development unless regeneration proceeds apace. Client states in the Third World could provide some of this timber. The USSR might find, as in agriculture, that although it has the potential to produce, the organization and legacy of its developmental policies preclude the achievement of self-sufficiency, even with highly restricted levels of demand.

In writing *The Disappearing Russian Forest,* we selected specific regions and time periods for analysis. The Soviet forest and wood-processing industries are too large and diverse to assess by individual enterprise. Throughout much of the period covered by this book (1960-1984), however, regional data offer the opportunity for comprehensive analysis of the resource and many processing sectors. Most of the period is bracketed by problems with information - the data drought of the Stalin and immediate post-Stalin eras, and the reassertion of a penchant for information secrecy after 1977, especially at the regional level, by Brezhnev, which has been maintained by his three successors. The period 1966-1982, however, was characterized by stability in the major regional classification of administrative units (Figure 1.3). In fact, with the exception of transferring Tyumen Oblast from the Urals to Western Siberia in 1966, and Bashkir ASSR back from the Urals to the Volga Littoral in 1963, the system was unchanged between 1961 and 1982. In December 1982, the composition of the major regions was modified by division of the Northwest into two separate regions - the North and the Northwest - and the transfer of Bashkir ASSR again to the Urals (Figure 1.4).

Where possible, this book utilizes the 1963-1982 schema of major regions. This system conforms to that used in the release of considerable regional data both for the forest and wood-processing sectors and for numerous other sectors of the Soviet economy. In those cases where recent data are only available for major regions as defined in the post-1982 schema and cannot be reworked for administrative subunits (oblasts, krays, and ASSRs), the book uses this modified system. Unfortunately, neither system is particularly acceptable to geographers because some of the major regions contain administrative units which seem to belong more appropriately elsewhere in the geographic scheme. The authors have divided the Soviet Far East, for example, into northern and southern subdivisions reflecting the quality of the timber resource, the levels of economic and urban development, and the quality of infrastructure. On the other side of the country, Kaliningrad Oblast of the Russian republic (RSFSR) is physically cut off from its associated republic by Lithuania and probably has more in common in economic development and physical environment with the Baltic republics than with Russia proper. The authors thus include it with the Baltics, and the Baltics with Belorussia, to form the West. Moldavia, although one of the 15 union republics, is combined in this study with the Ukraine to form the Southwest because of its economic and physical similarity to the southwestern districts of that republic. Given that the major regional variations in volume and spatial extent of Soviet timber occur within the RSFSR, the

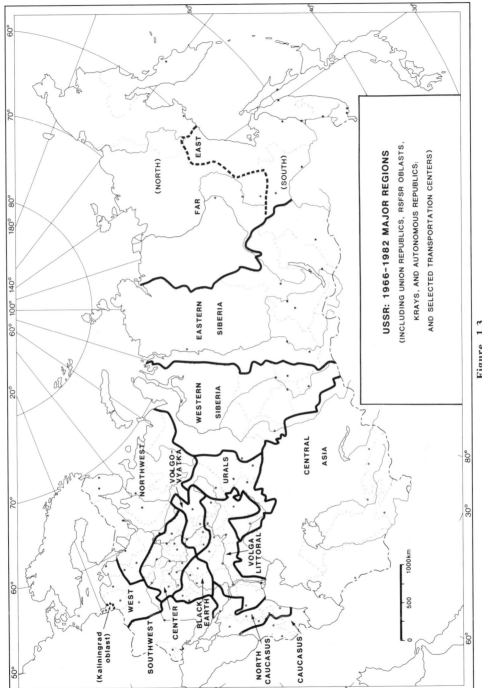

USSR: 1966-1982 MAJOR REGIONS

(INCLUDING UNION REPUBLICS, RSFSR OBLASTS, KRAYS, AND AUTONOMOUS REPUBLICS; AND SELECTED TRANSPORTATION CENTERS)

Figure 1.3

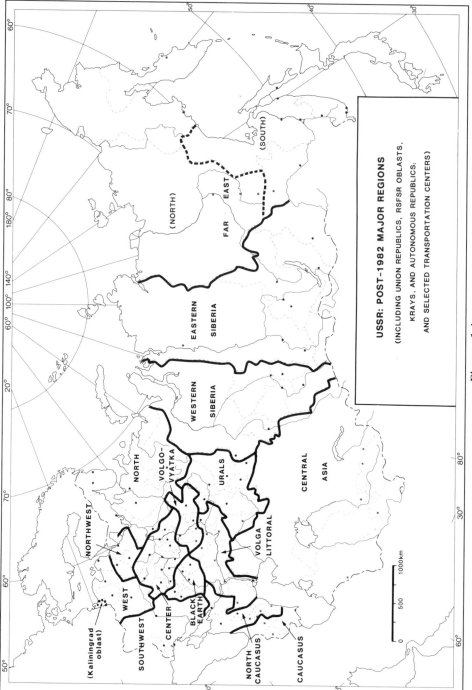

USSR: POST-1982 MAJOR REGIONS

(INCLUDING UNION REPUBLICS, RSFSR OBLASTS,
KRAYS, AND AUTONOMOUS REPUBLICS;
AND SELECTED TRANSPORTATION CENTERS)

Figure 1.4

authors feel that reduction of the number of regions outside the RSFSR to a minimum enhances analytical clarity and simplifies the major analyses which emphasize the contrasts between European-Uralian USSR and Asiatic Russia.

In using the Russian terms for the regions, *Povolzhskiy* and *Volgo-Vyatskiy*, the authors prefer to use *Volga Littoral* and *Volgo-Vyatka* in place of the somewhat more common, *Transvolga* and *Volga Vyatka*. *Black Earth* is a simplified version of the more cumbersome, *Central-Black Earth*, or the term, *Chernozem*, which may be unfamiliar to those not well acquainted with the USSR.

The authors have also decided in the interest of clarity to restrict the presentation of major data sets to benchmark years coinciding with the end of the five-year planning periods (except for 1960, which technically is the third year of the one and only seven-year plan). The book's focus on the period 1960 to 1985 (statistical data are current to 1984) coincides with the period of economic and geographic reorganization of the Soviet economy after Khrushchev's consolidation of power and his abrogation of the Sixth Five-Year Plan in 1958, and with the recognition that major heartland-hinterland spatial divisions of the economy were economically too important to be denied. The authors adhere to this temporal framework except where variations or inadequacies in the data require flexibility or estimation, and identify exceptions where appropriate.

The book is organized into nine chapters. An introductory chapter presents basic issues; six core chapters examine various aspects of Soviet wood industries; and a concluding chapter revisits our basic themes. Chapter 2 is a reader's "guide," including translation of specific terms and names and a discussion of data sources and limitations. Because the forests are integrated with important aspects of the Soviet economy and society through extensive institutional organization, Chapter 2 also identifies the major agencies responsible for mensuration and management of the timber resource and associated with its conversion into useful products for domestic and foreign consumption. Although the institutional system is so extensive that its analysis could comprise a separate monograph, Chapter 2 focuses primarily on the components formally affecting management and utilization of the resource and on important informal procedures and organizational deficiencies, such as nomadic logging and predatory harvesting.

Beginning the core section of the book, Chapter 3 examines the components of the Soviet commercial forest, the portion of the total forested land, and the actual growing stock that is accessible and deemed to have economic utility. This is a much smaller proportion of the total growing stock than is usually identified by most analysts, because the remainder lies beyond the geographical limit of supporting transportation and settlement infrastructure. Major forests of Eastern Siberia and the Far East are inaccessible or have adverse physical environments; domestic and foreign markets cannot be supplied from these areas under present market or administrative prices even in a centrally administered command economy.

Chapter 3 then completes its overview of the physical and institutional characteristics of the forestry and wood-processing industries by summarizing the current sectoral and spatial patterns of production and consumption and by briefly examining the most significant differences in these patterns in the periods preceding and following 1917. As in most components of the Soviet economy and society, the post-1917 period has witnessed full-scale regional industrial development and significant spatial shifts in the location of industrial production and consumption. Unlike other industries such as generation of hydroelectricity, smelting of aluminum, and production of automobiles, however, the pre-1917 Russian Empire had achieved important commercial developments in the forest and wood-processing sectors and had a long history of exporting timber to world markets. Some Soviet pulp and paper mills, for example, predate the Russian Revolution,some predate the invasion of Russia by Napoleon,and others were acquired from territorial annexations immediately preceding or following World War II.

Chapter 4 approaches the forest resource within the broad framework of world deforestation and alienation of forest land. Although the five Soviet inventories completed since accurate national mensuration commenced in 1961 reveal a consistent expansion of forested land, most of the increases have resulted from improvements in accuracy rather than from concerted reforestation. Forests are classified into three major groups according to industrial and nonindustrial priorities, and annual plans officially regulate the management, allowable cut, utilization, and regeneration of timber. Chapter 4, therefore, analyzes the management, maintenance, utilization, and silvicultural subsystems comprising the forest resource and concludes with an assessment of the major current and expected future developments associated with them.

Unlike deforestation in many tropical countries such as Brazil and Indonesia caused by population pressures and land clearing for agriculture, or the extensive deforestation of arid regions in Africa and India caused by the incessant growth in need for fuelwood, Soviet deforestation is caused by inappropriate harvesting and inadequate reforestation of logged areas. Degradation of the forest environment and removal of forest land from commercial forest production will ultimately affect domestic industrial and nonindustrial users of Soviet forests and may lead to restrictions in the Soviet export of timber and wood products.

Although a significant world exporter of roundwood and relatively unprocessed wood products, the Soviet Union nevertheless is a major producer of manufactured forest products, a role examined in Chapter 5. The past quarter century has been particularly significant for improvements in the output of chemically derived wood products, such as pulp, paper, paperboard, and wood chemicals, and in the comprehensive manufacturing of others such as plywood, particleboard, and fiberboard. Spatial patterns of production, however, have changed differentially according to the sector of the wood-processing industry. The major differences among regions for each sector are identified through shift-share analysis. Regional differences are caused by variations in the locational requirements of different technological processes, in the extent of interindustry backward and forward linkages, and in the differing degrees of interaction between weight loss during processing and the structure of Soviet rail tariffs.

Chapter 5 summarizes the spatial pattern of timber utilization among industrial users and refers to a previous linear programming assessment of regional timber supply and demand for 1970 and 1975 and for that anticipated by 1990 (Barr, 1983). The chapter's analyses permit present and anticipated commercial timber requirements to be related to analyses of foreign trade in timber and wood products in Chapter 7 and to be compared with the characteristics and volumes of growing stock among major Soviet regions in Chapter 4.

Whether accessible for commercial exploitation, all Soviet forests have environmental, social, and cultural significance. Chapter 6 reviews the importance of trees to the maintenance of major watersheds, ecosystems, and wildlife habitats. These include soil retention and runoff control on steep mountain and upland slopes, and systems of shelter belts developed on the arid southern agricultural margin. The nonindustrial uses of Soviet forests are then analyzed, particularly those associated with tourism, recreation, and nature preservation, and those related to the Soviet food program in which forest plants, fungi, and seeds are directly or indirectly consumed by humans. This last use has received extensive official support and attention since 1982, particularly as the forestry and forest-product sectors are now officially integrated into the USSR's program to improve the supply and quality of foodstuffs.

The role of forests in Soviet food supply, however, is relatively poorly understood outside the USSR. Except for the collection of mushrooms in many parts of Europe, most people outside the USSR do not rely on food products directly from the forest, except in relatively primitive indigenous societies of hunters and gatherers. In the USSR, however, many species of flora and fauna in the forests are utilized as nutrient supplements (and for medicinal purposes) to the undistinguished Soviet diet. With the continuing shortfalls in production of grain, meat, milk, and vegetables in the USSR, the Soviet government throughout the 1980s has stressed the integration of the forest environment into the national food program to improve the country's diet and nutrient balance. Obviously the forest immediately adjacent to populated areas has the most direct significance to most nonindustrial uses, but continuing depredation of the forest through inappropriate timber harvesting and toxic precipitation suggest that forests in the European-Uralian zone are most at risk.

Chapter 7 examines forests and international trade. Throughout most of the past quarter century, Soviet purchases abroad have increasingly included large amounts of food and feed grains to supplement domestic supplies and meet obligations to foreign client states. Forest-sector exports have been important throughout the Soviet planning period as a major means of earning hard currency with which to purchase foreign technology. Although the importance of timber and wood products to foreign exchange receipts have been overshadowed since 1973 by sales of petroleum, the recent fall in world energy prices is an appropriate reminder of the contribution of forest items to the diversity and stability of Soviet foreign trade.

Export of timber and wood products, however, is problematic because many accessible forests traditionally supplying export timber in the Northwest and the Yenisey-Angara valleys in Eastern Siberia have been depleted and are increasingly unable to meet the domestic and foreign demand for roundwood. In the short run, the USSR has met some timber obligations such as those to Finland by moving timber up to 5000 km by rail from Western Siberian forests. In the long run, however, Soviet foresters expect to ship large amounts of timber from Eastern Siberia and the Far East to world markets, particularly those in the Pacific rim, although the most prevalent species in these forests is larch and considerable volumes available for shipment may be diseased. Timber for export has to compete with domestic Soviet demand and investment priorities, including the allocation of funds to substitute capital for the dwindling supply of labor, especially physical labor in harsh, peripheral areas. Although Bulgarian and Korean "guest" workers are occasionally identified as contract loggers in areas such as the Komi ASSR and Khabarovsk kray to facilitate Soviet timber exports to their countries, the USSR has not yet developed an effective and systematic program to replace domestic labor with foreign workers or even with labor from Soviet Central Asia. Similarly, despite considerable improvement in technology at all levels of timber harvesting and processing, the substitution of capital for labor does not seem to have proceeded at an appropriate pace.

Soviet hard-currency export of timber and wood products is also an important key in facilitating the continuing transfer of foreign technology to Soviet primary and secondary industries, including the forest sectors themselves. Transfer of technology is analyzed in Chapter 8. In some cases, because the utilization of imported technology has enhanced the scale of plant operation and expanded the diversity and mix of raw material inputs and processed outputs, major individual enterprises have facilitated the spatial expansion of sectors into hitherto undeveloped regions.

Although forestry is one of the stable elements in the Soviet Union's foreign trade, continuing destruction of its accessible forests, or priority reassignment to other industries of incremental additions to the country's labor force, particularly among European Soviet peoples, might lead the USSR to curtail the export of timber and forest products, and even to import significant amounts of key items. Obviously this scenario is subject to influence by many unknown variables, but important precedents do exist in agriculture. Other precedents in the industrial sphere can be found in Soviet imports of raw materials after countries in the Third World have become its client states. Although the growing demographic imbalance between Central Asia and the European USSR might lead Soviet leaders to develop effective strategies for employing Central Asians on a contract, short-term basis in Siberian forests, this does not appear imminent. The export of raw materials like timber and relatively unprocessed wood products may be succeeded by greater foreign trade in highly manufactured goods, particularly if links within CMEA provide the technological breakthroughs necessary to ensure state-of-the-art goods for worldwide trade. Finally, even if the USSR continues to export from some regions, it might decide to forego long-distance domestic shipment of timber and to import timber and wood products to forest deficit areas, particularly in the western and southern European USSR. Many such imports could be high-value or purpose-specific from Scandinavia. Even the possibility of timber or wood product imports from Canada or the United States, for example, in the future may really not be a farfetched idea - both are already major grain exporters to the USSR.

Finally, the authors return in the concluding chapter to our initial questions of resource utilization. Resolution of the European-Uralian versus Siberia and the Far East debate through positive actions or by default has important consequences for the future development of Soviet forestry, timber production, and wood-processing. Chapter 9 assesses possible alternatives arising from different outcomes of this debate, and assesses their implications for management of the forest resource; for patterns of domestic industrial utilization and foreign trade; for nonindustrial use including international tourism; and for processes of technological change, particularly in relation to the traditional goal of autarchy, the pragmatic approach to trade with the West and the professed goal for greater integration within CMEA. The book concludes that the cumulative effect of inappropriate timber harvesting will probably prevent the USSR from reaping the full economic benefit from its forests enjoyed by many other nations, and may in the future require that country to import significant amounts of timber and wood products, particularly into specific regions of European USSR. The growing backlog of regeneration in the European-Uralian zone requires concerted and immediate investment priority to reverse a situation in which many of the best quality forest lands in the most accessible regions of the country are no longer able to support commercial forestry or the enterprises originally designated to use their timber.

The book's nine chapters are supplemented by a bibliography, figures, maps, and charts, and appendices with institutional information, Soviet terminology, and the Latin names of major timber species.

2
A Reader's Guide

This chapter contains basic terminology (Appendix 2.1), institutional organization and data resources associated with Soviet forestry and wood-processing; lists major species comprising Soviet forests by their Russian and Latin names (Appendix 2.2); identifies the abbreviations employed in the literature to represent major types of manufacturing units in the forest sector (Appendix 2.3); describes the managerial structure comprising ministries, agencies, organizations, and committees; and evaluates the literature and statistical sources of data which comprise the basis for subsequent analyses.

TERMINOLOGY

Western foresters and geographers alike often find some of the Soviet forest terminology to be different from that used elsewhere in the world. One of the main causes of this difference stems from the specific political economy of the USSR and the multi faceted classification of forests and administrations. The glossary comprising Appendix 2.1 includes many terms which appear frequently in Soviet tabular headings and textual classifications. Although much of the terminology associated with timber removals is actually similar to that used elsewhere, it too is included in the glossary to facilitate translation by geographers and other non-forestry analysts. It is derived from numerous sources, particularly the *Dictionary of Forestry in Five Languages - German - English - French - Spanish - Russian* (Weck, 1966), the *Anglo-Russkiy Lesotekhnicheskiy Slovar'* (Mozhayev *et al.*, 1983), and J. Holowacz (various years). This glossary was previously compiled by Barr to enhance his review of Vorob'yev *et al.* (Barr, 1982) and is reprinted here with permission.

The authors use a designation for Soviet tree species that is different from most other non-Russian works. Soviet foresters divide tree species into three groups: conifers (*khvoynye porody*), and two others (*myagkolistvennye* and *tverdolistvennye porody*). Some analysts translate these last two as softwood and hardwood deciduous species; others have grouped these species into a single designation of broadleaved species. Holowacz (various years), however, whose terms are used throughout this book, suggests that the appropriate translation for these two categories is shade-intolerant hardwood species (SIHS) and shade-tolerant hardwood species (STHS) (see Appendix 2.1), based on the locational characteristics of their growing stock.

The major USSR industrial timber species are listed by their English, Latin, and Russian names in Appendix 2.2, and their regional distribution is identified. The species are arranged according to Holowacz's tripartite classification.

The glossary and list of major timber species provided here, plus the abbreviations for types of manufacturing enterprises engaged in the forestry sector (Appendix 2-3), should enable readers to understand Soviet forestry and wood-processing in a manner comparable to that provided for North America by such authors as Sharpe *et al.* (1986), Conway (1982), and Haygreen and Bowyer (1982).

INSTITUTIONAL ORGANIZATION

The Soviet forest-products sector is part of the centrally administered Soviet economy. Most of it is planned, and almost all of its products accrue directly to the state. The Soviet Union has undertaken industrial planning since 1928 and now regularly organizes its industrial targets by five-year periods comprising various subperiodic targets. The five-year plans are confirmed by congresses of the CPSU held at five-year intervals. Planning and regular management, however, are carried out by a comprehensive governmental infrastructure overseen by the all-pervasive administrative structure of the CPSU. This system of industrial planning and operation is complex and has undergone significant modifications since its inception (concisely described in Kozhukhov, 1984, pp. 65-103). Soviet industrial activity is carried out by industrial ministries and state committees. It is coordinated by the Council of Ministers, which in turn is subordinate to the Supreme Soviet (and in effect to the CPSU). Some of these are national (all-union) organizations, others are joint union-republic organizations or individual republic organizations. Many have intermediate forms of organization (amalgamations and chief administrations) related to product lines and/or geographical areas.

In recent years production associations or amalgamations have emerged as a powerful organizational force grouping subordinate and allied enterprises into horizontally and vertically integrated organizations. They have also replaced many chief administrations. Amalgamations have grown from 608 in 1970 to 4295 in 1984 (*Narodnoye Khozyaystvo SSSR v 1984 godu,* 1985, p. 128); they included 18,507 subordinate enterprises and units and accounted for half of industrial production and personnel. Production occurs in enterprises, major integrated factories (*kombinats*) and associations. In 1984, 45,539 of these operated in the USSR; 12 percent were associated with forestry and forest products (*Narodnoye Khozyaystvo SSSR v 1984 godu,* 1985, p. 128).

Four organizations are responsible for the forest sector: (1) USSR *Minlesbumprom*; (2) USSR *Gosleskhoz*; (3) Councils of Ministers of Union Republics; and USSR *Glavmikrobioprom*. Their operations are subordinate to the USSR Council of Ministers.

1. The current organizational framework governing forest products dates from 30 October 1980, when the USSR Union-Republic Ministry of the Timber and Paper Industry (*Minlesbumprom*) was constituted from two previously separate ministries: the USSR Ministry of the Timber and Woodworking Industry (union-republic), and the USSR Ministry of the Pulp and Paper Industry (all-union) (Kozhukhov, 1984, p. 68). The two separate ministries themselves had been created out of one major ministry in June 1968 (Scherer, 1981, p. 18). *Minlesbumprom* carries out its undertakings directly through all-union industrial

amalgamations or jointly with republic councils of ministers through republic ministries of timber and wood-processing industries. These minstries, in turn, administer production amalgamations and enterprises which undertake logging; production of wooden housing; forest products, including furniture production; and a host of auxiliary activities found in modern industry everywhere.

2. Forestry is administered by the USSR State Forestry Committee (*Gosleskhoz*), which has a union-republic structure. It was formed in 1966 and administers 94.6 percent of the state forest (the remainder is administered by collective farms [2.3 percent] and other administrations [3.1 percent] [Kozhukhov, 1984, pp. 74-75]).

3. *Gosleskhoz* works with the Councils of Ministers of Union Republics to coordinate the work of republic ministries of forestry. These ministries undertake forestry activity in the republics and oversee kray and oblast forestry administrations and the ASSR ministries of forestry. Republic ministries and their subordinate administrations control various forestry enterprises and amalgamations.

4. Microbiological and hydrolysis industries are administered by the Chief Administration for Microbiology (*Glavmikrobioprom*) of the USSR Council of Ministers. It directly administers amalgamations and enterprises which carry out wood hydrolysis and the production of various microbiological products.

For greater simplicity in analysis, the authors of this book do not focus extensively on the administrative organization of Soviet forests unless it directly influences patterns of production or has caused major problems in resource utilization which could not be explained without reference to organizational structures. Production data analyzed throughout the book, therefore, represent the aggregate output of numerous organizations with varying levels of responsibility for forestry and forest products.

CHANGING FORTUNES OF ADMINISTRATIVE UNITS

A response to the poor performance of the forest industries in the USSR has often come in the form of ministerial reorganization. Thus, the ministry which oversees many of the forest-related branches of the national economy has been unified, disaggregated, and then reunified over the past 25 years.

The Central Committee of the CPSU and the Council of Ministers, as noted above, are ultimately the highest organs responsible for the performance of forest industries under the centrally controlled planning structure of the USSR. Despite the large-scale changes that have taken place in administrative organization, the basic division of forestry versus industrial exploitation has persisted.

Since 1966, the USSR State Forestry Committee (*Gosleskhoz*) has continually administered most forests. The industrial ministry, however, has not enjoyed such an uninterrupted administration. Before 1968, forest industries were controlled by one ministry: Timber, Pulp, Paper, and Woodworking. This national ministry was then split into two divisions: the Ministry of Timber and Woodworking, headed by Nikolai Vladimirovich Timofeyev, and the Ministry of Pulp and Paper headed by Konstantin Ivanovich Galanshin. After years of arguments between the ministries, as noted in Soviet press articles, and attempts to distribute blame for production shortfalls, the ministries were recombined in 1980 into one ministry, *Minlesbumprom*.[1] Timofeyev and Galanshin were in their 60s at the time and are assumed to have retired. Stepan Alekseyevich Shalayev, 52, took over as minister of *Minlesbumprom*, with two deputy ministers appointed under Shalayev: I. A. Yagodnikov for timber and woodworking, and M. I. Busygin for pulp and paper.

Recently, Busygin, who originally was general director for the construction of the Ust-Ilimsk timber industry complex (LPK), has taken over as minister in Shalayev's place. Busygin, in turn, has come under heavy criticism in the Soviet press for the continuing poor record of the timber, pulp, and paper industries. In September 1984, the CPSU Central Committee and the USSR Council of Ministers published a resolution critical of the performances of both *Minlesbumprom* and *Gosleskhoz*. The resolution called for better replanting, reforestation, use of deciduous species and by-products, and more mechanization of logging. It also ordered better oversight by provincial party committees of forest industry enterprises (*Pravda*, 23 September 1984, p. 1). In 1985, *Izvestiya* published an article on the wasteful record of the pulp and paper branch of *Minlesbumprom*, which was accused of a 100,000-ton-per-year shortfall in planned paper deliveries despite 7 billion rubles of investment between 1974 and 1984. Reporter Sukhachevsky blamed the style of management in the ministry (*Izvestiya*, 23 June 1985, p. 2).

Finally, Busygin himself came under attack in the Soviet press over the issue of pollution in Lake Baykal. An *Izvestiya* reporter, V. Rasputin, wrote that, in a meeting on the issue of the lake's condition, Busygin was evasive and bureaucratic, interested only in continuing to operate the pulp plant on the lake shore, rather than in the lake's ecology (*Izvestiya*, 17 February 1986, pp. 3, 6).[2]

Gosleskhoz was headed by Georgii Ivanovich Vorob'yev for many years, but he apparently was succeeded in 1986 by A. I. Zveryev. *Gosleskhoz* not only has managerial control over forests, but also supervises 20 research institutes. The duties of *Gosleskhoz* include conducting forest inventories; carrying out reforestation; and protecting forests from fire, insects, and disease.

Have all the reorganizational machinations over the years contributed overall to increased efficiency in forestry and wood-processing? Evidence suggests that decision making has *not* become more streamlined, because in addition to national structures, union-republic layers of bureaucracy still exist. In the timber and woodworking section of *Minlesbumprom*, over 3000 enterprises operate at the basic level. Blandon (1983, pp. 51, 53) has described the elimination of some layers of bureaucracy in the former Ministry of Timber and Woodworking and suggests that its reunification with the Ministry of Pulp and Paper was designed to strengthen links between producers and users. A delicate interplay of regional and administrative divisions, however, still remains within the timber industry. Anoshin *et al.* (1984, pp. 30-31) point out that, in the forest deficit zone, layers of organization on top of individual enterprises can include units such as *leskhoz* (forestry firms), *lespromkhoz* (forest-industry firms), *leskhozzag* (logging firms), *lesokombinat* (forest combines), and *lesokhozyaystvenniye ob'edineniye* (forest-industry amalgamations). In the forest surplus (forested) zones, such as the European North and Siberia, the *leskhoz* dominates the organizational structure and is often subdivided into ranger stations and sections. Combines and amalgamations (unions) are usually given names indicating regional orientation and in turn are divided into individual forest-industry firms (Kozhin and Styazhkin, 1976, pp. 23, 212-24). Firms at the lowest level are then subdivided into *lesopunkty*, logging units or areas. Some data suggest a relationship between number of logging areas in a *lespromkhoz* and volume of output (Charts 2.1 and 2.2), indicating that firms with more *lesopunkty* under their jurisdictions may harvest more logs.[3]

The rationale behind the creation of combines, amalgamations, and forest-product complexes has been the efficient integration of raw material extraction and production, and/or the integration of several processing steps to make use of by-products. For example, a sawmilling, woodworking combine would theoretically assure lumber supply from a mill, while its chip by-products would be utilized in the production of composition boards. Combines exist in three basic forms: (1) final-process-based, (2) raw-material-based, and (3) intermediate-output-based. Thus, combines may be both interbranch and intrabranch: several furniture enterprises could be united into a combine; logging firms could be joined; or lumber and composition board enterprises could form a combine (Glotov, 1977, pp. 157-58). Glotov (1977, p. 163) offers the example of the Primorskiy (Maritime) Lumber Woodworking Combine (DOK) with the following production capacity (cu. m):

Lumber	289,000
Chips	45,000
Particleboard	25,000
Window frames	354,000
Wood shavings	8,300
Furniture frames	30,000
Veneer sheets for furniture	20,000

When the forest product industries started to move to more remote areas and larger scales of operation, the form of organization known as LPK, or forest industry complex, was born. The concept included a large area of forest exploitation (logging) and transportation of logs to a town containing the heart of the LPK - a series of integrated processing plants which theoretically make optimal use of intermediate by-products. The first work on designing LPKs was conducted in 1963 by *Giprolesprom*, the Forest Industry Design Institute, later joined in this work by Leningrad's Kirov Forestry Academy (Glotov, 1977, pp. 167-70).

One of the earliest LPKs, at Bratsk in Eastern Siberia, began operations in 1971. It was designed to utilize 3.9 million cu. m of raw materials. Bratsk, however, did not achieve physical output targets or fulfill plans for profit goals and unit costs in the 1970s (Petrov, 1977). While a variety of factors may explain the problems at Bratsk, including labor turnover typical of Siberian complexes, the lack of vertical integration and shortfalls in raw materials supply may also have played a role. Despite these pitfalls, other LPKs have been constructed, including those at Syktyvkar in the Komi ASSR, Asino in Tomsk oblast, and Lesosibirsk and Krasnoyarsk in Krasnoyarsk kray. Major problems

Chart 2.1

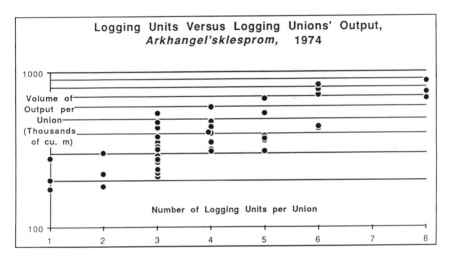

Chart 2.2

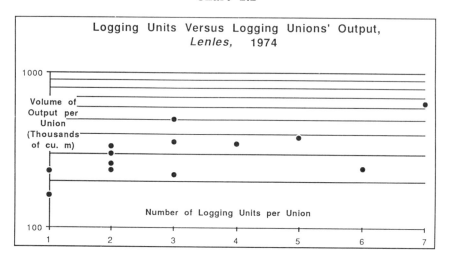

Logging Units Versus Logging Unions' Output,
Lenles,   1974

associated with many Soviet timber complexes are discussed in various articles in *CDSP* grouped under such revealing headings as "How a Siberian Timber Complex Fell Apart" (1984, vol. 36 [26], pp. 8, 12); "Reorganization in Timber Industry Asked" (1981, vol. 33 [31], pp. 10-11); "Process More Timber Near Cutting Sites" (1978, vol. 29 [51], pp. 7, 28); and "Siberian Regional Planning Hits Snag" (1977, vol. 29 [1], pp. 1-4).

Complaints expressed in the revealing article about the virtual collapse of the Krasnoyarsk timber complex (*CDSP*, 1984, vol. 36 [26], pp. 8, 12) confirm that difficulties in achieving integration with giant complexes continue to plague the forest industries. The *CDSP* material is derived from a visit by a correspondent of the influential Soviet newspaper, *Sotsialisticheskaya Industriya*, to the Krasnoyarsk LPK in 1984. This complex, according to the newspaper, now exists "in name only" because of its lack of integration. The wood chemical section of the complex must obtain raw materials (shavings and sawdust) from Irkutsk and Kemerovo; pulp for the Krasnoyarsk Pulp and Paper Combine (TsBK) is brought in from Bratsk. The article concluded that lack of leadership in the industry has resulted in the failure of the complex, because intricate material-supply ties among the units of the LPK cannot be maintained.

Another organizational bottleneck in the forest industries occurs in the area of technological developments. Research and Development (R&D) are accomplished both under *Gosleskhoz* and *Minlesbumprom*, and within academic institutes. The problem with R&D appears to be more in the realm of innovations (applied technology) than with inventions, because of the tenuous linkages between laboratory and field.[4] Testing on new equipment in the laboratory may produce results which are more optimistic than the equipment's actual performance at an enterprise. In 1975, for example, the L'vov Forest-Technical Institute tested a variety of new saws and found the profit produced by them to range from 1.06 to 1.58 rubles per cu. m of wood; once in use in an Arkhangel sawmill, however, the same equipment yielded a profit of only 0.76 rubles per cu. m (Mugandin, 1977, p. 53).

R&D is carried out within three units: the enterprise itself, offering some material incentives for new inventions developed by workers; the NII *(Nauchno-Issledovatel'skiy Institut)* (Scientific Research Institute), responsible for developing and testing inventions; and the design bureau, which plans new enterprises. (Examples of R&D organizations within *Minlesprom* are depicted in Chart 2.3; Chart 2.4 describes the functional organization of the design bureau,*Giprolestrans*.) In addition, *Gosleskhoz* oversees institutes for basic research on silvicultural management. One of the largest of these,*VSIILM* (All-Union Research Institute for Silviculture, Mechanization, and Economic Planning) is located at Pushkino in the Moscow greenbelt. Other major institutes under the supervision of *Gosleskhoz* include *LesNIILKh* (Leningrad Forestry Research Institute), *Dal'NIILKh* (Far East Forestry Research Institute), *Lesoproekt* (All-Union Air Photo Forest System), and *Soyuzgipropeskhoz* (All-Union State Planning/Prospecting Institute) (Anoshin *et al.*, 1984, p. 30).

Academic institutions also accomplish R&D. Both the Ministry of Higher Education and the USSR Academy of Sciences administer institutes which conduct research on forestry or on the forest-products industries. The Kirov Forestry Academy in Leningrad (*LLTA*) has a staff of 2500 and a student body of

Chart 2.3

Selected Research and Design Organizations Within *Minlesprom*

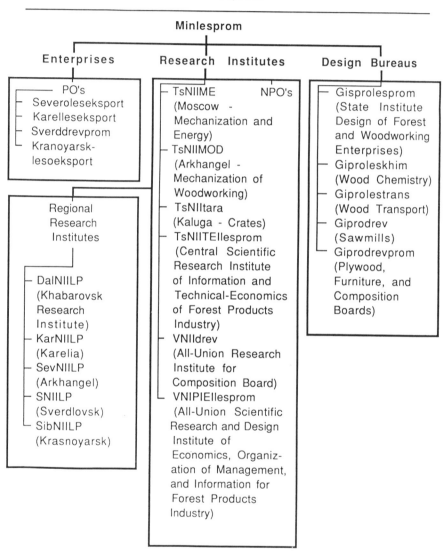

Minlesprom

Enterprises   Research Institutes   Design Bureaus

Enterprises	Research Institutes	Design Bureaus

PO's
Severoleseksport
Karelleseksport
Sverddrevprom
Kranoyarsk-
lesoeksport

Regional
Research
Institutes

DalNIILP
(Khabarovsk
Research
Institute)
KarNIILP
(Karelia)
SevNIILP
(Arkhangel)
SNIILP
(Sverdlovsk)
SibNIILP
(Krasnoyarsk)

TsNIIME   NPO's
(Moscow -
Mechanization and
Energy)
TsNIIMOD
(Arkhangel -
Mechanization of
Woodworking)
TsNIItara
(Kaluga - Crates)
TsNIITEllesprom
(Central Scientific
Research Institute
of Information and
Technical-Economics
of Forest Products
Industry)
VNIIdrev
(All-Union Research
Institute for
Composition Board)
VNIPIEllesprom
(All-Union Scientific
Research and Design
Institute of
Economics, Organiz-
ation of Management,
and Information for
Forest Products
Industry)

Gisprolesprom
(State Institute
Design of Forest
and Woodworking
Enterprises)
Giproleskhim
(Wood Chemistry)
Giprolestrans
(Wood Transport)
Giprodrev
(Sawmills)
Giprodrevprom
(Plywood,
Furniture, and
Composition
Boards)

Source: Mugandin (1977); Pavlov (1972); and Petrov (1977).

Chart 2.4

Organization of Giprolestrans (Wood Transport)
Design Bureau

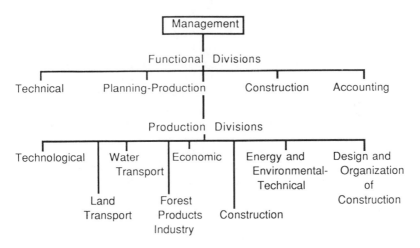

Source: Mugandin (1977); Pavlov (1972); and Petrov (1977).

12,000. *LLTA* offers a five-year program for engineers in addition to shorter programs and training for graduate students.

Despite the work of the R&D sector, forest industries are still criticized for being under mechanized and for not using profitably the capital investment assigned to them. Foreign technology (see Chapter 8) still plays a large role in the attempt to modernize this part of the Soviet economy. To the misguided postulate that forests are unlimited in the USSR, one might add that the forest-product sector may have suffered from the assumption that ministerial changes substitute for basic reforms in the system. Evidence suggests that the reorganizations of the past have not yet improved the performance of the industry.

SOURCES OF STATISTICAL DATA

Soviet reluctance to publish regional timber-harvesting data since approximately 1977 has greatly restricted the accuracy of analysis possible in the logging sector. In the relatively wide window of disclosure which seems to have existed from about 1960 to 1977, many Soviet published works provided extensive detail about the product mix and levels of cost of various products by region and frequently by enterprise. The annual *Narodnoye Khozyaystvo* volumes for the USSR and many union republics, especially the RSFSR, were rich in regional production data, and many individual studies by economists, geographers, and other industrial analysts provided the basis for extensive recalculation of production figures in our analyses of the country's space economy and regional geography. Unfortunately, this flexibility has been denied for most of the past decade as detailed sectoral studies have been discouraged; data sections in *Narodnoye Khozyaystvo* volumes have disappeared; and fugitive or sporadic references to economic and production data have been largely eliminated from the broad spectrum of publications comprising newspapers, magazines, trade journals and national and regional research publications.

The RSFSR *Narodnoye Khozyaystvo* volumes, however, have continued to provide some regional production data on key forest-sector products (lumber, plywood, paper, and paperboard), although not on timber harvesting. Furthermore, levels of reporting and forecasting have increased in association with the promulgation and publicizing of the Twelfth Five-Year Plan in late 1985 and early 1986. Many of the sources published between 1960 and 1975 contained projections which permit reasonable estimates of what may have occurred during the past decade, particularly when corroborated with some of the production data which have recently been published.

RELEVANT LITERATURE

The basic data supporting *The Disappearing Russian Forest* are derived from Soviet statistical handbooks, forestry research journals, individual monographs, and compendia provided by the United Nations Economic Commission for Europe. Supporting material has been obtained from previous studies by the authors and other analysts of Soviet forests and wood-processing industries, and from major translation media such as the *Current Digest of the Soviet Press* (*CDSP*) and *Soviet Geography*. Valuable information has also been provided during interviews with North American, Finnish, and Japanese industrialists who regularly participate in foreign trade and exchange of information with the USSR, but whose valuable personal insights and observations are not found in any published source.

In a broad sense, however, the base and inspiration for *The Disappearing Russian Forest* is the extensive study produced during the Association of American Geographers' project on Soviet Natural Resources in the World Economy. Analyses by the present authors and by specialists on other major components of the Soviet economy in the publication arising from that project obviate the need for providing extensive background or basic description of the USSR and its major resources here because they represent a current and invaluable starting point for the focus of the present book. The other indispensable source of reliable information and careful analyses concerning all Soviet resources and related developments comprises the "News Notes" accompanying each issue of *Soviet Geography*. Specialists like Victor Mote, Leslie Dienes, and Matthew Sagers have written extensively on topics germane to Soviet resources and regional developments and hence also to the present study. Although Western analysts of Soviet forests are relatively scarce, the body of recent work by Jarmo Eronen (1981, 1982b, 1984) in Finland on Soviet pulp and paper is particularly insightful, and that of Peter Blandon (1983) in the United Kingdom merits careful attention, particularly in the organization and conduct of logging. Although no longer directly active in the analysis of Soviet forests, some of the most careful and comprehensive assessments of the resource, methods of processing, and applications of specific types of technology is represented by the diverse and often unpublished reports of Jaroslavl Holowacz in Ontario. The authors acknowledge a deep gratitude to the assistance which Holowacz has provided since 1965 and for the quality of his work. These and other sources of information are appropriately discussed during analyses in each chapter.

Although evidence is not usually forthcoming on individual projects, the Soviet literature comprising research and administrative journals, and detailed monographs, is rich with data and discussion pertaining to individual topics, issues, problems, and regional developments. Much of the Soviet literature is supported by extensive field research and laboratory analysis. During the period covered by this book, the technical improvements in mensuration have meant that Soviet forests have access to increasingly accurate and representative inventory data. Physical and economic data supposedly measuring the same variable, however, often vary among and within Soviet publications because of a somewhat casual approach to the definition of terms and a lack of rigor in the utilization of consistent categories of information. This is particularly evident in figures expressing the spatial extent and physical volume of the forest - some represent the total growing stock for all administrations; others exclude the farming sector; and still others exclude forests utilized by non forestry ministries. Even data measuring forests under central state management may exclude certain categories of age, protective group, or degree of accessibility.

The data utilized in this book, however, have been carefully selected and verified for consistency in each analysis. Many are physical representations of variables and are compared through roundwood equivalents, the volume of roundwood required to produce a unit of each wood product. Economic variables are used when their importance is unequivocal, but Soviet forest economic data tend to be fragmented among many sources and to vary in composition and significance. For example, although individual examples employing economic variables are useful for illustrative purposes, great caution must be exercized when they are aggregated. Hence, the authors prefer to rely on many types of physical evaluation in their analyses; the techniques for measuring technology and products are consistent with their previous analyses and with those of other Western forest specialists. Although individual case studies of relatively unique projects are periodically reported by the Soviet press, the authors hesitate to use them as examples unless they clearly represent regional developments or technological and sectoral trends.

Despite the availability of an extensive Western and Soviet research literature, the question remains, however, "How adequate are our data?" Obviously the validity and reliability of national and regional forest data display shortcomings in most countries. This problem has only recently started to be overcome in Canada, for example, where most forest jurisdiction rests with the ten provincial governments. For the Soviet Union, however, most of the period covered in this book has involved extensive publication of statistical data and increasingly penetrating analyses by professional foresters. Unfortunately, access to appropriate decision makers and specialists by Western analysts remains virtually impossible; therefore, most of the insights and supporting evidence in each of this book's analyses are derived from the extensive literature published in the Soviet Union on forests and wood products.

NOTES

1. In March 1981, the new minister of *Minlesbumprom* reported in *Sotsialist-icheskaya Industriya* that the amalgamation was directly due to the lack of communication between the two ministries, particularly the inefficiencies in the Ministry of Timber and Woodworking, which were responsible for short-falls over the course of the Tenth Five-Year Plan (1976-1980) of wood equal to 17 percent of annual national requirements (*World Wood*, July 1981, pp. 18-19).
2. Discussed in *CDSP* (1986, vol. 38 [7], pp. 5-6, 22).
3. Blandon (1983, pp. 51-61) provides a detailed discussion of the Soviet log-ging structure under the former Ministry of Timber and Woodworking (*Min-lesprom*).
4. Poor linkages between design and application are not peculiar to forest pro-ducts, and have been discussed widely. Of particular note are studies by Am-man *et al.* (1977), and Martens and Young (1979).

APPENDIX 2.1. GLOSSARY

FOREST CLASSIFICATION AND ADMINISTRATION

Russian	*English*
Les	forest
Lesonasazhdeniye	standing forest
Devstvennyy les	virgin forest
Perestoynyy les	overmature forest
Dostupnyy dlya ekspluatatsiy les	accessible/exploitable forest
Ekspluatiruyemyy les	exploitable/usable/workable forest
Neekspluatiruyemyy les	nonexploitable or not currently being used
Ekspluatatsionnaya ploshchad'	timber limits/logging chance/area assigned to logging enterprises for exploitation/commercial timber land
Khozyaystvennyy les	managed forest
Stabil'no-khozyaystvennyy les	sustained yield management forest
Promyshlennyy les	commercial/industrial forest
Stabil'no-promyshlennyy les	perpetual/self-sustaining/stabilized forest resource base
Zashchitnyy les	protection forest
Lesistost'	degree/extent of forest cover
Lesnaya kul'tura	(forest) plantation/ (forest) planting
Lesnichestvo	ranger station
Lesnoye khozyaystvo/lesnoye delo/ lesovodstvo/lesopromyshlennost'	forestry/forestry practice
Ustroystvo lesov	forest system/forest organization/ forest regulation (in time and space)
Leskhoz	forestry firm
Predpriyatye po zagotovke lesa	logging enterprise
Khozyaystvo lesopol'zovaniya	logging operation/lumbering
Lesnoy fond	forest resource
Lesokhozyaystvennaya chast'	managed forest
Lesorastitel'naya zona	forest region
Lesorazrabotka	forest exploitation area/timber exploitation
Lesoseka	timber-cutting area
Lesorazvedeniye	afforestation
Lesovosstanovleniye	forest regeneration/reafforestation
Lesovozobnovleniye	forest regeneration/reproduction/ renewal/restocking/seedling crop/ young stand

Likvidnyy zapas — marketable volume (i.e., solid timber)

Glavnoye pol'zovaniye — principal cut/principal utilization

Promezhutochnoye pol'zovaniye — thinnings/intermediate forest use (i.e., cutting prior to the principal cut or cutting prior to the rotation cut)

Pobochnoye pol'zovaniye — nonindustrial use (i.e., use other than deriving wood fiber)

Myagkolistvennye porody — shade-intolerant hardwood species (e.g., poplar; birch; aspen, and, in USSR, basswood)

Tverdolistvennye porody — shade-tolerant hardwood species (e.g., oak; beech)

Khvoynye porody — conifers [e.g., pine; spruce (yel); fir (pikhta); larch]

Vozrastnye gruppy: — age groups (of forest stands):
  a) Molodnyaki — a) juvenile
  b) Sredne-vozrastnye — b) middle age
  c) Prispevayushchiye — c) approaching maturity
  d) Spelye i perestoynye — d) mature and overmature

Kategoriya zashchitnosti lesov: — forest protection classification:
  a) Lesa I gruppy — a) protection forests - sanitary and selective cutting only

  b) Lesa II gruppy — b) industrial forests in densely populated areas. Cut should not exceed mean annual increment in any forest

  c) Lesa III gruppy — c) industrial forests. Cut can exceed mean annual increment in a forest but not in a broad geographical area

Sanitarno-gigiyenicheskiye i ozdorovitelnye lesa — urban-centered forests (i.e., forests of sanitoriums associated with convalescence and preservation of health)

Somknutost' — stand density/stocking density

Somknutost' nasazhdeniya — stand density/density of stocking/ extent of crown cover or of complete canopy

Bonitet — site quality

Polnota — stocking (density)

Lesnye kategorii zemel': — forest land categories:
  a) Pokrytye lesom — a) forested forestry lands
  b) Ne pokrytye lesom — b) nonforested forestry lands

c) Nesomknuvshiyesya lesnye kul'tury   c) plantations in which crowns have not closed

Nelesnye kategorii zemel':   nonforestry land categories:
   a) Ugodya   a) miscellaneous usable lands
     -Pashni   -arable lands
     -Senokosy   -natural hay fields
     -Vody   -water bodies
     -Pastbishcha (vygony)   -open range
     -Dorogi, proseki, kanavy   -roads, rights of way, ditches

   b) Neispol'zuyemye zemli   b) unutilized lands
Pitomnik   forestry nursery
Lesnye kul'tury   plantations
Osnovnye lesoobrazuyushiye porody   principal forestry species
Zapretnye polosy   restricted zones/belts/regions/areas

TIMBER REMOVALS

Godichnaya lesoseka	annual cutting area
Fakticheski vyrubleno	actual cut
Prochiye rubki	other cuttings or removals
Obshchiy otpusk drevesiny	total removals of wood (i.e., all removals)
Polosno-pasechnye rubki	strip cutting
Polosnaya rubka	strip cutting, felling
Polosnaya sploshnaya rubka	progressive strip system/ progressive fellings
Rubka kulisnaya/cherespolosnaya	strip felling or cutting
Raschetnaya lesoseka	regulated/calculated allowable cut
Rubka	felled or felling quantity/cut/ logging quantity/ felled (timber)/ (timber) removals
Vyrubka	deforestation/felling of trees or timber/clear-felling/ felled or logged area
Vyrubka (vyrublennyy uchastok lesa)	felled/logged area
Obezleseniye	dis(af)forestation/deforestation/ forest liquidation
Istrebleniye/opustosheniye lesa	forest devastation or liquidation or destruction/deforestation
Godichnaya vyrubka	annual cut/yield/felling
Smetnaya vyrubka	calculated logging quantity/ calculated cut/quota to be cut/ felling budget/calculated felling volume
Rubki glavnogo pol'zovaniya	principal or main cut/use

Rubki ukhoda	improvement thinnings/ improvement fellings or cuttings/ tending cut/intermediate cutting or felling
Prokhodnye rubki	selective logging/thinning/culling (a form of intermediate cutting or felling)
Sploshnaya rubka/lesoseka	clear cutting, clear-cut area
Ukhod za lesom	tending of woods or forest
Vyborochnye rubki	cleaning/selection cutting/felling/ selective cutting or felling/free felling

NOTE ON CONVERSION FACTORS

Conversions are approximate and vary depending on type of wood and recovery factor.

1 hectare (ha) = 2.471 acres
1 ha = 10,000 square meters (sq. m)
1 cubic meter (cu. m) of logs = 0.253 thousand board feet (mbf) assuming 60% lumber recovery
1 cu. m of solid wood = 0.424 mbf

Source: Based on Barr (1982, pp. 455-56). Conversion information is from Williston (1976, pp. 484-85).

APPENDIX 2.2
MAJOR USSR INDUSTRIAL TIMBER SPECIES

CONIFERS/KHVOYNYE PORODY - Including:

Larch/Larix/Listvennitsa
Larix dahurica Turcz. ex Trautv./Listvennitsa daurskaya
Eastward from Khatanga and Lower Tunguska rivers; northward to 72d 30m; southward to headwaters of Sungara river; southern half of Kamchatka.
Larix maritima Sukacz./Listvennitsa primorskaya
Far East; mountain slopes of Tatar strait.
Larix sibirica ledeb./Listvennitsa sibirskaya
Northeastern European USSR and western half of Siberia; lower reaches of Yenisey River to 69d 40m and Pyasina River to 70d 15m north latitude; southward to western foothills of Altay and Sauru and Tarbagatau ranges (47d north latitude).
Larix czekanowskii Sz./Listvennitsa Chekanovskogo
Distribution similar to listvennitsa sibirskaya and daurskaya. Grows in Krasnoyarsk kray, Yakut and Buryat ASSRs, Irkutsk and Chita oblasts.
Larix sukaczewii Djil. Dyl./Listvennitsa Sukacheva

Extends westward from Ob and Irtysh rivers to eastern shores of Lake Onega.
Pine/Pinus/Sosna

Pinus koraiensis Siebold et Zucc./Sosna kedrovaya koreyskaya, kedr koreyskiy
Soviet Far East; between 42d 30m and 51d 32m north latitude, and 129d 50m and 140d 20m east longitude.

Pinus sibirica Du Tour./Sosna kedrovaya sibirskaya (stone pine)
Found almost throughout Siberia and widely in the Urals. Extends throughout an area circumscribed by the upper reaches of Vychegda River, northern Urals at 66d north latitude, the lower Ob and Yenisey (at 68d 12m), upper reaches of Aldan River, northern Mongolia, Altay (48d 15m) Mountains, and the southeastern Urals (57d north latitude).

Pinus sylvestris L./Sosna obyknovennaya
Found widely throughout the USSR from the Kola Peninsula (70d north latitude) and White Sea to the southern slopes of the Verkhoyansk Range and the Sea of Okhotsk. Its territory includes the Altay and extends into Central Asia (as far south as 48d 20m north latitude). Southern border in European USSR extends from southern Volkhynya and Kiev oblasts through Dnepropetrovsk, Saratov, Kuybyshev, and Chelyabinsk oblasts. Also found in eastern Crimea and in Transcaucasia.

Spruce/Picea/Yel'

Picea abies (L.) Karst./Yel' obyknovennaya
Primarily found in European USSR southward from wooded tundra to northern limits of the central Black Earth belt, westward to the Carpathian Mountains, and eastward to the Urals. Some growth in the southern tayga zone of Western Siberia as far east as the Irtysh River.

Picea ajanensis (Lindl. et Gord.) Fisch. ex Carr./Yel' ayanskaya
Typical alpine species found in the Far East on Kamchatka and on Sakhalin.

Picea obovata Ledeb./Yel' sibirskaya
Extends from the Northeastern European USSR through the Urals to Siberia with periodic occurrences along the Amur, in Transbaykal, and in the Sayan and Altay Mountains.

Fir/Abies/Pikhta

Abies sachalinensis Fr. Schmidt./Pikhta sakhalinskaya
Grows throughout Sakhalin and extends to Schmidt peninsula. Basic coniferous species in southern Kurile islands. Has vertical range up to 1000 m.

Abies sibirica Ledeb./Pikhta sibirskaya
Grows in the Northeastern European USSR, throughout much of Siberia (from Baykal in the East into the Altay Mountains and southwards into Central Asia). Grows at elevations up to 2000 m.

Abies holophylla Maxim./Pikhta tsel'nolistnaya or *man'churskaya, primorskaya*
Found in the far south of the Maritime oblast in the Far East in mountain elevations below 500 m.

Abies nephrolepis (Trautv. Maxim./Pikhta belokoraya, podkocheshuynaya, amurskaya
Corresponds to the distribution of Yel' ayanskaya in the Sikhote-Alin Mountains at elevations below 1200 m.

SHADE-TOLERANT HARDWOOD SPECIES (STHS)/
TVERDOLISTVENNYE PORODY - Including:

Oak/Quercus/Dub
   Quercus dentata Thunb./Dub zubchatyy
Found along the sea coast of the Maritime oblast, Soviet Far East.
   Quercus petraea (Mattuschk'a) Liebl./Dub skal'nyy, or *zimniy*
Grows in the southern Baltic states, in the Western Ukraine, in the Northern
Crimea, in the North Caucasus, and in northwestern Transcaucasia.
   Quercus robur L./Dub chereshchatyy, letniy
Extends throughout the European USSR; northern limit corresponds to a line
between Leningrad and Kirov; eastern extent is limited by the Ural Mountainss;
does not extend southeastwards past Orenburg, Saratov, and Volgograd. Extends
southward to mouth of Dneper and Novocherkassk. Also occurs naturally in the
Crimean and North Caucasian foothills.
   Quercus mongolica Fisch. ex Ledeb./Dub mongol'skiy
Grows in Amur oblast, Maritime kray, and southern two-thirds of Sakhalin
oblast.
Beech/Fagus/Buk
   Fagus orientalis Lipsky./Buk vostochnyy   or *kavkazskiy*
The principal forest species of the Transcaucasus. Also found in the Crimea.
   Fagus sylvatica L./Buk lesnoy   or *yevropeyskiy*
Grows in the Western Ukraine (Carpathian Mountains up to elevations of 1000
m, and Carpathian foothills), western Belorussia, Kaliningrad oblast, Moldavia,
and mountainous regions of the Crimea.
Ash/Fraxinus/Yasen'
   Fraxinus excelsior L./Yasen' obyknovennyy
Found throughout the European USSR. Northern limit corresponds to a line
between Leningrad and Cheboksary; southern limit extends from the mouth of
the Medveditsy River through Lugansk, Artem'evsk, Dnepropetrovsk, and
Kishinev. Some stands in the mountainous Crimea and the Transcaucasus.
Common in urban greenery plantations and in shelterbelts.
   Fraxinus mandshurica Rupr./Yasen' man'chzhurskiy
Found in the Far East in Amur oblast, Maritime kray, and southern Sakhalin.

SHADE-INTOLERANT HARDWOOD SPECIES (SIHS)/
MYAGKOLISTVENNYE PORODY - Including:

Birch/Betula/Beryeza
   Betula davurica Pall./Beryeza daurskaya, chernaya
Grows in southern districts of the Far East and Transbaykal.
   Betula costata Trautv./Beryeza rebristaya
Found in the mountainous forests of the Far East.
   Betula ermanii Cham./Beryeza kamennaya, Ermana
Grows along the Sea of Okhostk coast, on Sakhalin and Kamchatka, and along
the USSR northern tree line.
   Betula pendula Roth./Beryeza plakuchaya, povislaya, borodavchataya

Covers a significant portion of the European and Western Siberian forest zones. Occurs in pure and mixed stands.

Betula pubescens Ehrh./Beryeza pushistaya
Found in European USSR forests except in the Crimea. Extends northward to the tundra. In Siberia, extends northeastward into northern Yakutia and eastward in Transbaykal as far as the Yablonovyy Mountains.

Betula schmidtii Regel./Beryeza zheleznaya, Shmidta
Grows in the Far East in southern Maritime kray on dry, rocky slopes.

Aspen/Populus tremula L./Osina
Found throughout the European and Asiatic USSR

Basswood/Tilia/Lipa

Tilia amurensis Rupr./Lipa amurskaya
Found in the Far East from the middle Amur southwards and extends westward to the Dauriya. Grows on south-facing slopes often in mixed stands with Betula davurica and Quercus mongolica.

Tilia cordata Mill./Lipa mekolistnaya, serdtsevidnaya
Found in European USSR forests, including the Crimea and Caucasus, and in Western Siberia as far east as the Irtysh River. Occurs in the Alatau Mountainss near Krasnoyarsk and in the Altay. Northern European border extends from lakes Ladoga and Onega eastward to the mouth of the Vagi River, through Kotlas, across northern Perm oblast to the Urals.

Tilia platyphyllos Scop./Lipa krupnolistnaya
Found in western forests of the Ukraine and in the Caucasus. Extensively utilized in urban greenery in the Baltics, Belorussia, Ukraine, Crimea, Caucasus, and the RSFSR central provinces as far north as Leningrad, Moscow, and Perm. Also comprises urban greenery in Central Asia.

Alder/Alnus/Ol'kha

Alnus glutinosa (L.) Gaertn./Ol'kha chernaya, or *kleykaya*
Found throughout a large portion of the forest and wood steppe zones of European USSR, in the Crimea, Moldavia, North Caucasus, Western Siberia, Altay, and Northern Kazakhstan. Northern European boundary (usually no further north than 62d) extends from Petrozavodsk to Perm. Occasional clusters of this species are found further north.

Alnus incana (L.) Moench./Ol'kha seraya, or *belaya*
Extends northwards to the tundra and southwards to the wooded steppe and is occasionally found southeast from the Volga. Extends beyond the Urals to the Irtysh River. Also is found in the forests of the Greater Caucasus Mountain Range.

Source: Based on Atrokhin *et al.* (1982); Mozhayev *et al.* (1983); Buzykin (1984); and Sutton (1975, pp. 110-38).

APPENDIX 2.3. ABBREVIATIONS FOR SELECTED TYPES OF PRODUCTION IN THE FOREST-PRODUCTS SECTOR

Abbreviation	*Russian Term (and Translation)*
DOK	Derevoobrabatyvayushchiy kombinat (Woodworking combine)
DSK	Domostroitel'niy kombinat (Housing construction combine)
FK	Fanerniy kombinat (Plywood combine)
FMK	Fanerno-mebel'niy kombinat (Plywood-furniture combine)
FMZ	Fanerno-mebel'niy zavod (Plywood-furniture plant)
LK	Lesnoy kombinat (Forest combine)
LPK	Lesopromyshlenniy kompleks (Forest industry complex)
LZ	Lesnoy zavod (Forest plant)
MDF	Mebel'no-derevoobrabatyvayushchaya fabrika (Furniture-woodworking factory)
MDK	Mebel'no-derevoobrabatyvayushchiy kombinat (Furtniture-woodworking combine)
MK	Mebel'niy kombinat (Furniture combine)
TsBK	Tsellyulozno-bumazhniy kombinat (Pulp and Paper combine)
TsKK	Tsellyulozno-kartonniy kombinat (Pulp and Paperboard combine)

Sources: Compiled from Delimov (1972); Alekseyev (1977); and Glotov (1977)

3
The Record of Forest Utilization

Chapter 3 seeks to establish a basis on which subsequent chapters can identify and analyze specific problems concerning the Soviet forest and wood-processing industries. Many aspects of the utilization dilemma begin with choices on harvest and management. The major problems underlined in the chapter are: (1) underutilization of accessible European-Uralian and Siberian forests; (2) possible misemphasis by planners on eastern forests; (3) need for alternative patterns of consumption, harvesting, and use of waste materials and thinnings; (4) underestimation of the significance of intermediate cut; and (5) degradation of some forest stands due to deforestation processes.

GROWING STOCK AND ALLOWABLE CUT

The USSR has one-fifth of the world's forested area and over one-quarter of its growing stock (UNIDO, 1983, p. 12). Soviet resource and production data, however, often vary according to author and reporting agency. Confusion results as well from the large number of subdivisions into which the national forest area is classified. Thus 94.6 percent of the Soviet forests are administered by central forestry authorities, 3.1 percent are under long-term tenure with various ministries and agencies, and 2.3 percent are held by collective farms (Kozhukhov, 1984, pp. 74-75). The area administered by central forestry authorities (Honer *et al.*, 1985, Figure 2) is subdivided into land utilized as pasture by various cooperative organizations (9 percent of national total forest land); nonexploitable forests (protection or Group 1 forests, 13 percent of the total); and exploitable forests: restricted-use industrial and local forests (Group 2, 6 percent of the total) and exploitable commercial and reserve (inaccessible) forests (Group 3, 67 percent).

Published data, however, often exclude resource and production data from some of these categories or pertain only to selected industrial ministries and organizations. Data in the annual national and republic yearbooks *(Narodnoye Khozyaystvo)*, for example, seem to apply solely to the principal harvest by organizations of state significance. Some of these sources thus exclude thinning or improvement cuts which originate mainly in Group 1 and 2 forests. On the other hand, the sole recent economic geographical analysis of the Soviet forest resource includes data only for timber produced and shipped by *Soyuzglavlesa*, a subdivision of *Gossnab*, which allocates timber materials to various industrial enterprises (Vorob'yev *et al.*, 1979, p. 193). Reserves of standing timber in some Group 1 and 2 forests, however, become quite significant when the relative economic utility of various regions is evaluated, or when the merits of regeneration in the European-Uralian zone are weighed against those of logging remote Siberian virgin stands (discussed at length in Chapter 4).

Most of our knowledge about the current size and distribution of growing stock in the USSR derives from the last three national inventories (1973, 1978, and 1983). Atlthough many qualitative characteristics of the Soviet forest can be evaluated from the published report of the last inventory (Chapter 4), the regional distribution of the growing stock and its species mix requires a composite analysis based on all three inventory reports.

The 1978 inventory report (Drozhalov, 1979) reported a total forest area of 1257.3 million ha, a nonforested forestry area of 143.4 million ha (hectares), and 322.3 million ha of nonforestry land. The land area of the USSR is 2227.5 million ha (2240.2 million including the White Sea and the Sea of Azov). Land used by agriculture comprises 1047.3 million ha, but that pertaining to the State Land Reserve and forestry organizations (excluding long-term leases by kolkhozy and sovkhozy) totals 1112.1 million ha. Other landusers account for 68.1 million ha (*Narodnoye Khozyaystvo SSSR v 1984 g.*, 1985, p. 396). The centrally managed forested area was 729 million ha, of which 678 million (Table 3.1) comprised principal species, with the remaining 51 million ha consisting of bush, shrubs, willows, nuts, and fruits.

Most of the Soviet forest comprises conifers, particularly larch, pine, and spruce, which account for 70 percent of the principal species' area. Spruce and birch each comprise approximately one-eighth of the principal species' area; the relative share of aspen almost corresponds to that of fir. Seven genera with a variety of species thus comprise over 85 percent of the Soviet principal species' forested area. Their spatial distribution, however, varies considerably and inflates the utility of forests comprising pine and spruce, while it detracts from those dominated by larch (Table 3.2). The natural species composition enhances the utility of European-Uralian and Southern and Western Siberian forests and could, if sustained, obviate logging in Eastern and Northern Siberian forests, and in those of much of the Far East, which are dominated by larch.

The location of many shade-intolerant stands should promote their utilization, but the Soviet economy does not yet place an appropriate value on the readily accessible European-Uralian birch and aspen forests. Thus, the European USSR taiga comprises 78 percent conifers; the mixed forest belt, 53 percent; the wooded steppe, 25 percent; and the steppe, 12 percent. Through selective felling, the share of shade intolerant species has steadily increased in the European mixed forest, and that of shade tolerant species, particularly oak, has become more pronounced in the wooded steppe (Atrokhin *et al.*, 1982, p. 25). Consequently, this book stresses the importance of accessible European-Uralian and Siberian forests to the Soviet timber industry, particularly to the present day, and argues that these regions could sustain present total annual national harvesting levels of approximately 400 million cu. m if effective management and silviculture were undertaken.

Much of our current understanding of the spatial variation in the utility and significance of Soviet growing stock derives from the work of Vorob'yev *et al.* (1979). Their "economic-geographical" analysis uses several classification schemes to describe Soviet forests and the timber industry, although unfortunately it excludes any economic evaluation of regional forests. Nevertheless, their physical categories (area and volume of standing timber, designated usage, species composition, age, accessibility, type of harvest, site

Table 3.1
Principal Species Composition of Centrally
Administered Forests
(Millions of ha)

Species	Area	% of Total
Principal Species	678.0	100.0
Conifers - Including:	531.2	78.3
Larch	275.2	40.5
Pine	117.8	17.4
Spruce	81.1	12.0
Stone Pine	41.0	6.0
Fir	15.4	2.3
Shade Tolerant Hardwood Species (STHS) - Including:	32.3	4.7
Oak	9.8	1.4
Beech	2.6	0.4
Ash	0.7	0.1
Shade Intolerant Hardwood Species (SIHS) - Including:	114.0	17.0
Birch	88.6	13.0
Aspen	19.1	2.8
Basswood	2.7	0.4
Alder	2.5	0.4

Source: Drozhalov (1979, pp. 41-43).

Table 3.2
Species Composition of Forested Areas
(% of Areal Total)

	Conifers				Hardwoods					Scrub
	Total - Including:				SIHS	STHS - Including High Forest - Of which:				
		Pine	Spruce & Fir	Larch					Oak	Beech	
USSR[a]	75	17	14	38	17	3	2	1	<1	5
RSFSR	76	17	14	40	>16	2	<2	<1	>-	5
Northwest	80	32	47	<1	20	-	-	-	-	-
Center	46	28	18	-	51	3	1	1	-	-
Volgo-Vyatka	51	29	22	-	45	4	2	2	-	-
Black Earth	28	28	-	-	18	54	18	17	-	-
Volga Littoral	21	16	3	-	53	26	3	3	-	-
North Caucasus	10	8	-	-	16	74	37	13	24	-
Urals	77	18	54	-	15	-	-	-	-	-
RSFSR: Europe-Uralia	65	29	35	<1	30	5	<2	1	<1	<1
Western Siberia	69	35	6	6	31	-	-	-	-	-
Eastern Siberia	85	16	6	48	15	-	-	-	-	-
Far East	69	3	12	51	24[b]	7	2	2	-	-
RSFSR: Asia	79	13	9	50	13	2	2	<1	-	-
Belorussia	68	58	9	>-	28	<5	<5	4	>-	-
Baltics(Latvia)	68	51	17	>-	32	<1	<1	<1	-	-
Southwest (Ukraine)	47	36	11	-	11	41	31	21	9	1
Caucasus (Georgia)	19	4	15	-	8	66	61	7	49	7
USSR: Europe-Uralia	63	30	32	-	29	8	4	2	<2	-
USSR: Asia	78	13	9	49	13	2	2	<1	-	7

[a]Each row sums to 100 percent.
[b]Includes scrub.
Source: Derived from Vorob'yev *et al.* (1979, p. 78).

quality, and stocking) permit the resource to be qualitatively assessed and economic variables to be introduced from other sources.

The area and volume of standing timber (Table 3.3) vary throughout the country. At first glance, the large proportion of timber in the Northwest, Urals, Siberia, and the Far East appears to offer ample opportunity for development of logging and wood-processing, and to a large extent, this has occurred in the European-Uralian heavily forested regions. The sheer magnitude of the Soviet growing stock, however, is misleading because of important variations in other key physical criteria. A cental issue to consider is: why do regions with most of the standing timber not contribute concomitantly to timber harvesting or wood-processing?

In addition to its detail on regional distribution of timber, the classification scheme can provide information on inventory. The Soviet tripartite classification of forests (Table 3.4; Appendix 2.1) depends on their official role in the Soviet economy, especially on their location and social, cultural, and economic functions (UNIDO, 1983, pp. 13-14). Groups 1 and 2 emphasize resource conservation and environmental protection. They are significant in the European USSR where they comprise half of the state forest area. Forests in Group 1 receive the greatest degree of protection because they constitute urban greenbelts, shelterbelts, and erosion control; are adjacent to rivers and lakes; comprise forest reserves, parks, nut- and fruit-stands; or occupy sensitive tundra and subalpine areas. Forests in Group 2 combine economic and environmental functions and are located in heavily populated regions with well-developed infrastructure; they may have undergone extensive depredation from overharvesting. These forests require silviculture and controlled management to offset the effects of overutilization and demands by adjacent populations. The largest category is Group 3. These forests are suitable for commercial exploitation. They constitute 45 percent of the European state forest area and 84 percent of that in Asia. Some of these forests are available for harvesting, some are designated as reserves, and some are currently deemed inaccessible because they lack infrastructure or are otherwise economically not viable.

Four-fifths of Group 3 forests are conifers. These species comprise approximately half of Group 2 forests and between one-half and four-fifths of Group 1 forests. Asian Group 2 forests have major stands of pine (about one-third of the forested area), whereas Asian Group 3 forests are dominated by larch. On the other hand, European Group 3 forests are dominated by spruce and fir. These species are less significant in the other European groups, where oak (Group 2) and beech (Group 1) are the major species.

When Soviet foresters employ these three groups to estimate the industrial significance of regional forests (Vorob'yev *et al.*, 1979, pp. 122-24), they give the impression that timber harvesting should either occur in northern European-uralia or in Asia. Full use is permitted of forests in the five administative divisions of the North, in Kostroma oblast of the Center, and in Kirov oblast of the Volgo-Vyatka. Three divisions in the Urals, two in Western Siberia, all of Eastern Siberia, and the four divisions comprising the southern zone of the Far East are eligible for full industrial use. The Northwest, the rest of the Urals and Western Siberia, and the northern zone of the Far East, however, are allowed protected and use-restricted commercial logging. Except for the Far Eastern

Table 3.3
Distribution of Forested Area: Characteristics of Industrial Stands Under Central State Forest Management

	Forested Area	Total Growing Stock	% of Forested Area by Age Group of Stands				% of MOM[a] Comprising Stands of:			MOM as % of GS[c] Vol.	Utilization of CAC[b] for each Species (%)			
	Mill. ha	Mill. cu. m	J[a]	MA	AM	MOM	C[d]	SIHS	STHS		C	SIHS	STHS	Total
USSR	675,206	74,872	15	18	10	57	85	13	2	69				
RSFSR	646,102	72,216	14	17	10	59	86	(14 - both)		71	104	41		87
Northwest	68,806	7,366	20	17	5	58	89	11	0	72	104	79	62	87
Center	12,446	1,542	38	36	13	13	45	53	2	22	114	80	62	94
Volgo-Vyatka	9,911	1,209	42	25	9	24	57	42	1	44	102	92	92	95
Black Earth	1,113	125	48	35	10	7	19	47	34	13	89	58	32	61
Volga Littoral	8,925	1,023	27	31	14	28	20	62	18	38	114	82	80	99
North Caucasus	2,853	391	23	33	15	29	19	11	70	44	110	67	57	93
Urals	24,306	3,014	31	20	9	40	77	23	0	61				
RSFSR Europe-Uralia	128,360	14,670	26	21	8	41								
Western Siberia	75,716	9,655	7	15	15	63	68	32		72	44	16		30
Eastern Siberia	216,026	27,191	9	17	10	64	92	8		74	48	6		36
Far East	226,000	20,700	14	16	9	61								
(South)	70,216	8,948					77	15	8	70	53	13	15	45

(Region)	GS	CAC	J	MA	AM	MOM	C	SIHS	STHS			
(North)	155,784	11,752					99			74	12	13
RSFSR Asia	517,742	57,546	11	16	10	63	43	43	14	74	97	97
Belorussia	5,378	535	59	28	10	3	80	(20 - both)		6	97	97
Baltics (excl. Kaliningrad)	3,986	506	38	43	11	8				12	97	98
Estonia	997	121	39	38	12	11				18		
Latvia	1,714	228	35	47	10	8				11		
Lithuania	1,275	157	41	43	10	6				9		
West	9,364	1,041										
Southwest[e]	6,020	823	53	30	10	7	36	9	55	13	102	98
Caucasus	3,082	475	11	48	17	24	35	(65 - both)		36	56	64
USSR Europe-Uralia	146,826	17,009	28	23	8	41	77	19	4	53		
Central Asia	10,638	317					100			46		
(Excl. Kazakhstan)	1,538	25	19	31	20	29	71	29		48	57	58
Kazakhstan	9,100	292	11	16	10	63	87	11	2	74	58	66
USSR Asia	528,380	57,863	11	16	10	63				74	57	5

Note: Blanks spaces in table indicate that data are not available.

[a]J = juvenile stands; MA = medium age stands; AM = stands approaching maturity; MOM = mature and overmature stands.

[b]CAC = calculated allowable cut.

[c]GS = growing stock.

[d]C = conifers; SIHS = shade-intolerant hardwood species; STHS = shade-tolerant hardwood species.

[e]All data in this row except those in columns 1 and 2 refer to Ukraine only.

Source: Compiled and adapted from Vorobyev et al. (1979), various pages; Timofeyev (1980), pp. 17-18; and Lesnoye Khozyaystvo SSSR (1977, p. 57). Values are net of forests administered by collective farms, nonforestry ministries and agencies, or held under long-lease by sheep and reindeer herding enterprises.

Table 3.4
Forests by Categories of Designated Usage
(% of USSR State Forest Area)

Category of Protection and Permitted Use	USSR (Total)	European USSR	Asiatic USSR
Total	100.0	18.2	81.8
Group 1 - Including:	15.8	4.9	10.9
Greenbelts - Of Which:	1.5	1.1	0.4
Managed Forests	1.1	0.8	0.3
Field and Soil Protection	1.8	0.7	1.1
Resort Forests >-	>-	>-	
Restricted Zones Along Rivers, Lakes, and Other Water Bodies - Of Which:	5.8	1.3	4.5
Zones Adjacent to Spawning Rivers and Lakes	2.6	0.3	2.3
Protective Zones Along Roads	0.4	0.3	<0.1
Nut Harvesting Areas	1.1	>-	1.1
Protective Zones of Tundra Forests	4.3	1.0	3.3
Protective-Exploitable	>-	>-	-
Other	0.8	0.3	0.5
Group 2 - Including:	6.9	4.9	2.0
Operational	6.2	4.7	1.5
Designated Districts and Zones	0.2	0.1	0.1
Inaccessible >-	-	>-	
Zones Adjacent to Spawning rivers and Lakes, Fish Hatcheries, and Management Undertakings	0.1	-	0.1
Nonoperational	0.4	0.1	0.3
Group 3 - Including:	77.3	8.4	68.9
Operational	34.7	8.1	26.6
Designated Districts and Zones	0.9	>-	0.9
Reserve Forests	31.9	-	31.9
Zones Adjacent to Spawning Rivers and Lakes, Fish Hatcheries and Management Undertakings	0.5	0.2	0.3
Inaccessible and Nonoperational	9.3	0.1	9.2

Source: Derived from Vorob'yev *et al.* (1979, p. 89).

north, the other use-controlled commercial areas are accessible to markets and infrastructure and could, with effective forestry management, play an important and sustained role in the provision of timber. Furthermore, with appropriate changes in policy and landuse designation, many other areas, particularly in Europe, which are classified now as having "insignificant" industrial forests, could become important but limited suppliers of high-quality and/or special-purpose timber. Why, then, do these regions not contribute more? Many of the qualitative aspects of Soviet forests discussed below provide compelling evidence that rigidity through institutional organization and administrative classification might be leading Soviet planners and timber users to inappropriate development conclusions. Viable regional alternative strategies for obtaining timber and wood fiber are probably precluded from assessment, although this now may be changing as fiber shortages become increasingly acute in Europe-Uralia. Petrov *et al.* (1986, pp. 208-9) acknowledge that the allowable cut of conifers in the Group 1 and 2 forests of this zone has steadily increased since 1976 as the allowable cut from the area's Group 3 forests has declined following previous years' overcutting.

A factor frequently cited by Soviet foresters justifying the need for a greater shift of logging and wood-processing to eastern regions is the disproportionate share of mature and over-mature timber in these forests. Nearly three-fifths of the national forest pertains to this category, but the share is somewhat higher east of the Urals. As discussed in Chapter 4, this imbalance is exacerbated by the spatial variation in species and mean annual increment. It arises from the long history of agriculture and settlement in the European USSR, and the extent to which forests in this area were initially accessible for fuel and commercial exploitation, including export. European forests also have undergone the depredations of war and civil disorder to a much greater degree than those in Siberia and the Far East, and thus have larger proportions of stands in the juvenile and middle-age categories. The average annual increment per ha in all centrally managed forests was 1.38 cu. m in 1978, but this increment was much larger (2.13 cu. m) in such forests located in the European-Uralian zone. This sizable difference reflects both superior European growing conditions and the greater proportion of juvenile and middle-age stands in the region's forests. Mature and over-mature forests grow very little, if at all. Hence, logging in such forests is described as "the forced cutting method," which presumably implies extensive clear felling well in excess of mean annual increment (UNIDO, 1983, pp. 13-14). Unfortunately, this principle seems to have been used in the recent past throughout much of European-Uralian RSFSR without proportionate investments in silviculture, despite official policies aimed at regeneration (UNIDO, 1983, p. 13). This has produced not only a regeneration backlog, but also a serious disproportion in the age and species composition of accessible stands.[1]

The Soviet mean annual increment (MAI) (Table 3.5) is approximately 2.1 times greater than the annual volume of timber harvested by all producers. One-third of this MAI accrues to the European-Uralian USSR and represents 70 percent of the total annual harvest. The relative importance of this annual increment in Europe-Uralia is greater for deciduous species than for conifers. All species, however, grow much faster in the West than in Asia, and annual growth

Table 3.5
Mean Annual Increment (MAI) of Soviet Forests

	Total (Mill. cu. m/yr)				MAI/ha (cu. m/yr)		
	All Species	Conifers	SIHS	STHS	Conifers	SIHS	STHS
USSR	881	600	244	37	1.2	2.2	1.6
RSFSR	821	568	229	24	1.2	2.2	1.6
Northwest	86	61	25		1.1		
Center	40	17	23		1.1		
Volgo-Vyatka	28	13	15		2.9		
Black Earth	4	1	<1	2	3.7		
Volga Littoral	24	4	14	6	3.0		
North Caucasus	7	<1	1	6	2.1		
Urals	49	26	22	1	1.8		
RSFSR Europe-Uralia	238	122	101	15	1.5	2.6	2.5
Western Siberia	99	52	47		1.2		
Eastern Siberia	275	221	54		1.2		
Far East	209	173	27	9	[0.8(N)-1.5(S)][a]		
RSFSR Asia	583	446	128	9	1.1	1.9	1
Belorussia	16	10	5	1	2.7	3.5	2.1
Baltics	12	7	5		2.7	[3.2-3.9]	[2.5-3.6]
West	28	17	10	1			
Southwest	23	12	2	9	4.3	[3.6-5.1]	3
USSR Europe-Uralia	292	151	114	27	1.6	2.7	2.4
USSR Asia	589	449	130	10	1.1	1.9	0.8

[a]N = Far Eastern North; S = Far Eastern South; data pertain to conifers only.
Source: Vorob'yev *et al.* (1979, various pages); Sinitsyn (1976, p. 31);
Spravochnik Lesnichego (1965, pp. 653-54).

per ha in southern European regions such as the Ukraine exceeds that of Yakut ASSR by 5.4 times.

Important differences in quality of site and stocking density also distinguish European forests from those in Asia (Table 3.6). European regions south of the main forested area have larger portions of their forest stands rated high quality with full or average stocking than those in Asia. European-Uralian forested regions like those in the East are dominated by medium-quality sites with full or average stocking. Thus, extensive European areas south of the forest surplus regions have superior growing conditions, better quality forests, more cost-effective and established infrastructure, and cheaper access to domestic and foreign markets than those east of the Urals. Major European-Uralian forest regions have superior MAI per ha than those in the East, but their site qualities and stocking densities are similar. Thus, other things being equal, the more favorable northern European locations relative to markets and sources of labor should significantly enhance their utility compared with the development alternatives offered by peripheral regions in Siberia and the Far East.

The regional imbalance in MAI per hectare, the sizable magnitude of annual growing stock, and the superior site qualities and stocking densities all favor Europe-Uralia. Advocates of unlimited eastern relocation of logging should carefully consider whether effective forestry management in western regions might not offer a viable production alternative for many forms of timber and fiber.

The authors view the forest industry's situation in the USSR as a "Russian dilemma" because almost all Soviet mature timber (99 percent), including mature coniferous timber (99.4 percent), is found in the RSFSR (Table 3.7). Approximately four-fifths of all mature timber is found east of the Urals. Eastern Siberia alone has approximately two-fifths of the nation's mature coniferous timber, a share which is twice that of the European-Uralian zone. Three-fifths of that in the European-Uralian zone, however, are found in the Northwest; one-fifth is in the Urals, and the remainder is distributed throughout other European regions. Some of these other regions have a high relative proportion of coniferous mature timber in their growing stock but its absolute magnitude is small. Furthermore, a significant share of their mature timber is administered by collective farms and nonforestry ministries and administrations: 16.2 percent in the Baltics and 29.9 percent in Belorussia, for example.

Accessibility varies east and west of the Urals. Although approximately 55 percent of Soviet mature timber volume is situated in accessible or potentially accessible forests, these forests comprise 87 percent of the European-Uralian growing stock but only 48 percent of that in the Asian RSFSR. As expected by their designation, almost all Group 2 European forests, and even four-fifths of Asian Group 2 forests, are accessible. The overwhelming advantage of Asian regions over those in the European-Uralian RSFSR is substantially reduced when mature timber in accessible and potentially accessible regions is calculated (Table 3.8). Although still dominant, the ratio of RSFSR Asia to Europe-Uralia is only 2.8:1 for conifers, 2.3:1 for SIHS, and 2.6:1 for STHS. For all species, the ratio is 2.7:1. Given severe environmental and economic constraints on eastern timber harvesting and wood-processing, the supposed superiority of

Table 3.6
Distribution of Forest Stands by Site Quality
and Stocking Density
(% of Total Stands)

Site Quality[a]		High			Medium			Low		
Stocking Density[b]	Total	F	Av	Sp	F	Av	Sp	F	Av	Sp
USSR	100	6	4	<1	20	41	8	3	12	5
RSFSR	100	5	3	<1	21	42	8	3	13	5
Northwest	100	>4	>2	>-	28	41	>3	>3	15	3
Center	100	55	23	<1	13	8	<1	<1	<1	>-
Volgo-Vyatka	100	41	16	<1	24	16	1	1	1	>-
Black Earth	100	51	16	1	19	12	<1	>-	1	>-
Volga Littoral	100	28	11	1	31	27	2	<1	<1	>-
North Caucasus	100	24	19	1	23	28	2	1	2	<1
Urals	100	16	9	<1	35	35	>1	2	2	>-
Western Siberia	100	5	5	1	17	47	7	4	12	2
Eastern Siberia	100	2	2	<1	26	48	6	1	12	3
Far East	100	1	2	<1	13	41	14	4	16	9
Belorussia	100	44	21	<1	19	13	<1	1	1	>-
Latvia	100	43	21	1	21	13	1	-	-	-
Lithuania	100	45	21	1	20	12	<1	<1	>-	>-
Ukraine	100	62	16	<1	13	7	<1	1	<1	>-
USSR Europe-Uralia	100	19	9	<1	27	31	2	2	8	1
USSR Asia	100	2	3	<1	18	45	10	3	13	6

[a]High-site quality contains Class 2 and above according to the M. M. Orlov Scale; medium-site quality contains Classes 3 and 4; low-site quality contains Class 5 and below.

[b]Stocking: F = fully stocked, 70 percent density and above; Av = average stocking, 31-69 percent density; Sp = sparsely stocked, 30 percent density and below.

Source: Derived from Vorob'yev *et al.* (1979, p. 83).

Table 3.7
Volume of Mature Timber in Forests Under Central State Forest Management
(by Forest Group)
(Millions of cu. m)

	All Groups				Conifers			
	Total	Group: 3	2	1	Total	Group: 3	2	1
USSR	51,367	43,931	2,272	5,164	43,943	38,649	1,441	3,853
RSFSR	50,857	43,859	2,120	4,878	43,682	38,588	1,365	3,729
Northwest	5,318	4,498	275	545	4,748	4,096	178	474
Center	289	76	119	94	100	54	21	25
Volgo-Vyatka	527	284	161	82	302	163	91	48
Black Earth	16		5	11	3		2	1
Volga Littoral	387	181	102	104	78	21	29	28
North Caucasus	166		69	97	32		11	21
Urals	1,831	1,062	535	234	1,415	881	369	165
RSFSR Europe-Uralia	8,534	6,101	1,266	1,167	6,678	5,215	701	762
Western Siberia	7,001	6,186	115	700	4,760	4,186	29	545
Eastern Siberia	20,414	17,905	608	1,901	18,456	16,433	561	1,462
Far East	14,908	13,667	131	1,110	13,788	12,754	74	960
RSFSR Asia	42,323	37,758	854	3,711	37,004	33,373	664	2,967
USSR Europe-Uralia	8,894	6,101	1,397	1,396	6,825	5,215	765	845
USSR Asia	42,473	37,830	875	3,768	37,118	33,434	676	3,008

	SIHS				STHS			
	Total	Group: 3	2	1	Total	Group: 3	2	1
USSR	6,424	4,734	680	1,010	1,000	548	151	301
RSFSR	6,340	4,723	640	977	835	548	115	172
Northwest	570	402	97	61				
Center	181	22	94	65	8		4	4
Volgo-Vyatka	218	121	67	30	7		3	4
Black Earth	8		2	6	5		1	4
Volga Littoral	238	122	58	58	71	38	15	18
North Caucasus	18		3	15	116		55	61
Urals	413	181	164	68	3		2	1
RSFSR Europe-Uralia	1,646	840	485	313	210	38	80	92
Western Siberia	2,241	2,000	86	155				
Eastern Siberia	1,958	1,472	47	439				
Far East	495	403	22	70	625	510	35	80
RSFSR Asia	4,694	3,875	155	664	625	510	35	80
USSR Europe-Uralia	1,696	848	516	332	373	38	116	219
USSR Asia	4,728	3,886	164	678	627	510	35	82

Source: Compiled from *Lesnoye Khozyaystvo SSSR* (1977, p. 39).

Table 3.8
Volume of Mature Timber in Accessible and Potentially Accessible Forests
(by Forest Group)
(Millions of cu. m)

	All Groups				Conifers			
	Total	Group: 3	2	1	Total	Group: 3	2	1
USSR	28,168	24,414	2,080	1,674	22,589	20,084	1,307	1,198
USSR Europe-Uralia	7,762	5,758	1,382	622	6,022	4,901	792	329
USSR Asia	20,406	18,656	698	1,052	16,567	15,183	515	869
RSFSR	27,868	24,353	1,939	1,576	22,427	20,033	1,239	1,155
RSFSR Europe-Uralia	7,564	5,758	1,258	548	5,934	4,901	733	30
RSFSR Asia	20,304	18,595	681	1,028	16,493	15,132	506	855

	SIHS				STHS			
	Total	Group: 3	2	1	Total	Group: 3	2	1
USSR	4,981	3,958	645	378	598	372	128	98
USSR Europe-Uralia	1,521	820	494	207	219	37	96	86
USSR Asia	3,460	3,138	151	171	379	335	32	12
RSFSR	4,916	3,943	606	362	525	372	94	59
RSFSR Europe-Uralia	1,483	820	463	200	147	37	62	48
RSFSR Asia	3,433	3,128	143	162	378	335	32	11

Source: Compiled from Vorob'yev *et al.* (1979, pp. 46-47).

Asian forests over those in Europe-Uralia needs careful scrutiny in relation to the
location of major timber consumers (Chapter 5).

Annual timber harvesting seems to take place within a relatively loosely
enforced calculation of annual allowable cut. The total annual allowable cut for
all organizations is 680 million cu. m, of which 61.5 percent is coniferous; 36
percent SIHS; and 2.5 percent STHS. The allowable cut in the European-Uralian
zone comprises 41 percent of the national total and represents 35 percent of the
allowable harvest of conifers but 49 percent of that for SIHS. Slightly over one-
half of the European-Uralian allowable cut comprises conifers, whereas their
proportion in forests east of the Urals is over two-thirds. Most of the European-
Uralian allowable cut is allocated to the RSFSR, with two-fifths accruing to the
Northwest and one-quarter to the Urals. If deciduous species are excluded from the
calculation, the share of the Northwest increases to over one-half of the
allowable cut; the Urals remains at one-quarter. Clearly the allowable deciduous
cut favors those RSFSR regions south and west of the major coniferous forests
which coincide with the major Soviet domestic markets. As demonstrated in
Chapter 4, regeneration of harvested forests in these areas with conifers such as
pine and spruce could obviate the need for some peripheral development east of
the Urals.

The calculated allowable cut in accessible and potentially accessible forests
under central state forestry management (Table 3.9, Chart 3.1) is 636.7 million
cu. m, approximately 43 million cu. m less than reported in the previous
paragraph for all organizations. For all forest groups within the RSFSR, the size
of the Asian allowable cut compared with that for Europe-Uralia is 1.6:1 for all
species; 2:1 for conifers; 1.2:1 for SIHS; and 0.8:1 for STHS. Admittedly the
advantage of Asia over Europe-Uralia (Chart 3.2) is much higher for the conifers
of Group 3 (2.6:1), but Asia is vastly inferior in relation to the allowable cut of
conifers in Group 2. The data in Table 3.9 strongly suggest that qualitative
aspects of the forest resource do not dictate the need for a major shift of logging
toward the East, although the cumulative effect of poor logging practices
undoubtedly adversely affect many European-Uralian forests. Comprehensive data
on production and transport costs for logging enterprises throughout the Soviet
Union, however, would probably refute the much vaunted superiority of eastern
development over sustained-yield management in the West for timber destined for
westward shipment in primary or derivative form.

One of the major drawbacks facing eastern forests is the very large share of
their total growing stock in reserve and inaccessible forests (Chart 3.3). The
sheer size of this resource, essentially comprising conifers (Table 3.10),
particularly larch, makes these forests a tempting target for traditional industrial
planners who view them as a type of "free good," which they are if the cost of
infrastructure and labor is ignored or discounted under some social or political
priority. If the Soviet Union lacked timber in European-Uralian and accessible
Siberian regions, the allowable cut in peripheral regions might justify its cost of
development. The calculated allowable RSFSR annual cut in accessible or
potentially accessible regions exceeds that in the reserve and inaccessible forests
by a ratio of 3:1. The magnitude of the accessible allowable cut itself exceeds all
forms of annual harvest by approximately 1.5 times. Much of the Soviet forest
is unlikely to be developed, therefore, unless relatively fortuitous circumstances

Table 3.9
Calculated Allowable Cut in Accessible and Potentially Accessible Forests Under Central State Forest Management
(Millions of cu. m)

	All Forest Groups				Group 3			
	Total	Conifers	SIHS	STHS	Total	Conifers	SIHS	STHS
USSR	636.7	403.3	218.1	15.3	479.5	334.2	139.0	6.3
USSR Europe-Uralia	250.0	137.5	103.3	9.2	131.6	91.7	38.4	1.5
USSR Asia	386.7	265.8	114.8	6.1	347.9	242.5	100.6	4.8
RSFSR	618.9	395.3	210.7	12.9	478.2	333.2	138.6	6.4
RSFSR Europe-Uralia	235.5	131.2	97.1	7.2	131.6	91.7	38.4	1.5
RSFSR Asia	383.4	264.1	113.6	5.7	346.6	241.5	100.2	4.9

	Group 2				Group 1			
	Total	Conifers	SIHS	STHS	Total	Conifers	SIHS	STHS
USSR	106.4	47.2	54.1	5.1	50.8	21.9	25.0	3.9
USSR Europe-Uralia	86.0	35.4	47.1	4.4	31.5	10.4	17.8	3.3
USSR Asia	19.5	11.8	7.0	0.7	19.3	11.5	67.2	0.6
RSFSR	95.5	41.8	49.6	4.1	45.2	20.3	22.5	2.4
RSFSR Europe-Uralia	76.5	30.2	42.8	3.5	27.4	9.3	15.9	2.2
RSFSR Asia	19.0	11.6	6.8	0.6	17.8	11.0	6.6	0.2

Source: Compiled from Vorob'yev *et al.* (1979, p. 57).

Chart 3.1

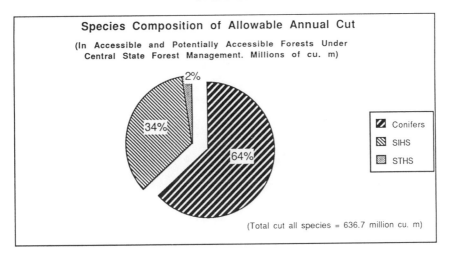

Species Composition of Allowable Annual Cut

(In Accessible and Potentially Accessible Forests Under Central State Forest Management. Millions of cu. m)

2%

34%

64%

Conifers

SIHS

STHS

(Total cut all species = 636.7 million cu. m)

Chart 3.2

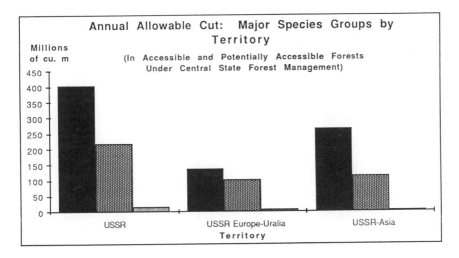

Annual Allowable Cut: Major Species Groups by Territory

Millions of cu. m

(In Accessible and Potentially Accessible Forests Under Central State Forest Management)

450
400
350
300
250
200
150
100
50
0

USSR

USSR Europe-Uralia

USSR-Asia

Territory

Chart 3.3

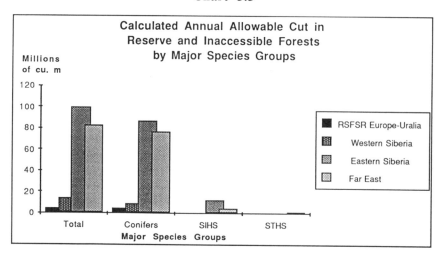

Table 3.10
Calculated Annual Allowable Cut in Reserve and Inaccessible
Forests[a] (Millions of cu. m)

	Total	Conifers	SIHS	STHS
USSR	201.2	178.1	21.9	1.2
RSFSR	<201.2	<178.1	21.9	1.2
Northwest	>4.5	4.1	>0.4	
North Caucasus	>-		>-	
RSFSR Europe-Uralia	4.6	4.1	0.5	
Western Siberia	13.7	9.2	>4.5	
Eastern Siberia	100.1	87.5	12.6	
Far East	82.7	77.3	4.2	1.2
RSFSR Asia	<196.6	<174.0	21.4	1.2
USSR Europe-Uralia	4.6	4.1	0.5	
USSR Asia	196.6	174.0	21.4	1.2

[a]Reserved for future or other (unspecified) uses.

Source: Compiled from Vorob'yev *et al.* (1979, p. 57).

such as a trunk railway constructed for nonforestry purposes should change any region's accessibility.

Some of the cause for present regional imbalances within the Soviet growing stock probably can be attributed to inappropriate past definition of annual allowable cut and hence underinvestment in regeneration. Eronen (1982b, p. 277) suggests that the Soviet Union may use five methods for determining annual allowable cut and cites Glotov (1977, p. 77) in noting that the USSR revised these calculations three times between 1951 and 1973. Glotov (1977, p. 20) states that the annual allowable cut was "insufficiently grounded," suggesting thereby that reliable information from periodic inventories was not forthcoming until 1973. Between 1951 and 1973, the annual allowable cut was reduced from 1,752 million cu. m (1,354 million cu. m of conifers) to 620 million cu. m (393 million cu. m of conifers) (Glotov, 1977, p. 74). Only mature stands are taken into account in determination of annual allowable cut. Inclusion of younger stands, for example, in thoroughly managed forests would enhance regional productivity; improve the general utility of accessible forests; and obviate many new investments in peripheral regions, including the BAM and AYAM service areas. Eronen (1982b, p. 277) observes that the Soviet allowable cut is smaller than that in similar conditions in Scandinavia which is based on total growth. If growth in young Soviet stands were included in the allowable cut, thinnings could be designated as pulp wood and utilized by the pulp and paper industry.

Eronen (1982b, p. 277) also suggests that Soviet methods for estimating growing stock produce smaller results than those employed in Scandinavia because they do not include annual mortality, overestimate the area of coniferous forest, and are made after the principal cut, not several times during the rotation.

When the 1973 allowable cut is compared to the actual harvest for such previous years as 1949, 1953, and 1961, Glotov (1977, p. 21) demonstrates that most European regions suffered extensive depredation of their growing stock, particularly forests in the Baltics, Belorussia, the Center, the Ukraine, and the Transcaucasus. In all these regions, rates of overcutting coniferous species exceeded those of deciduous stands. By 1973, the overcutting had ceased in the composite forests of all regions, although it still occurred in coniferous stands in Belorussia and the Center. Overcutting in composite Uralian forests and European timber surplus regions was not reported by Glotov in 1949, 1961, or 1973, but their coniferous stands were overcut in 1961 and 1973. Uralian conifers were also overcut in 1953. Obviously the total resource is not being utilized (Table 3.3) when deciduous stands are undercut and coniferous forests consistently are overutilized. This imbalance becomes even more significant in face of the deteriorating balance in regeneration between conifers and deciduous species. One-third of the Soviet mean annual increment occurs in European-Uralian forests, but only half of the new growth comprises conifers. Two-thirds of the Asian annual increment is in coniferous stands, but the deciduous species contribute twice as much to the annual increment as to the total Asian forested area. These imbalances in harvesting and regeneration have major policy implications for Soviet foresters because they suggest alternative patterns of consumption and regional timber harvesting could be pursued.

TIMBER HARVESTING

Soviet statistical handbooks normally report levels of timber harvesting which combine output of the planned and unplanned sectors. In 1965, for example, the planned sector produced 90 percent of the reported timber harvest and 92 percent of the commercial timber reported (Holowacz, 1968, p. 7). The composite figures, termed industrial removals of roundwood here, are made up of commercial roundwood and fuelwood obtained in the final cut and during forest rehabilitation or renewal work (*lesovosstanovitel'nye rubki*) in forests of state significance and on collective farms. They exclude timber obtained through intermediate or thinning cuts. The final cut pertains to mature and over-mature timber; the renewal cut pertains to stands in flooded areas or those damaged by wind, storm, fire or pests (UNIDO, 1983, p. 14). The final and renewal cuts pertain mainly to Group 3, but also partially to Group 2, and intermediate harvesting occurs in all groups.

In 1984, for example, 44.7 million cu. m of marketable timber was derived from intermediate harvesting, 322 million cu. m from the final cut and forest renewal work in state forests, and 45.8 million cu. m from collective farm forests (*Narodnoye Khozyaystvo SSSR v 1984 g.*, 1985, pp. 187, 400). The total harvest was at least 412.5 million cu. m, and not simply the industrial timber harvest of 367.8 million cu. m reported in the annual statistical yearbook. Industrial removals thus were perhaps 11 percent lower than total harvesting because they excluded the intermediate cut. Furthermore, the total harvest presumably excludes informal or personal harvesting by rural inhabitants for fuel and construction. These removals are classified as nonindustrial removals of roundwood in Table 3.11 based on Blandon (1983, pp. 247-48) who obtained them from a 1976 Soviet source. Regional production throughout this book, however, refers to industrial removals, as these are the only consistent regional harvesting data published in the annual yearbooks (particularly before 1976).

Soviet annual industrial removals peaked in the mid-1970s just below 400 million cu. m (Table 3.11) and declined to a consistent figure of 357 million cu. m by the 1980s as better use was made of wood waste and low quality timber. Four-fifths of the industrial harvest comprises conifers (United Nations, 1984, p. 4). Almost one-half of the removals (45 percent) constitute saw and veneer logs, 16 percent is pulpwood, 21 percent is other industrial wood, and the remainder is fuelwood. The last year for which data are available, 1984, shows an increase in commercial harvesting over that of any of the previous four years of approximately 12 million cu. m. Soviet efforts to curtail expansion of harvesting and increasingly to substitute waste materials and intermediate cuttings for roundwood may not be succeeding.

The intermediate cut, nevertheless, is relatively significant in some European regions (Table 3.12), especially those which are usually termed timber deficient. This book contends that steady improvement in forestry will likely produce larger volumes of intermediate cut, particularly from Group 2 forests and some Group 1 stands if the derived timber were deemed to be economically worth using.[2] A considerable portion of the intermediate cut south of the Northwest and Volgo-Vyatka (Table 3.13) is deciduous timber; all intermediate harvest is small

Table 3.11
Timber Harvesting of Roundwood
(Selected Years 1913-1984)
(Millions of cu. m[s])[a]

Year	Industrial Removals			Nonindustrial Removals	
	Total	Commercial	Fuel	Total	Fuel
1913[b]	60.6 (67.0)	27.2 (30.5)	33.4 (36.5)	232.0	204.0
1928	61.7	36.0	25.7	242.0	215.0
1930	147.2	96.7	50.5	n/a[c]	n/a
1935	210.1	117.0	93.1	223.0[d]	201.0[d]
1940	246.1	117.9	128.2	136.0	130.0
1945	168.4	61.6	106.8	140.0	130.0
1950	266.0	161.0	105.0	100.0	92.0
1955	334.1	212.1	122.0	70.0	63.0
1960	369.5	261.5	108.0	40.0	30.0
1965	378.1	273.6	104.5	38.0	32.0
1970	385.0	298.5	86.5	37.0	30.0
1975	395.0	312.9	82.1	35.0	29.0
1980	356.6	277.7	78.9	n/a	n/a
1984	367.9	282.8	85.1	n/a	n/a

[a]Cu. m(s) refers to volume of solid timber.

[b]1913 data pertain to the territory of the USSR included within the boundaries which existed until 17 September 1939 (data enclosed in parentheses pertain to territory included in the Russian Empire in 1913).

[c]n/a = Data are not available.

[d]Values for 1932.

Source: *Promyshlennost' SSSR, Statisticheskiy Sbornik* (1957, p. 249); *Narodnoye Khozyaystvo SSSR v 1967 godu* (1968, p. 272); *Narodnoye Khozyaystvo SSSR, 1922-1982* (1982, pp. 200-201); *Narodnoye Khozyaystvo SSSR v 1984 godu* (1985, p. 187); *SSSR v Tsifrakh v 1982 godu* (1983, p. 68); P. Blandon (1983, p. 248 - for nonindustrial removals of roundwood in turn based on Lobovikov and Petrov [1976]).

Table 3.12
Distribution and Relative Importance of
Intermediate Cut

	% of USSR Total Intermediate Cut	% of Total Industrial Removals in Each Region
USSR	100	10
RSFSR	63	7
Northwest	9	3
Center	11	17
Volgo-Vyatka	8	10
Black Earth	2	38
Volga Littoral	8	23
North Caucasus	2	32
Urals	9	5
RSFSR Europe-Uralia	49	10
Western Siberia	n/a[a]	6
Eastern Siberia	n/a	3
Far East	n/a	7
RSFSR Asia	14	4
Belorussia	9	42
Latvia	4	54
Lithuania	3	45
Estonia	3	45
Ukraine	16	54
USSR Europe-Uralia	85	16
USSR Asia	15	5

[a]n/a = Data are not available
Source: Compiled fro Vorob'yev *et al.* (1979, p. 60);
RSFSR regional data were calculated from Timofeyev (1980,
pp. 30-41).

Table 3.13
Size and Basic Species Composition of Principal and Intermediate
Timber Harvested in European (Non-Uralian) USSR
(% of Total Type of Each Harvest)

	Principal Cut					Intermediate Cut				
	Total	C[a]	D	LC	AC	S&F	Total	C	D	LC	AC	S&F
USSR Europe	100	66	34	17	53	30	100	43	57	6	15	79
RSFSR Europe	100	68	32	16	53	31	100	36	64	7	17	76
Northwest	100	87	13	17	52	31	100	65	35	10	25	65
Center	100	40	60	16	54	30	100	35	65	5	18	77
Volgo-Vyatka	100	51	49	14	53	33	100	48	52	11	22	67
Black Earth	100	17	83	13	56	31	100	32	68	2	9	89
Volga Littoral	100	28	72	17	59	24	100	17	83	4	10	86
North Caucasus	100	12	88	13	55	32	100	4	96	5	5	90
Belorussia	100	47	53	20	54	26	100	50	50	6	11	83
Latvia	100	58	42	18	52	30	100	74	26	4	16	80
Lithuania	100	38	62	20	53	27	100	58	42	13	22	65
Estonia	100	59	41	17	49	34	100	71	29	10	27	63
Ukraine	100	46	54	20	53	27	100	40	60	1	6	93

[a]C = conifers; D = deciduous; LC = large-size commercial timber; AC = medium-size commercial timber; S&F = small-size commercial timber and fuelwood.

Source: Compiled from Vorob'yev *et al.* (1979, p. 59).

size commercial timber or fuelwood. This wood has utility, however, if chipped and shipped to regional pulp, fiberboard, or particleboard mills, most of whose products originate in the European-Uralian zone (Chapter 5).

Thinnings and sanitary removals now contribute over one-half of the total timber output of such regions as the Ukraine (Burdin *et al.*, 1980, p. 64, state that in 1977 this cut contributed 7.3 out of 13.2 million cu. m). Honer, Hegyi, and Bonnor (1985, p. 8) state that the Ukraine's annual output is 10 million cu. m of which 60 percent originates from plantation thinnings. As recently as 1983, however, the Ukraine's true output must have been much higher than the industrial removals total (10.6 million cu. m) in the annual statistical yearbook (*Narodnoye Khozyaystvo Ukrainskoy SSR v 1983 godu*, 1984, p. 109) if thinnings and sanitary removals are added to the total as Burdin's methodology suggests. These thinnings comprised 8.8 million cu. m in 1983, of which merchantable timber accounted for 7.8 million cu. m. The published industrial removals seem to include timber from the principal cut and from renewal work in Forests of State Significance (the national total of this cut has been published annually since 1982, and some republics have followed suit) plus a component from remaining forests which are administered by collective farms. The 1983 Ukrainian total is thus probably closer to 18.4 million cu. m when merchantable thinnings are included, approximately 70 percent more than reported output. In a different example, Estonian industrial removals in 1984 totaled 2.6 million cu. m. That republic, however, seems to use a different accounting methodology and to include 1.1 million cu. m of merchantable thinnings with industrial timber removals (*Narodnoye Khozyaystvo Estonskoy SSR v 1984 godu*, 1985, pp. 55, 140; Burdin *et al* ., 1980, p. 64). Similarly Lithuania's total output in 1984 of 2.7 million cu. m of industrial timber seems to include almost 1 million cu. m of merchantable thinnings (*Narodnoye Khozyaystvo Litovskoy SSR v 1984 godu*, 1985, pp. 43,138). Whether or not thinnings and sanitary removals are included in the published total, however, they nevertheless amount to a large volume of timber (36 out of 42 million cu. m in 1977), especially from forests in the Baltics, Belorussia, the Ukraine, and the European-Uralian regions of the RSFSR (Burdin *et al*, 1980, p. 64).

Soviet industrial timber production has undergone important regional shifts (Table 3.14) during the period analyzed in this book. Regional data on timber harvesting have been unavailable since 1975 although regional production of key wood products continues to be published despite periodic hiatuses (Chapter 5). Soviet loggers have retreated from all European-Uralian regions of the RSFSR except the Northwest. Without increased harvesting in the Northwest, the absolute decline in timber output would have been almost 55 percent greater during the period 1960-1975. Logging in the West, however, remained almost static during this period, probably due to the major contribution of improvement fellings to total output. Total timber production in the Southwest, on the other hand, declined significantly. The net increment to annual output over this period came from the Asian RSFSR, particularly Eastern Siberia followed by the southern zone of the Far East. As shown in Chapter 5, this additional output has added considerably to the Soviet average length of haul of timber and wood products because major markets remain in the European USSR and in European export markets. The westward and southward flows of roundwood and wood

Table 3.14
Regional Shift in Industrial Removals of Timber (1960-1975)
(Thousands of cu. m)

	1960	% of Total	1975	% of Total	Change (1960-1975)	%Change (1960-1975)
USSR	369,550	100.0	395,039	100.0	25,489	6.9
RSFSR	336,365	91.0	366,900	92.9	30,535	9.1
Northwest	89,829	24.3	97,300	24.6	7,471	8.3
Center	32,601	8.8	29,700	7.5	-2,901	-8.9
Volgo-Vyatka	38,242	10.3	30,300	7.7	-7,942	-20.8
Black Earth	1,308	0.4	900	0.2	-408	-31.2
Volga Littoral	12,572	3.4	11,300	2.9	-1,272	-10.1
North Caucasus	5,131	1.4	3,200	0.8	-1,931	-37.6
Urals	65,086	17.6	58,400	14.8	-6,686	-10.3
RSFSR Europe-Uralia	244,769	66.2	231,100	58.5	-13,669	-5.6
Western Siberia	25,135	6.8	33,000	8.4	7,865	31.3
Eastern Siberia	45,416	12.3	69,200	17.5	23,784	52.4
Far East	20,640	5.6	33,200	8.4	12,560	60.9
(South)	15,637	4.2	28,600	7.2	12,963	82.9
(North)	5,003	1.4	4,600	1.2	-403	-8.0
RSFSR Asia	91,191	24.7	135,400	34.3	44,209	48.5
Belorussia	7,301	2.0	6,190	1.6	-1,111	-15.2
Baltics	8,222	2.2	9,028	2.3	806	9.8
Kaliningrad	405	0.1	400	0.1	-5	-1.2
West	15,928	4.3	15,618	4.0	-310	-1.9
Southwest	13,712	3.7	9,841	2.5	-3,871	-28.2
Caucasus	1,584	0.4	741	0.2	-843	-53.2
USSR Europe-Uralia	275,993	74.7	257,300	65.1	-18,693	-6.8
Central Asia	2,366	0.6	2,339	0.6	-27	-1.1
USSR Asia	93,557	25.3	137,739	34.9	44,182	47.2

Source: *Narodnoye Khozyaystvo SSSR v 1970 godu* (1971, p. 225); *Nararodnoye Khozyaystvo RSFSR v 1970 godu* (1971, pp. 97-99); *Narodnoye Khozyaystvo SSSR v 1975 godu,* (1976, p. 273); *Nararodnoye Khozyaystvo RSFSR v 1975 godu* (1976, pp. 87-89).

products add to the existing heavy burden on the Soviet railways. which has also intensified as the output of other raw materials destined for European markets has increased in Siberia and the Far East. The major issue raised by increased logging in Siberia and the Far East, therefore, relates to the degree of alternate sources of roundwood or wood fiber which could be generated in Europe-Uralia to offset the higher cost of transportation and labor associated with eastern forests.

PRE-1960 PATTERNS OF LOGGING

The major commercial coniferous forests of the Soviet Union did not undergo large-scale utilization until the introduction of central planning in 1928 (Table 3.11). Timber, however, was a major source of domestic fuel for rural and urban residents until the discovery and exploitation of large gas and oil fields in the 1950s and the advent of mass-produced centrally heated apartment buildings in urban areas after 1956.

The first decade of Soviet rule entailed forest utilization similar in manner and location to that of Tsarist times. It sustained the peasants' need for fuel (over four-fifths of the population lived in rural areas, primarily in European USSR) and sustained the lumber, pulp, and paper industry, which was chiefly located in the West and Northwest from Leningrad oblast south to the northwestern Ukraine. Most commercial timber was harvested in areas tributary to Leningrad for conversion in adjacent mills or for export to western Europe in exchange for manufactured timber products, equipment, chemicals, technical expertise, and British coal. Major administrative and industrial consumers of paper were concentrated in Leningrad, then St. Petersburg. Despite the shift of national administration to Moscow in 1918, the Tsarist imprint on consumption patterns of commercial timber was not immediately lessened. Furthermore, prerevolutionary levels of industrial production generally were not reached again until the end of 1926 (Glotov, 1977, p. 7).

With the advent of national central planning and industrial development in 1928, forests in the traditionally peripheral northeastern and eastern regions of European RSFSR, which had played an essentially "colonial" role in Tsarist times, became the focus of new investment in timber and wood-processing (Rodgers, 1955, p. 93; Glotov, 1977, pp. 7-14). By the outbreak of World War II, two-thirds of national timber harvesting occurred in the European North, the Northwest, the Central Industrial Region around Moscow, the upper Volga, and the Urals (Rogers, 1955, p. 96). Eastern Siberia and the Far East accounted for nearly 10 percent, and the remainder was dispersed throughout the country.

Major regional rivers and their tributaries facilitated movement of timber for industrial consumption and export, but the railway system, which had been put in place in the last decades of Tsarist rule and expanded in the first two Soviet decades, permitted large-scale movement of timber from numerous rail-water intersections to emerging centers of national industrial consumption in the Central Industrial District, the eastern Ukraine, and the Urals (Glotov, 1977, pp. 7-14; Timofeyev *et al.,* 1967, pp. 73-87, 141-55). The expanding rail system also ensured that traditional areas of consumption in the Leningrad region and Belorussia, and markets for Soviet timber in western Europe could be satisfied with additional amounts of timber from previously unexploited forests. Much of Belorussia, all of the Baltic states, and the southern half of Sakhalin Island were not included in the USSR between the two world wars.

Forest industries, despite their significance to industrialized countries such as Finland, Sweden, Canada, and the United States, did not receive high priority in the prewar central allocation of Soviet investment funds. Myriad competing demands by sectors of the economy deemed crucial for forced industrialization, autarchy, and national survival have traditionally left the forest industry in an inferior technological position with many unrealized opportunities for product and regional growth. Pre-World War II timber production was mainly intended to satisfy domestic demand for fuelwood, for roundwood in unprocessed form during construction, and for roundwood which had received minimal processing (into items such as rough planks, beams, and squared building logs). Export commitments chiefly took the form of roundwood, but the volume of export on the eve of World War II comprised less than 1 percent of commercial timber harvested in the country. (Export of all forms of roundwood in 1975 at the peak of post-World War II annual timber felling still comprised less than 6 percent of the commercial roundwood produced in the USSR.) Surprisingly, however, in some years of early forced industrialization, timber was the most important export commodity and contributor to the national budget, but the significance of timber exports declined during the worldwide depression of the 1930s (*Vneshnyaya Torgovlya SSSR 1922-1981*, 1982, pp. 52-53; *Lesnoye Khozyaystvo SSSR za 50 Let (1917-1967 gg.)*, 1967, pp. 16-24; Timofeyev, 1980, pp. 52-212, 223-27).

The timber industry prior to and just following World War II did not engage significantly in comprehensive forms of processing or expand into major forests peripheral to the European-Uralian industrial axes. Product and spatial growth of the wood-processing industry was greatly hampered by shortages of skilled workers in the major regional forests and away from traditional processing centers. Facilities inherited from prerevolutionary times thus provided locational inertia, most notably those of the major timber converters, integrated pulp and paper mills. Two-thirds of the country's pulp and paper in 1937 was produced in the European North, the Northwest, or the Central Industrial District (these regions had slightly more than one-fifth of the total population). The fourth major paper producing region, the Urals, contributed 13 percent of the 1937 output and had 7 percent of the country's population (Rodgers, 1955, p. 96).

Surveys of timber reserves for quality, volume and species composition were inadequate, and facilities for product movement and handling by river and rail were deficient. As a result, fuel for industrial heating and material converting was in short supply. Furthermore, the major accessible forests of central and eastern European Russia acted as significant intervening opportunities between the established regions of industrial timber consumption and the vast forests which lay in northern European Russia and east of the Urals.

Following post war recovery and the significant growth in the country's industrial prowess, administative and industrial sectors have generated large demands for forest products. The sale of raw materials such as timber (second in importance only to petroleum) in various forms has helped finance the transfer of technology from the West to the USSR. Growing domestic and foreign marketing of timber and wood products, therefore, has weakened many economic, institutional, and geographical barriers which previously hampered the forest industry. By 1960, although the European-Uralian RSFSR still produced two-thirds of the country's timber, modest decline had occurred in the Northwest and the Center as production shifted slightly in favor of the Volgo-Vyatka and Urals regions. The industry was still concentrated in the traditional Soviet European-Uralian harvesting areas, although total output of industrial timber increased 77 percent between 1937 and 1960 (*Narodnoye Khozyaystvo SSSR v 1970 godu,* 1971, p. 222).

The harvesting pattern between 1940 and 1960 maintained a relatively stable output of 110 to 115 million cu. m from what the Soviets term "forest deficient" or "lightly forested" regions, and derived an increment of 118 million cu. m from "forest surplus" or "much forested" regions, whose total output increased to 254 million cu. m in 1960 (Narodnoye Khozyaystvo SSSR v 1970 *godu,* 1971, p. 223). These latter regions are essentially those described above under the general expansion of the timber industry in recent times. East of the Urals, the increment in output from the Far East between 1940 and 1960 was only 3.6 million cu. m, whereas that of Western and Eastern Siberia was 35.6 million cu. m, hardly a major component of the growth in total output from all forest surplus regions during this period (*Narodnoye Khozyaystvo RSFSR v 1970 godu,* 1971, pp. 96-99). As noted above, growth since 1960 has favored eastern regions. Thus, we can observe three basic periods in Soviet timber harvesting: (1) the period prior to the mid-1930s which favored traditional areas; (2) the period from the late 1930s until 1960, which witnessed spectacular increases in harvesting from European-Uralian forest surplus regions; and (3) the past quarter century, which has seen the absolute decline in timber from European-Uralian forests offset by increased output from Siberia and the Far East. As observed elsewhere in this book, the development of timber harvesting seems to have been associated with expediency in logging rather than effective forestry, particularly before 1973.

The extent and legacy of forest degradation through overcutting and environmental depredation during the first 70 years of Soviet rule are extremely difficult to evaluate. There is no reliable evidence to suggest that timber harvesting prior to 1928, the commencement of central planning, or during the five planning periods prior to 1956 (the first complete analysis of all Soviet forests) was conducted with any true reference to allowable cut and sustained-yield management. Prerevolutionary logging by up to 2 million peasant loggers in European Russia and by forced laborers in forests of the European North and the Urals has been described as rapacious, predatory, and completely ignorant of management principles (Timofeyev *et al.,* 1967, p. 74). Tseplyayev (1965) has reported that, despite the 1888 law by the Tsarist government to conserve the forest, between 1888 and 1908 in European Russia alone 3 million ha of forested land were cleared and the general forest area declined by over 9 million ha: "In pre-revolutionary logging anarchy prevailed: the exchequer, the aristocracy, mining enterprises, military authorities, and private landowners treated the forests with impunity and with total disregard for their conservation and replacement" (Tseplyayev, 1965, p. 144). Vorob'yev *et al.* citing Tsvetkov's analysis of changes in the extent of European Russian forests from the end of the seventeenth century to 1914, note that about 70 million ha of forest were cleared in European Russia during that period (Vorob'yev *et al.*, 1980, p. 25).

Soviet practices until well after World War II were probably not fundamentally different from those of Tsarist times or from contemporary practices in most of the world's forests. Soviet concern in the 1920s was with recovery to output levels existing before 1914; goals in the 1930s and 1940s were related to expediency, rationalized when necessary by the general opinion that forest reserves were "incredibly immense" and that economic growth and national survival justified short-term exploitation of the forests. If the figures published in the first post war statistical handbooks are true indicators of planners' estimates of the forest resource, we can conclude that even the 1950s were marked by large-scale ignorance of sustained yield-management. The annual allowable cut against which annual harvesting was measured exceeded the annual increment of the forests by a factor of 2.5 (by 3 in the early 1950s). It was not drastically reduced until after the comprehensive inventories of the 1960s. If permissible levels of cutting are adjusted by a factor of two and one-half, forests were regularly being overcut in the Northwest (58 percent), the Center (130 percent), the Volga-Littoral (128 percent), North Caucasus (40 percent), and the Urals (42 percent). In the non-Russian western regions, however, the factor of overcutting was extreme: Ukraine (4 times), Belorussia (3 times), Lithuania (5 times), Latvia (2.5 times), and Estonia (two times) (*Promyshlennost' SSSR. Statisticheskiy Sbornik*, 1957, p. 247).

Although these estimates are extremely crude, they suggest that the volume of overcutting and hence deforestation, if aggregated over the period extending from the late 1930s to 1960, would have affected large areas of forest. Indeed, recent estimates of the remaining mature and overmature timber supplies in many RSFSR European forests suggest this was the case (discussed in Chapter 3).

When peacetime deforestation is added to the volume of depredation experienced during World War II in many of these same regions, the impression is created that major areas of the European USSR have experienced deforestation. The exact regional volume and form of deforestation probably has resulted in extensive uneconomic areas of forest (Blandon, 1983, p. 5) characterized by dominant stands of poor quality poplar, birch, and alder, and sparse, irregular, or immature stands of conifers.

In his assessment of the Soviet pulp and paper industry in 1955, Rodgers (1955, pp. 100-3) parenthetically commented on wartime devastation of forests in the Baltics, the Northwest, and the Center, and on the forest depredation committed by the Japanese during their tenure on Sakhalin Island from 1905 to 1945. In view of the battles waged during the war on the territory of the Ukraine, Belorussia, and the Baltic republics, we assume that numerous forests must have suffered extensive damage. Forests certainly were used as part of the military strategy by both belligerents (Miller, 1972, pp. 186-202). Aggregate production of commercial roundwood during the four Soviet war years, however, was only 230 million cu. m or twice that for 1940 alone. Production of fuelwood, however, was approximately 450 million cu. m (Timofeyev *et al.*, 1967, p. 154). Military consumption of fuelwood, especially in areas related to heavy concentrations of military forces, on both sides of the front lines, must have placed great demands on local timber supplies. Vorob'yev *et al.* (1980, p. 35) report that approximately 20 million ha of forest were felled or destroyed in areas occupied by the Nazis or subject to military activities. They note that, where logging intensified elsewhere in the USSR to offset the loss of timber production in the western areas, actual cutting, especially in central regions, far exceeded the levels of established annual allowable cut. Given that allowable cut prior to the 1960s was itself exaggerated by a factor of at least 2.5 or 3, then the resulting deforestation must have been pronounced, particularly in central regions, which had already undergone centuries of forest depredation.

CONCLUSIONS

The first four decades of Soviet rule were associated with consolidation of power; development of central planning; years of war and destruction; and periods of reconstruction, recovery, and incremental investment. The country's industrial economy was engaged in a struggle for surival, probably at any cost, rather than in a balanced and managed use of elements of the natural environment, such as those represented by the contemporary extensive forests of European Russia, the Urals, and accessible Siberia. Events of the past quarter century, however, have probably been more indicative of "normal" Soviet practices, particularly with the apparent growth in environmental consciousness during the 1970s (assessed in Pryde, 1972 and 1983).

The major problem in utilization of Soviet forests seems to rest with programs and policies of sustained yield, particularly the establishment of meaningful timber prices and the implementation of effective efforts toward regeneration. Many forests are still being "mined" or "high-graded"; others are undergoing depredation through the uncontrolled intervention of nomadic loggers, who are destroying the resource base allocated for major mills. Timber close to markets is not being utilized fully when the species mix of the forests is deemed unsuitable. By now, however, further progress and enhanced resource utilization probably cannot be achieved in the USSR without important modifications to existing administrative and operational procedures. In particular, the central planners' understanding of the spatial dimensions underlying the national space economy must be revised (Vorob'yev *et al.,* 1980, pp. 26-45; Thornton, 1980, pp. 30-31; Barr, 1970, pp. 118-28; and Barr, 1983).

The problems presented in Chapter 3 have related to decisions made about utilization of forests. Levels of management, investment in inventory capability, and reforestation or silviculture suggest that, to this point in time, the USSR has achieved only a minimal level of effective forest utilization. The spatial distribution of the actual growing stock, the relatively limited accessibility of the gross Siberian and Far Eastern standing timber reserves, and the superior physical environments of many European-Uralian forestry lands over those of the East all suggest that the future of timber harvesting may have to be rethought. Greater intensity and more attention to transportation costs and labor shortages may generate a return to European forestry lands in the next century, as future spatial patterns of harvesting may come to resemble those of the period prior to 1937 when European, not eastern regions, dominated levels of output.

NOTES

1. Plantations are usually stocked with pine, spruce, or larch; in so-called warm climatic areas, oak is the preferred species (UNIDO, 1983, p. 15).
2. Additional support for this argument was obtained by one of the authors (Barr) in September 1986 from the major Soviet forestry and wood-processing exposition at Moscow's VDNKh (Exhibition of the Achievements of the National Economy), including evidence provided during informal discussions with its service personnel and large displays of material linked to the Twelfth Five-Year Plan.

4
The Wood Basket

Utilization of timber in the Soviet Union is commonly approached through examination of physical demand for roundwood and wood products rather than through economic evaluations of timber resources and the volumes of growing stock of individual species.[1] The growing stock is so large and extensively distributed that it tends to be taken as given in discussions of regional development or analyses of such industries as pulp, paper, paperboard, lumber, and plywood. The forest regeneration backlog of nearly 138 million hectares in the USSR suggests, however, that the Soviet timber resource has not escaped from the problems of deforestation and environmental degradation common to most other countries, including Canada.[2]

This chapter examines the significance of major Soviet forests to regional development by reviewing the 1983 forest inventory in relation to the drive for more intensive utilization of raw materials.[3] The 1983 inventory offers strong support for the view that important regional advantages in utilization of the timber resource can be derived in the Soviet Union through achievement of stability in timber production within existing European-Uralian wood-processing regions and accessible logging areas of Siberia. Soviet regional timber reserves are overwhelmingly conditioned by spatial variations in the qualitative and locational (including distance) characteristics of the forest itself. They are also affected by the degree of willingness among central forestry and industrial agencies to view forest exploitation as a form of harvesting rather than an exercise in high-grade mining. The perceived need to develop increasingly remote stands of virgin timber is influenced by the extent to which forests in existing areas of infrastructure are utilized and regenerated, and by the degree of recovery of wood waste from logging and processing sites.[4]

ARGUMENTS ON REGIONS AND PRICING

Soviet forestry literature is extensive and increasingly research-based, with the measurement of the forest resource becoming scientific and, therefore, more accurate during the past two decades. Descriptions of the resource and evaluations of the commercial uses of timber abound in Soviet and Western literature; they have been extensively utilized and referenced in previous work by the authors of this book (Braden, 1983; Barr, 1982, 1983, 1984, forthcoming) and by Eronen (1981, 1982, 1983, 1984).

The major problem in Soviet industrial analyses seems to lie in the very size and visibility of the forest resource. Many Soviet analysts wax eloquent on the vast reserves of timber in the European North, Siberia, and the Soviet Far East. They note the relatively large share of mature and overmature timber in these forests, the proportions of juvenile stands in European-Uralian forests, and the prevalence of deciduous species in forests closer to the industrial heartland of the USSR (approximately the western two-thirds of the population triangle). Furthermore, in all major Soviet primary industries except iron ore, the prevailing wisdom and calculations of the so-called economic effect of utilizing various deposits appear to favor the exploitation of "spectacular" eastern deposits to offset declining reserves in the European-Uralian zone. The Soviet indicator of profitability is a surrogate for regional price and cost differentials, but is based on f.o.b. calculations which exclude a crucial variable in regional policy, namely transportation cost. The apparent negative economic characteristics of associated higher exploitation and transportation costs are of necessity overlooked in oil, gas, coal, hydroelectric, and other sectors. Alternative areas of supply are few, and the hardships and penalties associated with peripheral resource extraction are accepted. A general momentum seems to extend this enthusiasm for development of eastern resources uncritically to the area's forests although the annual increase in the cost of producing 1 cu. m of roundwood varied between 0.7 percent and 3.6 percent from 1971 to 1978.[5] European alternatives do exist in forestry as in agriculture, iron and steel, and nuclear power.

The Soviet forestry literature and the forestry program adopted by the Twenty-Sixth Congress of the Communist Party of the Soviet Union (CPSU) in 1981 envisaged sustained yield management, comprehensive utilization of wood material, and improvement of the quality of the growing stock. Specific attention was paid to European-Uralian forest utilization, including the development of special timber plantations to support that region's pulp and paper industry (Mikhaylov and Bronina, 1984, p. 5). These goals were reaffirmed by the Twenty-Seventh CPSU Congress in February and March 1986. Efficient utilization of resources is a major element of the drive to double the USSR's production potential by the year 2000, and many of the improvements required in economic performance are predicated on "radical improvements" in the utilization of natural resources ("Osnovnye Napravleniya Ekonomicheskogo i Sotsial'nogo Razvitiya SSSR na 1986-1990 Godu i na Period do 2000 Goda," 1986, p. 13). Although also calling for more effective investment in Siberia and the Soviet Far East, the CPSU seems to be taking much greater cognizance of judicious investment in those regions than it did previously.

The discrepancy between the location of virgin stands of timber and the major consumers of roundwood or wood fiber in the USSR is described by Anuchin (1986, pp. 200-1) as the "geographical scissors" (or discrepancy) syndrome. Closure of the gap between them requires extensive investment in eastern infrastructure, but also 1.5 to 2 times greater capital cost for timber harvesting and primary manufacturing of wood products than in Europe-Uralia. Anuchin (1986, p. 201) concludes that the only way to justify greater logging in Siberia and the Far East is to transfer labor to these regions from the European USSR. Westward shipment of roundwood in large quantities cannot be justified. Although representing one of the most forthright statements to date, Anuchin's argument overlooks the problem of labor's unwillingness to relocate eastward, the high costs of investment in the East (which he only notes in passing), and the general lack of necessity to relocate if appropriate forestry practices were adopted and true economic alternatives were recognized in Europe-Uralia.

Although taxes and pricing are discussed in Chapter 8, their impact on location of harvesting should be noted here. Soviet prices for logs are based on costs; timber prices were reset by *Gosplan* in 1967 and again in 1982. Roundwood prices are differentiated according to cost, tax (i.e., stumpage fee), and f.o.b. and c.i.f. According to Blandon (1983), taxes average 10 percent of cost; they are added to timber costs to determine the price of timber f.o.b. before transport costs are added. Taxes vary throughout seven zones; the tax per cu. m in the most accessible zone may be eight to ten times greater than in the most remote zone to encourage harvesting in peripheral regions. Coniferous species such as pine have a tax index of 100 compared with that for birch of 50 and other deciduous species of 20 to 25. Taxes are higher for trees with diameters in excess of 25 cm to encourage harvesting of smaller trees. Taxes diminish within harvesting regions according to five zones to encourage the use of timber most remote from road, rail, or raft loading points. Taxes are also reduced if complete harvest of a plot occurs and less desirable species are harvested. Loggers are taxed for the full harvest whether or not they leave standing timber and, therefore, are theoretically encouraged to utilize all the growing stock in a stand.

Transport costs, however, are excluded from the tax calculation. Blandon (1983) notes that the differential effect of taxes for utilization of deciduous species is offset by c.i.f. price calculations which apply to these species at a lower rate than for conifers. Hence, while the f.o.b. tax on birch is 50 percent that on pine, the c.i.f. price is 70 percent. Blandon also suggests that the price differential for smaller-diameter trees is insufficient to offset their higher relative transport costs. Some of these tax components seem to run counter to planners' stated preferences for using more deciduous species and smaller-diameter trees, because the zonal factor outweighs these components in the tax equation. This equation may actually encourage selective harvesting in remote stands and promote a prevailing behavioral environment of regional environmental depredation and future species imbalance.

As a result of such thinking, much of the literature related to wood-processing which espouses a partisan approach to eastern development, pays little attention to non-Siberian or non-Far Eastern alternatives. Thus, on the one hand, the Soviet forester, Belov (1983, p. 225), demonstrates unequivocally that effective management and utilization of timber can reduce depredation of the country's forests. Analysts of wood-processing, such as Kazakov (1984, p. 12), state that, in the future the USSR will need "to process wood comprehensively and to utilize waste through integrated processing, . . . and to transfer the center of gravity of logging and processing to eastern regions of the country."

On the other hand, other analysts, such as Kozhukhov (1984, p. 63), note that major future increments to the supply of basic wood products will originate from integrated production complexes in heavily forested Siberian and Far Eastern regions, but they also state that the cost structure of using these forests should be evaluated. Kozhukov further notes that, while these forests effectively represent free goods in that they have been created without capital investment, their climatic environments are far less favorable than those in the European USSR. Their productivity is low (less than 100 cu. m per ha), their site quality is poor, and their average treetrunk diameter does not exceed 24 cm. Furthermore, argues Kozhukhov, their utilization will occur in undeveloped circumstances.

Development of related infrastructure and construction organizations costs 2 to 2.5 times more than in European regions. Using eastern timber to supply European processors entails average hauls of at least 3000 km. Because eastern regeneration cycles can be three times longer than those in the western USSR, the process of regeneration will take too long to ensure sustained-yield forest management and continuous supply of timber to the region's mills. Consequently, another solution is needed: intensification of regeneration, production, and utilization in European-Uralian forests. Kozhukhov adds, however, that Siberian and Far Eastern timber should be utilized more comprehensively in regional complexes so that raw, semi-finished, and finished products can be delivered to all customers as efficiently as possible.

The reluctance of Soviet analysts to subject eastern forest projects to deeper scrutiny may reflect two constraints: first their criticism would fly in the face of official development policy, and second, utilization of Eastern forests without due regard for their effective regeneration would at least buy time for the Soviet economy to organize an effective sustained-yield forest system in the European-Uralian zone over the next 30 to 50 years. This could effectively compensate for the "mining" or depletion of the extensive eastern peripheral forests.

Although having little apparent influence in determining the regional distribution of wood-processing, many of these forest analysts are publishing cogent analyses of the relative merits of sustained utilization of accessible forests (including those in South-central Siberia). Underlying their arguments is the often overlooked fact that timber resources are a spatially extensive phenomenon, whereas minerals, hydroelectricity, and coal - even oil and gas - are reasonably punctiform or capable of relatively constrained primary-gathering networks and concentrated or high-volume bulk movement to market. They worry about the ever-increasing length of haul of timber to market. They note the problems of accessibility in Northern, Siberian, and Far Eastern forests; the harsh environmental conditions for labor and equipment; the seasonality of harvesting and movement of timber; and the physical remoteness of logging sites from settlements, infrastructure, and domestic markets. They imply that investment capital could be more effectively utilized not only in reforestation in the European-Uralian zone but in renovating existing processing plants in that zone. In many cases, established mills, settlements and transportation links in western regions are in jeopardy because the forests have been ruthlessly exploited in the past and appropriate reforestation has not been undertaken.

In light of these considerations and the imputed advantages of effective European-Uralian forest management over unconstrained growth of logging east of the Urals, the incomplete but compelling evidence presented by the major thinkers in Soviet forestry must be evaluated for the support it lends to our understanding of the regional alternatives which users of this resource may seek to adopt in the future.

RESOURCE INVENTORY

Western analysts such as Eronen (1982b) and Honer, Hegyi, and Bonnor (1985) have noted the improved accuracy of forest mensuration and greater reliability in the manner of establishing permissible cutting limits which have occurred during the past two decades. The first reliable data on the entire USSR forest was obtained in 1957 (Gusev *et al.*, 1981, p. 10). Inventories taken in 1961, 1966, 1973, 1978, and 1983 are considered methodologically reliable by Soviet foresters, especially in evaluation of remote or peripheral forests in the North, Siberia and the Far East. The data published after each of the last three inventories are particularly consistent with previous publications; improvements in survey methods, mensuration technology including use of satellite imagery, and electronic data processing suggest that these inventories reflect a state-of-the-art approach to resource measurement. Many decisions associated with utilization of Soviet forests made prior to the mid-1960s, therefore, probably reflect a methodologically and technically inadequate data base and may have promoted expediency in the utilization of all forests.

The growing scientific approach to forest mensuration and more profound understanding of biophysical constraints on silviculture evident in the Soviet forestry literature have produced by the 1980s a body of thought (e.g., Shutov *et al.*, 1984; Petrov and Morozov, 1984) which seems to be more reliable and less dogmatic or ideologically constrained than at any previous period of Soviet development. Thus, although we still do not have detailed economic analyses of spatial alternatives in timber utilization, we now seem to have reliable physical or technical evaluations of developmental alternatives.

1983 FOREST INVENTORY

The report on the 1983 inventory (all references here to this inventory are from Drozhalov, 1984) reveals relatively minor changes compared to that for 1978. Major changes occurred between the 1973 and 1978 inventories. Survey accuracy thus seems to have stabilized and the rate of change in alienation of forest land in European USSR may have diminished.

AREA AND VOLUME

Three-quarters of the Soviet population lives in the European-Uralian region, an area comprising 25.5 percent of the forested area, 27.3 percent of the total growing stock, 19 percent of the forest land, and 18.3 percent of the nation's mature timber. State forests comprise forested, nonforested, and nonforestry lands (Table 4.1). The volume of total USSR forest land increased between 1978 and 1983 by 2.1 million hectares to 1259.4 million hectares although that in the European-Uralian zone decreased by 0.7 million ha to 239.5 million ha. Collective farms exercised jurisdiction over 1.6 percent, various ministries and administrations including state farms controlled 4.5 percent, and the remaining 93.9 percent was under the jurisdiction of central forestry agencies. The relative shares of the central agencies and of the collective farms have declined slightly during the past decade. Collective farms continue to be transformed into state farms. Centrally administered lands are transferred to other organizations and landuse categories, or they are removed from the land reserve for industry, settlement, and infrastructure.

Approximately 10 percent of the centrally administered forest land is held as long-term leases, primarily associated with reindeer and sheep herding. This land is utilized by nonforestry ministries and agencies and collective farms, and probably should be viewed as separate from concepts of "managed" forests. Due to its location, this long-term lease land comprises (1978 data) only 5.4 percent of the central forest agencies' forested land. (This accounts for the difference between 710 million ha reported in 1973 for central state forestry agencies [Table 4.2] and 675.2 million ha reported in Chapter 3 [Table 3.3].) Almost all of this leased forest in the European USSR is associated with reindeer range in the Northwest, and 80 percent of the leased land in the Asian USSR is used for reindeer grazing in the northern Far East. The remainder mainly supports sheep in Central Asia.

The regional share of forest land held by collective farms and nonforestry organizations varies greatly (1978 data) among the major regions. In the European USSR, collective farms administer 7.4 percent of the forested land, and nonforestry ministries, etc. are responsible for 10.3 percent of the forested land. Together with collective farms, these organizations' jurisdiction over forest land amounts to 31 percent in the Center, 19 percent in the Volgo-Vyatka, 29 percent in the Black Earth, 46 percent in the Ukraine, 24 percent in Belorussia, and between 29 percent and 42 percent in the Baltic republics. In Soviet Asia, however, they exercise jurisdiction over only 3 percent of state forest land. The share of state forest land amenable to coherent management by central forest administrations is thus greatest in northern European forests, in the Urals, in Western and Eastern Siberia, and in the Far East.

With better mensuration, especially in northern and eastern peripheral regions, the forested area has increased steadily throughout the five accurate reporting periods (Table 4.2). Forested lands comprise 64 percent of lands administered by central forestry agencies; 12 percent are classified as nonforested forest land, and the remaining 24 percent are excluded from forestry (Table 4.1). Forested land administered by central state forestry agencies, however, varies (Table 4.1) from 78 percent of the European forest land to 62 percent of that in Asia. In the Northwest it accounts for 71 percent of the forest land, but in the Far East it is only 55 percent. The nonforested forest land represents a regeneration backlog - forestry land currently in a deforested or inadequately forested condition. The ratio of forested to deforested land is thus 5.7:1; this regeneration backlog is approximately twice the size of the total area which has undergone some kind of regeneration since the Revolution in 1917 (Table 4.3). The relative importance of deforested land varies among regions; it is notable in Siberia and Central Asia (Table 4.1). In major resource areas, however, this regeneration backlog is significant throughout the forests of the RSFSR, especially east of the Urals.

The European-Uralian zone contains 33 percent of Group 1 (protection forests) forested area, 74 percent of Group 2 (restricted industrial forests) forested area, but 12 percent of Group 3 (general industrial forests) forested area. Because most commercial harvesting occurs in group 3 forests, and because four-fifths of their area lies outside the European-Uralian zone, the conclusion is frequently drawn both in the USSR and abroad that logging must be based in these forests. This expectation is compounded by the fact that most Soviet mature and overmature

Table 4.1
Landuse Composition of State Industrial Forests Administered by
Central State Forestry Agencies
(% of Areal Total)

	Total Forest Lands	Total Forestry Lands	Forestry Forest Lands								Nonforestry Forest Lands							
			Forested Lands			Nonforested Lands						Miscellaneous Usable Lands				Rights of Way	Unutilized Lands
			Total[a]	Including Plantations: Closed	Unclosed	Total[b]	Unspecified	Understocked	B&DS[c]	Cutover	Total	Arable Lands	Natural Hay Lands	Grazing Lands	Water Bodies		
USSR[a]	100	76	64	1	<1	12	1	6	4	1	24	-	<1	<1	<2	<1	21
RSFSR	100	76	64	<1	<1	12	1	7	4	1	24	-	<1	<1	<2	<1	22
Northwest	100	76	71	>	<1	5	-	<1	1	4	24	-	<1	-	3	<1	21
Center	100	94	87	5	3	7	4	>	>	3	6	2	1	-	-	1	2
Volgo-Vyatka	100	96	86	4	3	10	7	-	-	3	4	-	1	-	<1	1	2
Black Earth	100	92	85	19	6	7	2	1	-	4	8	<1	2	-	1	>1	4
Volga Littoral	100	92	85	5	4	7	2	1	-	4	8	>	2	-	-	<1	4
North Caucasus	100	89	81	4	3	8	2	1	-	5	11	<1	1	1	<1	<1	8
Urals	100	85	82	1	2	6	-	-	<1	<6	12	>	2	<1	<1	<1	9
RSFSR Europe-Uralia	100	82	77	3	<2	5	<2	<1	1	<3	18	<1	<1	<1	<2	<1	14
Western Siberia	100	61	55	-	-	>6	-	4	2	<1	39	-	<1	-	<5	-	33
Eastern Siberia	100	83	76	-	-	7	-	>3	<4	>1	17	-	-	<1	1	>	16

Region															
Far East	100	73	55	-	18	-	9	8	>1	27	-	<1	>	1	26
RSFSR Asia	100	74	62	>	12	-	7	<5	<1	26	-	<1	<1	<2	23
Belorussia	100	93	88	3	5	3	1	-	>2	7	<1	1	<1	<1	4
Estonia	100	71	65	3	6	4	1	-	>1	29	1	>1	1	1	22
Latvia	100	82	77	3	5	3	-	-	2	18	1	1	1	<1	11
Lithuania	100	87	84	2	3	2	-	-	1	13	>1	2	>1	3	5
Ukraine	100	91	84	4	7	6	>	>	1	9	<1	>1	>1	>3	5
Moldavia	100	95	81	8	14	10	-	-	4	5	-	1	<1	2	4
Georgia	100	92	86	1	6	3	3	-	-	8	-	-	>3	<1	4
Azerbaydzhan	100	90	80	2	10	7	3	-	-	10	<1	1	3	1	4
Armenia	100	85	66	3	19	14	5	-	-	15	-	-	>5	-	8
USSR Europe-Uralia	100	83	78	5	5	2	<1	<1	>2	17	>	<1	<1	<2	13
Kazakhstan	100	76	48	4	28	11	14	<1	<2	24	<1	2	9	1	11
Uzbekistan	100	72	27	6	45	18	25	>	2	28	<1	>	13	<1	14
Turkmenistan	100	71	20	5	51	37	14	-	-	29	-	-	>17	-	11
Tadzhikistan	100	46	24	3	22	13	9	-	-	54	-	-	11	>2	40
Kirgizia	100	45	31	2	14	7	6	-	-	55	-	<1	26	<1	27
USSR Asia	100	74	62	>	12	<1	7	4	<1	26	-	<1	<1	<2	23

[a] Percentages in this column have been rounded. They represent values of forested area shown in Table 3.3, column 1. Thus total USSR forested lands administered by central state forestry agencies excluding long-lease grazing comprise 64.7 percent of total forestry forest land or 675,706 million ha.

[b] Figures in this column represent an area of regeneration backlog. Thus 12 percent of total forestry forest land, or 124,653 million ha administered by central state forestry agencies represents an area of regneration backlog or an area currently existing in a deforested condition.

[c] B&DS = burned and destroyed stands.

[d] 100 percent of the total USSR comprises 1043.49 million ha of state forests administered by central state forestry agencies excluding long-lease grazing lands. (When long-lease grazing lands are included, the total comprises 1162 million ha.)

Source: Compiled and adapted from Vorob'yev et al. (1979, pp. 31, 32, and 35); and Sinitsyn (1976, pp. 8-23).

Table 4.2
USSR Forest Resource

Forested Area and Related Growing Stock, from Inventory
on 1 January of Stated Years

	1961	1966	1973	1978	1983
Total Forested Area (Millions of ha)	738	747	769	792	811
Collective Farm Forest	32	26	20	20	19
Industrial Forest - Including: Forest Administered by Central State	706	721	749	772	792
Forestry Agencies	687	691	710	729	745
Total Growing Stock (Billions of cu. m)	80	80	82	84	86
Collective Farm Forest	2	2	2	2	2
Industrial Forest - Including Forest Administered by Central State	78	78	80	82	84
Forestry Agencies	76	76	76	77	79

Source: *Narodnoye Khozyaystvo SSSR, 1922-1982* (1982); *Narodnoye Khozyaystvo SSSR*, (latest annual volumes); Drozhalov (1979, 1984); Nikolayuk (1975); Tseplyayev and Gusev (1967), and Ponomarev (1963).

Table 4.3
USSR Forest Management by Central State Forestry Agencies

Forest Restoration and Afforestation

Years	Total	Seeding/ Planting	Assisted Natural Regeneration
1917-1937	1,835[a]	1,326[a]	509[a]
1938-1941	1,054	964	90
1942-1945	245	165	80
1946-1949	2,182	1,373	809
1950	1,088	729	359
1955	1,188	582	606
1960	1,577	824	753
1965	2,011	1,223	788
1970	2,354	1,290	1,064
1975	1,363	1,275	1,088
1980	2,454	1,358	1,096
1984	2,167	972	1,195
Total, 1917-1984	71,388	39,609	31,779

Years	Managed/ Regulated	Improvement Thinnings and Selection Fellings		Marketable Volume
1950	20.7[b]	2,523[a]	24.2[c]	n/a
1955	31.7	2,365	21.0	n/a
1960	41.3	2,699	22.3	n/a
1965	39.5	3,110	30.0	25.4[c]
1970	41.6	3,823	44.1	36.7
1975	46.0	3,979	49.7	40.4
1980	46.8	3,919	52.6	42.4
1984	47.8	3,923	54.9	44.7

[a]Figures are in thousands of ha.

[b]Figures are in millions of ha.

[c]Figures are in millions of cu. m(s) - refers to volume of solid timber.

Source: Early Soviet periods and 1917-1981 total are from J. H. Holowacz (various years) and *Lesnoye Khozyaystvo SSSR za 50 let* (1967). Remainder are compiled from *Narodnoye Khozyaystvo SSSR. 1922-1982* (1982), and latest annual volumes of *Narodnoye Khozyaystvo SSSR*.

timber is found in Group 3 forests and that because the growing stock is biologically in jeopardy in such stands, removal of these stands would provide the basis for future regeneration and general improvement in land productivity. These expectations, however, ignore the spatial or geographical realities of many Group 3 forests, particularly their remoteness, harsh climate, topography, species composition, and slow regeneration.

AGE AND SPECIES MIX OF STOCK

Mature and overmature stands make up 52 billion of the 86 billion cu. m total national growing stock; 43 billion cu. m of the mature and overmature stands comprise conifers. In the last interinventory period (1978-1983), the national area of mature and overmature stands decreased by 13.1 million ha, including 2.4 million ha in the European-Uralian zone. This decrease occurred chiefly in coniferous forests. Nevertheless as in previous periods, the relative share of mature and overmature species remains significant in the USSR at 53 percent of total forested area. Even in the European-Uralian zone, however, mature and overmature species comprise 37 percent of the forested area. Their share of the forested area in the North, Northwest, Urals, and Volgo-Vyatka - the regions of chief timber reserves in the European-Uralian zone - comprises 82 percent of the coniferous forested area. Inappropriate harvesting practices in these regions are particularly harmful if they lead to destruction or premature cutting of the relatively small share of the stands comprising the age group "approaching maturity."

But the opposite age structure prevails in the European lightly forested regions; juvenile stands are predominant (46 percent of the forested area in the Ukraine, 51 percent in Belorussia, 39 percent in the Black Earth region, for example). Depletion of the forests in previous periods and the small present proportion of mature timber thus precludes intensive timber harvesting in the near future.

Central forestry organs (1983 data) administer 745 million of the 811 million ha of forested land (Table 4.2); approximately 566 million ha comprise coniferous stands. Of these 745 million ha of forested land, 689 million ha represent principal stands (539 million ha - 78.2 percent - of these are conifers), 56 million ha are low shrub formations, and nearly 1 million ha are occupied by nut-bearing and other species). The total area of principal stands includes 40.5 percent larch, 17.5 percent pine, 11.9 percent spruce, 6 percent Siberian stone pine, 2.3 percent fir, 13 percent birch, 2.7 percent aspen, 0.4 percent alder, and 0.4 percent basswood; shade tolerant species (oak, beech, ash, maple, etc.) comprise most of the remaining 5.3 percent. Environmental constraints limit most of the shade-tolerant species to the European-Uralian zone, and most of the Siberian stone pine and larch stands to Eastern Siberia or the Far East (Appendix 2.2).

Soviet authors note that because of its widespread distribution in eastern regions, larch will become the basic raw material for wood-processing in the Twelfth Five-Year Plan (presumably for industries deriving their raw material from eastern forests, in the authors' opinion). Furthermore, "future development of Siberia is related to the utilization of larch for local needs, needs of other

Soviet regions, and for forest-product exports" (Bokshchanin, 1982, p. 3). Most Soviet larch is found in eastern Siberia (77 percent of total national larch volume) and in the Far East (21 percent of total national larch volume). Larch comprises approximately one-half of the coniferous forest volume of eastern Siberia and almost three-quarters of that of the Far East. Bokshchanin (1982, p. 9) predicts that by the 1991 to 1995 period, larch will comprise 40 percent of the harvest in eastern Siberia and 60 percent of that in the Far East; he reports that the annual harvest of larch in the early 1980s had already reached 2 million cu. m in Irkutsk Oblast and comprised 40 percent of the export volume from the Far East. If the last official figures on all roundwood harvested in Irkutsk Oblast (1975) are taken as a base, the annual harvest of larch comprises only 6 percent of the timber harvest (official figures do not likely include the cut by "nomadic" loggers, which is a major problem in eastern Siberia).

The species composition of all Soviet forests is highly problematic, however. We cannot assume that domestic or foreign customers will adjust willingly or rapidly to larger volumes of larch in their timber consumption mix, although foreign experience with utilization of larch and numerous deciduous species and Soviet shortfalls of accessible coniferous timber seem to be stimulating greater awareness of their commercial properties in the USSR (Bobrov *et al.*, 1984, and Shcheglov *et al.*, 1984). As noted below in Chapter 7, for example, Japanese plywood manufacturers are beginning to accept larch experimentally. Nearly 21 percent (155.5 million ha) of the forested area administered by central state forestry organs is situated in the European-Uralian zone. Coniferous species comprise 63.6 percent, shade-tolerant species, 7.2 percent, and shade-intolerant species 28.5 percent. The remainder comprises various shrubs, willows, and other species. The traditional overcutting of conifers in this zone plus the poor performance of natural regeneration and the insufficient investment in silviculture have adversely affected the age composition of stands in these forests; in particular, the prevalence of immature stands of conifers and the proportion of deciduous trees, especially shade-intolerant species, have increased.

Despite the increase in area of coniferous forest in Asiatic and heavily forested European-Uralian regions, a large share of the stands regenerated after logging conifers comprises deciduous species, an undesirable process in terms of commercial sustained-yield management. In European regions, this process reportedly has been halted, although much remains to be done to improve the species composition of the forest. Drozhalov's (1984) analysis of the 1983 inventory relates the adverse change in species composition of forests in the heavily forested regions to inadequate silviculture after the felling of mature stands. This problem is exacerbated by insufficient equipment and shortages of labor. Furthermore, the introduction of forest-harvesting machinery has increased the incidence of destruction of new growth (the understory of new trees) and juvenile stands, thereby retarding the rate of new forest regeneration. Until this problem is overcome, Soviet foresters recommend that available equipment be limited to forests without significant understories.

In forests administered by central state forestry organs, 82 percent of the growing stock comprises coniferous forest, but 67 percent of the coniferous forest is classified as mature or overmature. Shade-tolerant and -intolerant species make up only 18 percent of the growing stock and only half of their area is mature or overmature forest. Of the increase in growing stock in the interinventory period, 47 percent occurred in coniferous stands. The dilemma facing Soviet foresters is thus related to the need to reduce, in the interests of sustained-yield management, the excessive share of mature and overmature stands without adversely changing the species composition of the forest. In theory this could be facilitated by effective regeneration and silvicultural practices; in reality, natural and human regeneration are inadequate, and undesirable deciduous species are increasingly occupying prime forest regions.

In the European-Uralian zone, for example, with one-quarter of the centrally administered volume of growing stock, conifers comprise 65 percent, but their share of growth in the last interinventory period was only 52 percent. The problem associated with this imbalance is particularly associated with shade-intolerant species (in some cases a larger regeneration of shade-tolerant species like oak would be desirable), which comprise 27 percent of the volume of growing stock but accounted for 36 percent of the interinventory growth in volume. As yet, these species are inadequately utilized by Soviet wood-processors, although calls for improvement in this matter have been registered for decades.

COMMERCIAL FOREST

When conservation and accessibility are taken into consideration, 385 million ha or 55.1 percent of the Soviet forested area is available for commercial timber harvesting. In the European-Uralian zone, however, the commercial timber-harvesting area is 128 million ha, or 85 percent of the regional forested area. The area commercially available outside this region is almost entirely located in Siberia and the Soviet Far East; it comprises approximately 257 million ha or almost exactly twice that of the European-Uralian zone.

In addition, a very large area - 184 million ha - mainly found east of the Urals is classified as reserve forest largely because of its remoteness and adverse physical environment. Great geographical variation in environmental adversity may be gauged from inventory figures released on the distribution of forest land in *gornye lesa* (mountain forests). Approximately 40 percent (474 million ha) of Soviet forest land comprises *gornye lesa*; half of this forest is composed of forested land, and two-thirds of the 26 billion cu. m growing stock reported from the 1978 inventory (Livanov, 1983, p. 4) is listed as mature or overmature. Of the total *gornye lesa*, 65 percent of the area is found in the Far East, 25 percent in eastern Siberia, but only 5 percent in the European-Uralian zone and 5 percent throughout the remainder of the country. Given that 90 percent of this forest area is found in eastern Siberia and the Far East (*gornye lesa* comprise 39 percent of the forested land area in eastern Siberia, 56 percent of that in the Far East, but only 28 percent of that in the Urals and 2 percent of that in the Northwest), then some of the adverse topographical limitations on forests of those peripheral regions are immediately apparent (*Lesnoye Khozyaystvo SSSR*, 1977, p. 19). Of the total national growing stock in the *gornye lesa*, 56 percent of the volume is situated on slopes over 20 degrees, and 30 percent is found on slopes of 20 to 30 degrees (Livanov, 1983, p. 4). Approximately 50 million cu. m is harvested annually (agencies are not specified) from *gornye lesa* in the USSR although the volume from slopes in excess of 15 to 20 degrees is only 4 million cu. m (Livanov, 1983, p. 4).

The volume of national commercial forest is set at 28.6 billion cu. m or 58 percent of the volume of mature and overmature stands. In the European-Uralian zone, however, the commercial forest comprises 88 percent of such stands. Despite increases in the overall volume of growing stock throughout Soviet forests, the volume of commercial stands declined in the European-Uralian zone during the interinventory period by 3 percent (260 million cu. m). Nevertheless, more precise mensuration and the extension of regulated utilization in various categories of European protected forest in the 1978-1983 period increased the volume of forest available for commercial exploitation by 3 percent. This increase apparently mitigated the full impact of decline in commercial forest during this period.

In addition, some 1.25 billion cu. m (70 percent of which is conifer) of mature and overmature timber in Group 1 forests are proposed for utilization in the near future. At present, the annual allowable cut of 38 million cu. m in these forests is only half utilized. Over 40 million cu. m of timber was being harvested annually by 1975 from intermediate cutting (Kolesnichenko, 1981, p. 9), largely from Group 1 forests. As noted in Chapter 3, this cut, important in the overall supply of wood although not included as part of the annual allowable cut, is particularly important in the European-Uralian zone where most Group 1 forests are situated. When conducted throughout all groups of Soviet forests, intermediate cutting as a form of improvement cut could account for 50 percent of the annual Soviet timber supply (Kolesnichenko, 1981, p.9). Proponents of sustained yield forestry in the USSR now frequently refer to the guidelines for economic and social development of the USSR from 1981 to 1990 which require foresters to undertake the gradual transition toward a forest industry based on sustained and coherent utilization of its resource, including improvement in the quality composition of the forest. Sennov (1984, p. 3) claims that this transformation is to be accomplished on the basis of effective improvement felling.

Despite such hopes, secure supplies of timber in reality depend on the commercial forests of the USSR, particularly those in the North and Urals economic regions of the European-Uralian zone having large proportions of mature and overmature stands (Drozhalov, 1984, p. 62). Their volumes of growing stock, however, are continually diminishing partly in relation to the objective of reducing the proportion of older timber, but partly because the appropriate measures are not being undertaken to guarantee replenishment of the resource. Drozhalov (1984, p. 62) fears that a large discrepancy between rates of harvesting and regeneration will lead to extensive fluctuations in logging and to rapid exhaustion of the resource. Thus, the allowable principal cut exceeds the mean annual increment by 86 percent in Archangel, 69 percent in Murmansk, 56 percent in Komi, 45 percent in Vologda, and 29 percent in Karelia, and by 22 percent in Kirov and Perm oblasts or territories. Although the volume of growing stock is still great in the European-Uralian regions, the reserves of mature and overmature timber which constitute the basis for designation of commercial forests have a life expectancy (at existing levels of utilization) of 13 years in Kostroma, 20 years in Kirov and Vologda, 30 years in Karelia, and 50 years in Archangel and Komi. The extent of current middle-aged forests and those approaching maturity in these regions is too small to ensure future replacement of their mature timber now being harvested or to sustain their present levels of logging. Hence one of the major recommendations of the 1983 inventory report apparently incorporated into the Twelfth Five-Year Plan was to reconcile the gross discrepancies between utilization and regeneration of timber in European-Uralian forests, at least in the pulp and paper industry. (The 1978 inventory report seems to have had a similar effect on the Eleventh Five-Year Plan's goals but not on its actual procedures.)

In the optimistic and data-rich 1960s, figures of overcutting were regularly published for logging regions of the USSR, many of which today are described as having extremely undesirable forests. Although permissible levels of principal harvesting are lower than the annual increment, actual harvesting practices suggest that the commercial forests will be exhausted within 4 years in Belorussia, 9 years in the Ukraine, 8 to 10 years in the Baltics, and 10 years in the Black Earth region. Their levels of allowable principal cut were meant to reflect continual increases in the maturing of growing stock and to permit achievement of rotation cutting within 15 to 20 years (Drozhalov, 1984, p. 62).

QUALITY OF GROWING STOCK

Differences in physical environment among major forest regions are reflected in the quality of the resource. Nationally, 11 percent of the USSR is classified as high-yield forest, 49 percent as average yield, and 40 percent as low-yield. In the European-Uralian forests, however, the proportions of forest distributed among these groups are almost equal. With steady improvements in the age structure, increases in forested area, and increases in silviculture, the annual increment in growing stock is now rated at 931 million cu. m, representing an increase of 25 million cu. m over previous estimates. Approximately one-third of the annual increment accrues to European-Uralian forests which register an MAI per hectare of 2.2 cu. m compared to the national average of 1.35 cu. m. The annual increment of this region is nearly 310 million cu. m, which represents approximately three-quarters of the total timber harvest in the USSR from all sources, 97.5 percent of the total volume of timber harvested nationally by central state forestry organs, (*Narodnoye Khozyaystvo SSSR v 1983 godu*, 1984, p. 378), or 113 percent of commercial roundwood removals.

Most Soviet and Western descriptions of timber harvesting in the USSR focus on the logging volumes associated with commercial roundwood (275 million cu. m in 1983), or a larger figure associated with total "industrial" removals (356 million cu. m in 1983) as customarily reported in the annual *Narodnoye Khozyaystvo* volumes. The same volumes, however, under the section of natural resources and conservation, report a logging figure which lies between these two amounts (318 million cu. m in 1983) and which seems to include commercial roundwood harvested for the main wood-processing ministry plus improvement fellings which also seem to be consumed by that ministry.

The largest figure (356 million cu. m) expresses removals ("principal cut") for some 34 ministries and departments but excludes that comprising improvement fellings and other cutting. Wood for undisclosed users is harvested mainly in the Northwest, Volgo-Vyatka, the Urals, Siberia, and the Far East (Burdin *et al.*, 1980, pp. 64-65). A large share of the total annual cut, however, is consumed as fuel - approximately 100 million cu. m. Hence, the foregoing categories presumably include portions of this fuelwood, although Dienes and Shabad (1979, p. 33) note that the official figures do not include firewood gathered by the population for its own use. The total annual cut of approximately 410 million cu. m cited by Burdin *et al.* (1980, p. 64) and by Belov (1983, p. 224), although itself considerably in excess of what the wood-processing and statistical literature would have us believe, still seems to understate the annual cut.

Belov (1983, p. 225) states that the main wood-processing ministry takes 54 percent of the annual harvest of 410 million cu. m. The forestry ministries of the RSFSR, Ukraine, Belorussia, the Baltics, and of unspecified other republics take 22 percent (half of which comprises improvement and "sanitation" fellings), and the ministries of the fuel industry, transportation, ferrous metallurgy, agriculture, and unspecified others - the so-called independent loggers - take 24 percent. Although obviously an oversimplification due to omission of any consideration of timber size or species composition, these estimates strongly demonstrate what could be achieved in the European-Uralian zone with effective forest management.

One of the major factors detracting from full utilization of the potential of Soviet forested land is the imbalance between planned timber harvesting and the "trade" mix of timber designated in the allowable cut. To "fulfill the excessive planned harvesting volumes of commercial roundwood," analysis of the 1983 inventory notes that the best, high-yielding stands have been cut first, with the result that the composition of commercial forests has continually diminished. The present mature and overmature forests of the North and the Urals have lower than average yields which are close to those expected from forests approaching maturity. In Archangel (141 cu. m/ha) and in Kirov (212 cu. m/ha) yields in these two types of forest are equal, but in other regions forests approaching maturity exceed the mature forests in average volume of growing stock per ha: by 12 cu. m in Vologda, by 27 cu. m in Karelia, and by 31 cu. m in Komi. To overcome the depletion of quality timber within mature forests, Drozhalov (1984) recommends that timber harvesting be related to the wood-product mix which given commercial stands can support.

REGENERATION

In addition to better matching of product plans and growing stock profiles, effective silvicultural practices have great importance for improvements in the regional efficacy of Soviet timber management. The Soviet regeneration backlog of approximately 138 million ha (including all forest lands) appears to be growing, not declining as implied by the 1983 inventory. If we estimate that annual harvesting occurs on between 3.5 and 4 million ha, the levels of reforestation (Table 4.3) are inadequate by 1 to 1.5 million ha.[6] The quality of reforestation, particularly in terms of levels and success rates of seeding and planting, is also subject to debate among Soviet foresters. Unknown additional areas suffering annual depredations from fire, disease and insects obviously raise the real annual need for reforestation still further.

Areas listed in the inventory as reforested, however, belie low prevailing levels of stocking density and the unsatisfied need for improvement felling in many forest stands. Some 31 million ha of forest stands, of which 19 million are in the European-Uralian zone, apparently are overstocked and need improvement felling; an additional 24 million ha require "sanitary" felling. Other areas of endeavor for improving forest productivity, particularly in the European-Uralian zone, include greater use of intermediate cut, improved road access to stands in the major forested regions, greater use of normally less-desirable species, and extended rehabilitation of the national state-designated forested wetlands (80 percent of their 71 million ha are concentrated in this zone [Drozhalov, 1984, p. 63]).

THE GREAT GEOGRAPHY DEBATE

Regional alternatives in Soviet timber utilization appear to fall within the broad category of debate so effectively assessed by Dienes: pro-Siberian development versus strengthening of the European economic core.[7] The arguments presented in this chapter confirm that development of eastern forests need not occur because of an inevitable or irreversible depletion of growing stock in the European-Uralian zone, although many Soviet analysts, especially in relation to the wood-processing industries, accept eastern resource utilization as being axiomatic. Most foresters, however, demonstrate, in physical or biological terms, that effective management and regeneration of the resource could lead to a much greater utilization of European-Uralian forests and could alleviate the need to extend development into the harsh environments of eastern forests. At the same time, however, cutting practices in all regions are deemed unsatisfactory from the standpoint of environmental protection or rotation cut. Furthermore, industrial consumption within the east should be satisfied by regional production of major wood products and structural timber, but levels of production in eastern Siberia and the Far East, however, exceed those necessary to meet regional unprocessed and processed timber needs in the majority of products. European-Uralian regional timber supplies and consumption of wood products are supplemented by the output from eastern regions, although this is uneconomic in many cases, especially in roundwood and low-value timber commodities. Although boldly suggesting that, to alleviate pressure on the European environment, the logging industry should be relocated to eastern regions, or forests should be more effectively managed and utilized in the West, Voyevoda (1980, p. 31) notes that the USSR pursues both policies simultaneously in order to refurbish the European-Uralian resources and eventually to increase their utility to the national economy.

Some regional diversity in Soviet timber-development strategy[8] has been pursued in recent decades, although the impact of the natural environment on forest regeneration has been insufficiently understood (Voyevoda, 1980, p. 32). Furthermore, the full implications of improvement felling are not known. To

Voyevoda (1980, pp. 32-4), this is a labor-intensive process, an uneconomic activity in many cases which needs to be avoided. In addition, greater extraction of minerals from the forest soil by the remaining trees is alleged to encourage its degradation unless supplemented by mineral fertilizers. Given that the outcome of improvement felling is not sufficiently predictable, Voyevoda (1980, pp. 32-33) argues that foresters need to have at their disposal a reliable reserve supply, a process which is being met by greater reliance on heavily forested regions, particularly those of Siberia. According to this reasoning, expenditures on silviculture in the western, heavily-populated regions mean that expenditures on development in the East are not as expensive as otherwise expected. This argument, however, seems to confirm that eastern developments are not evaluated in terms of the cost of regenerating their associated forests, or of moving timber and wood products to European USSR markets. Eastern timber utilization is essentially viewed as a mining operation with little long-term consideration for the environment or for sustained management of the resource.

Some analysts, however, take a completely didactic approach to eastern forests and dismiss all obstacles or supposed disadvantages in order to support current national political policy. Their statements and prognoses are reminders that the academic and scientific establishments in which informed planning opinion is formulated in the USSR still have proponents of regional development perhaps removed from spatial and economic reality as evidenced by the following statement by Timofeyev (1979, p. 141):

> Despite the harsh climate, difficult terrain, and heavy demands for capital investment, the development of the forest sector of Siberia and the Far East has many economic advantages over other regions of the country. Moreover, production of commercial roundwood, lumber, chemical pulp and other processed wood products rightly does not have competitors today in other regions of the country. This is primarily explained by the impossibility of achieving similar large scales of production elsewhere in the USSR.

Although also unable to offer comprehensive cost estimates of regional development alternatives between forests of the West and the East of the USSR, most rigorous analysts cite negative eastern cost influences which supposedly place the exploitation of those forests at a great disadvantage. Voyevoda, for example, cites the harsh climate, low population density, and distance from the economic heartland as factors which even the system of regional coefficients, allowances and longer annual vacations cannot overcome. Furthermore, the higher priority accorded other primary sectors in the east means that they can outcompete forestry for limited supplies of labor and that they have better records of labor turnover and higher productivity. In addition myriad environmental factors act adversely on eastern populations. Other exercises (Blam *et al.*, 1982, pp. 142-49) in deriving optimal values for regional utilization of roundwood also are unable to provide unequivocal evidence that development of Siberian forests offers greater utility to the Soviet economy than that which can be obtained from forests in the European-Uralian zone. Part of the problem in interpreting such studies is related to the lack of detail provided on the assumptions and constraints built into the models and the extent to which the location and product mix of existing processing units is considered immutable.

In their extensive review of mathematical programming models used in Novosibirsk to derive and validate recommendations for Siberian development, Soule and Taaffe (1985, p. 95) note that

> most of the quantitative approaches used in Soviet regional analysis in general, and Siberian development specifically, are still in the experimental stages and are used in preplanning and long-term projections rather than in operational planning

and that "rigorous analytical approaches" are

> constrained by the complexity of regional problems in general and by the specific difficulties of inadequate information, including the existing price system, unresolved methodological issues, limitations on computer capacities, and the intricacies of incorporating important noneconomic variables.

With perhaps unusual candor, Voyevoda (1980, pp. 84-85) notes that the inclusion of specific factors in regional comparisons can greatly affect the relative merits of eastern or western regions. In one set of examples, he demonstrates that harvesting timber in Krasnoyarsk kray is 19 percent more effective than in Komi ASSR, although this advantage changes greatly as variables are added or subtracted, and that many unknown relationships cannot be evaluated because of the simultaneous interaction of specific variables. Many estimates exclude the cost of raw materials and transportation, and eastern regions can be made to appear advantageous when these important associated costs are overlooked. Furthermore, the problem of deriving models of regional preference is compounded by the absence of an effective theoretical base for systematic sector analysis. Thus, in an example drawn from Kemerovo oblast, Voyevoda (1980, pp. 84-85) shows how one section of *Gosplan* RSFSR determined that logging Kemerovo was between 2.3 to 3.7 rubles more expensive per cu. m than bringing timber from Krasnoyarsk, Irkutsk or Tomsk regions; analysts in another agency, *Sibgiprolesprom,* however, ascertained that 3 to 3.5 rubles could be saved per cu. m by logging in the Kuzbas instead of bringing timber from Tomsk or Krasnoyarsk regions.

Modeling by Voyevoda and associates (cited in Voyevoda, 1980, p. 269) in the 1970s on sectoral and regional development of the forest industry, despite many methodological problems including those identified above, gives us some idea, however, of possible future patterns of logging in the USSR. Their optimization seems to have made few allowances for changes in the intensity of wood-processing or for advances in silviculture, although they did include allowance for improvement felling and for greater utilization of deciduous species. They concluded that, in the near future (1976-1990), logging related to principal cut and improvement felling could expand in the European-Uralian zone, although levels of possible increase are smaller than those in eastern regions.

The figures in Table 4.4 serve to illustrate how the future appeared to analysts in Novosibirsk in the mid-1970s. Their projection serves to reinforce the arguments made throughout the present analysis that greater use of European-Uralian forests is possible assuming the political will to force substitution of deciduous species, the utilization of low-quality timber, and the full adoption of effective silviculture. This same political will must ensure greater use of deciduous species in Siberia as well, a point often overlooked in analysis of the Soviet forest because of our customary preoccupation with the size of the eastern larch forest. Furthermore, the estimates of Voyevoda (1980) rest on many assumptions which are not fully known. The estimates of possible increases during the 1976-1990 period predate the growth in desire for intensive utilization of resources apparently affecting investment decisions in the 1980s. The estimates also probably include levels of subsidization of eastern projects, including those associated with the BAM which reflect political and social priorities rather than strict economic considerations. Finally, the Novosibirsk estimates and much of their accompanying discussion indicate that evaluation of European-Uralian alternatives versus those of Siberia and the Far East likely will become even more rigorous in the future. Research and planning organizations in the USSR are evaluating more of the key variables affecting regional physical planning of the distribution of resource industries even though the reliability of strictly economic criteria may not be improving.

CONCLUSIONS

Regional alternatives in Soviet timber utilization appear to fall within the broad category of debate so effectively assessed by Dienes (pro-Siberian development versus strengthening of the European economic core). Assessment of the 1983 Soviet forest inventory in relation to many other Soviet analyses confirms that development of eastern forests need not occur because of an inevitable or irreversible depletion of growing stock in the European-Uralian zone. Many Soviet analysts, however, especially those with partisan attitudes toward the wood-processing industries, accept major shifts toward eastern resource utilization as being axiomatic. Levels of production in eastern Siberia and the Far East, however, exceed those necessary to meet regional unprocessed and processed timber needs in the majority of products. European-Uralian regional timber supplies and consumption of wood products are supplemented by the output from eastern regions, although this is probably uneconomic in many cases, especially in roundwood and low-value timber commodities.

Greater investigation is needed of regional variations in silviculture; improvements in technology for effective utilization of roundwood, including deciduous species and larch; and the impact which shortages of capital and labor will have on forestry and wood-processing investment in eastern peripheral regions, including the service area of the BAM and the AYAM railways. Soviet literature on economic developments associated with the BAM or associated railways in the Far East tends to be lacking in precision and detail, which suggests that detailed planning on resource utilization, including timber, is still

Table 4.4
Estimated Total Possible Regional Increases in
Logging Volumes for the Period, 1976-1990[a]
(Mllions of cu. m)

Region	C[b]	D[b]	Total
Volga Littoral	+0.7	+7.5	+8.2
Urals	-4.6	+5.8	+1.2
Remainder of North and South European-Uralian RSFSR	+4.8	+26.3	+31.1
West	-3.5	+6.8	+3.3
Southwest	+1.8	+4.3	+6.1
Western Siberia	+8.7	+14.5	+23.2
Eastern Siberia	+34.2	+14.4	+48.6
Far East	+21.5	+8.0	+29.5

[a]Total is used here to designate the total increase in levels of annual output over the 15-year period; each figure includes wood derived from principal cut and from improvement felling.

[b]C = conifers; D = deciduous species.

Source: Compiled from Voyevoda (1980, p. 272).

incomplete (for example, Morozova, 1983, pp. 129, 133, 141; and Ayzenberg and Sobolev, 1982, pp. 17-18, 116-20). Even the recent book by Chichkanov and Minakur (1984) on regional analysis and forecasting, which purports to illustrate its theoretical formulations with evidence from the Far East, is lacking in the type of convincing evidence which should be forthcoming from a region supposedly undergoing significant expansion of its infrastructure.

Eastern forests will obviously be utilized, especially to fulfill regional demand for unprocessed roundwood and some export obligations of roundwood, chips, and lumber to Pacific markets. Areas accessible to the Soviet rail network will likely continue to ship roundwood to the European-Uralian zone for consumption in unprocessed or processed form. The key factor warranting investigation in these and associated spatial developments, however, is the rate of growth of logging and wood-processing in various regions, and the extent to which substitutions can be made in the supply of raw material to existing consumers from greater efficiency in the utilization of accessible forests, especially those in the European-Uralian zone. The evidence presented in this chapter suggests that mining of the eastern resource in the near future may be undertaken as part of an effort to buy time while major areas of the European-Uralian forest are regenerated to sustain rotation cutting, providing that such forests are efficiently exploited. Kalinkin (1984, pp. 21-24), for example, notes that the chaotic actions of "nomadic" loggers performed for numerous nonforestry ministries and agencies seem to be destroying the viability of many large wood-processing complexes in Siberia itself. Problems in silviculture and delays in the introduction of rigorous planning in wood-processing are serving to delay and/or offset the adoption of alternatives needed for more effective regional management and utilization of Soviet forests.

NOTES

1. Basic descriptions of forests, timber utilization, and many associated issues are provided in *Lesnoye Khozyaystvo SSSR* (1977); Nikolayuk *et al.* (1982); Prokhorchuk *et al.* (1981); Timofeyev (1980); and Vorob'ev *et al.* (1979, 1982). The work by Stepin (1982), however, stands out as a major attempt to provide economic analyses of the spatial economy of Soviet forests. A comprehensive economic evaluation of eastern development including many sectors of the economy is provided by de Souza (1985). The present chapter focuses on the 1983 inventory (Drozhalov, 1984); all the foregoing forestry references rely on previous inventories.
2. Forest land administered by the State Forestry Committee represents (1978) 134.3 million ha of this regeneration backlog throughout the USSR, and 9.9 million ha in the European-Uralian zone (Ivanyuta, Kozhukhov, and Moiseyev, 1983, pp. 30-31). A recent English-language assessment of this topic and related inventory matters is provided by Honer, Hegyi, and Bonnor (1985, p. 2).

    Honer and Bickerstaff (1985, pp. 11-12) note that Canada's forests have a growing stock of 21.5 billion cu. m, of which 14 billion cu. m are available for harvest; the remainder comprises immature and regeneration stands. The growing stock is depleted from harvesting, fires and pests by 287 million cu. m each year, but growth, regeneration, and silviculture replace 338 million cu. m. Approximately 22 million ha of productive forest land in Canada represents a regeneration backlog (this category more than quadrupled in area between 1965 and 1985 [p. 26]); this amounts to about 10 percent of the forestry land base and deprives the country of 38 million cu. m of annual volume increment. Twenty percent of the 2.2 million ha depleted of growing stock each year goes out of production and is "not satisfactorily restocked." Annual additions to stocked land comprise 1.8 million ha, of which 0.2 million ha are subject to artificial regeneration; the remaining 1.6 million ha accrue from natural regeneration. On forestry lands with approved management plans, 186 thousand ha of productive forest land annually are taken out of production.

Honer and Bickerstaff (1985, p. 41) note that Canada has a sufficient supply of mature and overmature timber to meet harvest needs. With immature stands, cutting levels can be maintained or even expanded but the productive forest land base is being eroded by "regeneration failures and land withdrawals. Data for this latter cause do not exist." (Almost half of Canada's forest inventory data are over ten years old and "many have not been updated" [p. 11].) Old growth timber will prevent Canada from running out of wood, but relevant data "tend to mask the local and regional shortages that do exist." Honer and Bickerstaff (1985, p. 41) state that the forestry land base can only be maintained through silviculture and that "all cutover lands must be restocked immediately to ensure continued economic prosperity from our forests."

3. Honer and Bickerstaff (1985, p. 22) observe that, in Canada, for example, forestry "is largely practiced at the extensive level of management intensity." They define extensive management as trying to maintain a merchantable timber supply; the regeneration of depleted areas; some protection from insects, disease, and fire; and establishment of guidelines for permissible levels of harvesting. Intensive management, however, seeks to improve the productive base; natural levels of productivity; genetic quality of species; silvicultural practices such as "cleaning, thinning, fertilization, improvement cuts and pruning in established stands;" and the efficacy of protection measures.

4. The Soviet literature on the substitution of wood waste or rejected timber for commercial roundwood is extensive. At present, an estimated 110 million cu. m of such material is available annually from the activities of all timber-harvesting agencies, although only two-fifths is deemed economically recoverable (three-fifths of the 62 million cu. m available to the major ministry is deemed economically recoverable); the respective volumes actually available, however, are even smaller - 33 percent and 47 percent. This subject is carefully discussed in Livanov, *et al.* (1980, pp. 3-9).

5. Reports on the visit of M. S. Gorbachev ("Uskorennoye Razvitiye Ekonomiki Sibiri i Dal'nego Vostoka," 1985) to Western Siberia in September 1985 attest to the role of national production goals in forcing the eastern development of high-profile sectors such as fuel and energy. These primary industries then become important to some related regional processors

(e.g., petrochemicals) in the name of "intensification" and to other sectors such as pulp and paper which are energy-intensive or which in aggregate consume large amounts of energy. Increasing costs of production are stated to be chiefly due to increasing length of hauling roundwood, rising costs of building logging roads, corrections to pay schedules between 1973 and 1975, introduction of new depreciation allowances in 1975, etc. (Burdin *et al.*, 1980, p. 241).

6. This rough approximation is based on an annual cut of 410 million cu. m and an average stocking of 106.3 cu. m per ha. On the other hand, Belov (1983, p. 224) states that 2.5 million ha are harvested annually for the principal cut, improvement felling occurs on over 2.3 million ha, "forest sanitation" cutting on over 1.7 million ha, and unspecified cutting on approximately 300 thousand ha. Thus, directly (2.5 million) or indirectly (4.3 to 4.4 million), some 6.8 to 6.9 million ha are affected by annual cutting.

7 The detailed assessments made by Leslie Dienes (1982, 1983) suggest overwhelmingly that much of the development of Siberia and the Far East cannot be explained in terms of coherent economic analysis except for the crash development and exploitation of some specific raw materials such as petroleum, coal, gold, or other material supplies deemed essential for the economic and military development of the USSR. Siberia and the Far East seem to the present authors to offer an overwhelming psychological imperative to Soviet developers and planners which carries a logic of its own. Perhaps the assault on new, undeveloped regions offers a greater psycho-political challenge than the careful, rather tedious management and husbanding of accessible resources such as the forests of the European-Uralian zone.

8. One of the ways in which the development of wood-processing has been accommodated in European-Uralian regions and in the East has been to expand and reequip existing plant and equipment in the former while developing major new investments in the latter *(Sovetskiy Soyuz,* 1975, pp. 181-82).

5
Forests and Industry

Given the regional constraints on forest distribution and harvesting discussed thus far, what patterns of industrial use may be identified? Chapter 5 first examines the utilization of industrial timber in the USSR by product sector and analyzes the regional shifts which have occurred in wood-processing since 1960, the benchmark year used in this book for modernization of Soviet forestry and forest products. The influence of transport modes and tariffs on the spatial distribution of wood-processing is then evaluated, followed by evaluation of the changing integration of timber in peripheral regions with processing plants in established Soviet regions. The chapter concludes with an assessment of how national and regional plans are likely to affect the wood-processing sector in the near future, and the extent to which regional shifts in logging and investment may affect the spatial organization of forest products.

The structure of Soviet timber supply and demand by type of raw material and sector of production is calculated below. All units of production are converted into roundwood equivalent to facilitate the estimation of total supply and consumption balances. This method is consistent with earlier studies by Barr (1970, 1983) and Barr and Smillie (1972), but calculation of the 1984 structure here utilizes some new international conversion factors (United Nations, 1982). Consumption of roundwood is increasingly supplemented by utilization of wood waste, particularly some form of wood chip. Wood-processing continues to reflect the growing investment in sheet products, especially particleboard and fiberboard, which were almost nonexistent among Soviet industries in 1960, and in paperboard for various forms of packaging. The current mix of production among Soviet wood-processing industries is compared with estimates by Barr (1983) for 1970 and 1975. Although Barr (1983) has previously offered a scenario of likely output in 1990 based on changes which occurred prior to 1975, recent declines in the output of lumber and the continuing unavailability of regional output data on minor wood products and timber suggest that the 1990 estimate probably reflected more what the Soviet Union might have done rather than what is occurring.

TIMBER SUPPLY AND DEMAND

Previous calculations by Barr (1970, 1983), and Barr and Smillie (1972), are compared in this section with estimates of the 1984 structure of Soviet timber supply and sectoral output mix. One of the major problems in assessing the aggregate output of forest products is comparability among the various items. Comprehensive and consistent economic data measuring the commercial production of Soviet forest-sector products are not available. Criteria employed in other industrial countries reflecting value added during manufacture, or selling value of factory shipments, cannot be utilized in assessments of the Soviet case. Regional employment data similarly are not published. Many authors simply describe the percentage change in the spatial distribution of individual industries and refrain from aggregate analyses. Nevertheless, we cannot fully comprehend whether Soviet claims of major eastward movement of forest-product investments are significant relative to the national pattern of total forest investment unless the major industries can somehow be aggregated.

The authors rendered individual industries' output into comparable units by converting all output of processed items into into roundwood equivalent, i.e., the volume of roundwood required for their production, designated cu. m(r) in Table 5.1. This technique assumes that international conversion factors (United Nations, 1982) are sufficiently reliable to be applied to each industry's output in all regions, even though the age of individual factories varies significantly. Conversion factors are widely used by international agencies to ensure comparability among nations when economic data are unreliable or unavailable. The factors vary among countries, however, and reflect important differences in technology and production process. In the Soviet case, despite the variation in age and origin of much forest-product technology, we have no choice but to apply conversion factors uniformly to all regions. The results, therefore, are subject to question but do at least facilitate some form of comprehensive analysis. The use of conversion factors not only permits use to ensure that total supply equals total demand, but also facilitates the generation of regional balances in net timber consumption. Some regions have significant surpluses which are shipped long distances, mainly by rail, to timber processors and consumers of wood in round form in other regions. These flows can be assessed with various optimality criteria to ascertain the economic viability of the spatial system and the imputed wisdom of further production, additional investment, or enhancement of reforestation programs in deficit areas.

The present analysis focuses on the years 1960, 1975, and 1984. The first year represents an important date in the modernization of Soviet industry. Investment increased in peripheral regions, and large amounts of capital started to be injected into forest-product sectors, particularly into technologically sophisticated products such as particleboard, fiberboard, and various chemical pulps which characterize the varied and productive wood-processing sectors of advanced industrial nations. The year 1975 is the last for which RSFSR regional output of both timber and forest products has been published, and is consistent with earlier, rather specialized work by Barr (1983) which supplements many of the observations made in the present analysis. The year 1984 is used because it is the basis for the *Narodnoye Khozyaystvo* volumes available in mid-1986. Refreshingly, the RSFSR volume provides important data on the 1984 regional (oblast, kray, ASSR) output of lumber, plywood, paper, and paperboard. The USSR volume also provides for the first time production data on glulam timbers ("structural glued-laminated timber products") apparently used in the USSR as roof trusses to span large distances in public (e.g., sporting, exhibition) and agricultural storage facilities (*Sovetskiy Entsiklopedicheskiy Slovar'*, 1982, p. 382). Industrial output of these items seems to have commenced in 1970 when the USSR produced 3000 cu. m and reached 168,000 cu. m in 1984 (*Narodnoye Khozyaystvo SSSR v 1984 godu*, 1985, p. 188). The regional location of this

Table 5.1
USSR Industrial Timber Supply and Demand
(Volume in Thousands of cu. m[r])

Supply	1960	% of Total	1975	% of Total	1984[a]	% of Total
Commercial Roundwood	261,513.00	98.1	312,902.00	89.7	282,840.00	83.3
Industrial Fuelwood	5,005.10	1.9	22,200.00	6.4	20,000.00	5.9
Wood Chips and Mill Waste	13,300.00	3.8	36,490.00	10.7	36, 490.00	10.7
Imported Roundwood	175.90	0.1	286.17	0.1	248.74	0.1
Total Supply	266,694.00	100.0	348,688.17	100.0	339,578.74	100.0
Total Supply for Domestic Consumption	262,265.30	98.3	331,819.17	95.2	323,981.74	95.4

Demand						
Lumber	162,556.20	61.0	176,346.94	50.6	155,361.24	45.8
Plywood	4,269.80	1.6	6,950.10	2.0	5,330.00	1.6
Chemical Pulp	11,179.80	4.2	33,516.00	9.6	39,949.70	11.8
Groundwood Pulp	2,328.00	0.9	4,206.00	1.2	5,397.17	1.6
Sleepers	11,930.30	4.5	9,741.18	2.8	9,952.95	2.9
Matches	756.20	0.3	1,104.93	0.3	1,408.70	0.4
Fiberboard	128.50	0.0	779.00	0.2	1,001.84	0.3
Particleboard	209.00	0.1	5,144.10	1.5	7,968.46	2.3
Total of Above Major Wood-processing Industries	193,357.80	72.5	237,788.25	68.2	226,370.06	66.7
Tanning-extractive Material	784.50	0.3	1,012.50	0.3		
Material for Processing Acetic Acid	523.00	0.2	800.00	0.2		
Packing Wood	9,142.88	2.6				
Pitprops	24,000.00	9.0	14,300.00	4.1		
Poles	3,500.00	1.3	6,272.00	1.8		
Ship and Marine Timber	2,400.00	0.9	2,400.00	0.7		
Construction and Miscellaneous Timber	37,700.00	14.1	60,103.54	17.2		
Total of Above Nonprocessed Uses	68,907.50	25.8	94,030.92	27.0	97,611.68	28.7
Roundwood Export	4,428.70	1.7	16,869.00	4.8	15,597.00	4.6
Total Demand	266,694.00	100.0	348,688.17	100.0	339,578.74	100.0
Total Domestic Demand	262,265.30	98.3	331,819.17	95.2	323,981.74	95.4

[a]1984 production data are from *Narodnoye Khozyastvo SSSR v 1984 godu* (1985, p. 187); some are estimated from 1975 data; export and import figures are from *Vneshnyaya Torgovlya SSSR v 1984 godu* (1985, pp. 27, 40); supply of chips is estimated from Livanov *et al.* (1980, pp. 3-9); fuelwood estimate is for 1980 obtained from Timofeyev (1980, p. 298) as the difference between the total amount of material available to replace roundwood and the supply of wood chips and mill waste.

Narodnoye Khozyastvo SSSR v 1975 godu (1976, p. 790) notes that the 1975 commercial timber removal figure includes 29 million cu. m of fuelwood for industrial consumption. This probably inflates previous 1975 estimates by Barr (1983).

All 1984 conversion factors are from United Nations (1982) (Conversion factors for previous years are from Barr [1970], pp. 24-25). Lumber conversion factor is 1.62; plywood conversion factor is 2.5; chemical pulp conversion factor is 4.9; fiberboard and particleboard - 1984 output divided by 1975 output times 1975 roundwood equivalent; groundwood pulp: calculated from *Narodnoye Khozyastvo SSSR v 1984 godu* (1985, p. 189); sleepers and matches 1984 figure is calculated by subtracting the 1975 actual figure from the 1990 estimate in Barr (1983), and prorating this anticipated 15-year (1975-1990) change over the 9-year period, 1975-1984.

1960 data - calculated from various sources; 1975 data - from Barr (1983).

Blank spaces indicate that data are not available and could not be reliably estimated.

industry is not indicated in the national or republican statistical yearbooks but probably is oriented toward the European-Uralian zone because of the major uses of this product and the awkwardness associated with transporting the final product. These structures are not included in Table 5.1 because of their small aggregate output and the absence of national or international conversion factors. We suspect, however, that the conversion factor for lumber probably would reflect well the roundwood equivalent because the product essentially is an aggregate of sawn boards. In this case, the 1984 output would equal 272,000 cu. m(r), a sum slightly larger than the total USSR import of roundwood (Table 5.1).

Throughout most of the period analyzed here (1960-1984), the Soviet Union steadily improved the amount of useful material recovered from each cubic meter of industrial timber (Table 5-1). During this same period, the output of industrial timber and commercial roundwood peaked and leveled off at approximately 356 million cu. m and 275 million cu. m, respectively, until 1984 when they both increased (by 12 and 7 million cu. m, respectively). Soviet policy, however, throughout this period has stressed the need to reduce roundwood consumption in the production of forest products and significantly to increase the utilization of wood chips, particles, and various forms of wood refuse, including suitable types of fuelwood. Although this substitution is clearly continuing, the recent upsurge in the output of industrial roundwood attests to the fact that adequate investment has not been made in the means to recover and utilize wood waste despite many indications that planners, politicians, and foresters are more than aware of the important economies achieved by such activity in other countries. Similarly, the wood material derived from intermediate harvesting and improvement felling (discussed in Chapter 3) represents an important source of fiber but is not included in the planned sector and does not appear necessary to balance supply and demand in Table 5.1. Some of the wood chips, however, may be derived from this intermediate source.

The relative importance of lumber output has declined significantly during the last quarter century from three-fifths of total processed output to well less than one-half, although an absolute decline did not occur until after 1975 (Tables 5.1 to 5.3). Domestic use of lumber has been offset by greater use of concrete and other nonwood materials in construction and by the greatly expanded output of composition boards (Table 5.3). Changes in output for each of the three subperiods analyzed here (1960-1975, 1960-1984, and 1975-1984) are summarized in Charts 5.1 to 5.3. The major wood-processing industries continue to consume approximately two-thirds of Soviet timber and fiber supply, although severe limitations in the data for 1984 prevent us from identifying which sectors continue to dominate the use of timber in unprocessed form. The greatly expanded output of paperboard, however, has probably reduced the volume of wood used in packaging and crates (Tables 5.2 and 5.3). The consumption of wood for packing both in crates and shipping containers has also probably been reduced by the greater use of standard metal containers on railroads and ships and by the use of plastics for domestic and retail distribution of beverages.

Table 5.2
Changing USSR and RSFSR Output of Major Forest Products
(Thousands)

		1960		1975		1984	
		USSR	RSFSR	USSR	RSFSR	USSR	RSFSR
Lumber[a]	cu. m	105,556.0	83,568.0	114,511.0	93,513.0	95,902.0	78,650.0
Plywood	cu. m	1,353.6	899.9	2,199.4	1,559.0	2,132.0	1,546.5
Fiberboard	sq. m	67.6	62.7	410.0	330.1	526.0	421.0
Particleboard	cu. m	160.8	91.8	3,957.0	2,581.7	6,190.0	4,139.0
Groundwood Pulp[b]	tons	931.0	730.0	1,682.4	1,428.4	2,060.0	1,749.0
Chemical Pulp	tons	2,281.6	2,090.6	6,840.0	6,428.7	8,153.0	7,723.0
Paper[c]	tons	2,420.8	1,940.8	5,215.0	4,317.5	5,862.0	4,917.0
Newsprint	tons	433.8	431.0	1,100.9	1,100.9	1,651.4	1,532.0
Paperboard	tons	806.1	490.5	3,369.5	2,513.9	3,965.0	2,814.0

[a]Newsprint figures used to be published in tons; they are now published in square meters. In 1970, for example, 1100.9 thousand tons are now shown in *Narodnoye Khozyaystvo SSSR v 1984 godu* (1985, p. 189) as 21.4 billion sq. m. Thus, 1 ton = 19.438.64 sq. m. Current data are expressed here, however, in tons.

[b]Groundwood pulp figures have been previously estimated by Barr (1970, 1983). The 1984 groundwood figure is derived as per Table 5.1; RSFSR share is assumed to be consistent with 1975.

[c]Paper includes newsprint.

Source: most 1960 data are from Barr (1970); newsprint data are from *Narodnoye Khozyaystvo SSSR v 1970 godu* (1971, p. 228); others are from *Narodnoye Khozyaystvo RSFSR v 1970 godu* (1971, p. 103). 1975 data are from Barr (1983). 1984 data are from *Narodnoye Khozyaystvo SSSR v 1984 godu* (1985, pp. 188-89); and *Narodnoye Khozyaystvo RSFSR v 1984 godu* (1985, pp. 81-86).

Table 5.3
% Change of USSR and RSFSR Output of Major Forest Products

	1960-1975		1960-1984		1975-1984	
	USSR	RSFSR	USSR	RSFSR	USSR	RSFSR
Lumber	8.5	11.9	-9.1	-5.9	-16.3	-15.9
Plywood	62.5	73.2	57.5	71.9	-3.1	-0.8
Fiberboard	506.5	426.5	678.1	571.5	28.3	27.5
Particleboard	2,360.8	2,712.3	3,749.5	4,408.7	56.4	60.3
Groundwood Pulp	80.7	95.7	121.3	139.6	22.4	22.4
Chemical Pulp	199.8	207.5	257.3	269.4	19.2	20.1
Paper	115.4	122.5	142.2	153.3	12.4	13.9
Newsprint	153.8	155.4	280.7	255.5	50.0	39.2
Paperboard	318.0	412.5	391.9	473.7	17.7	11.9

Chart 5.1

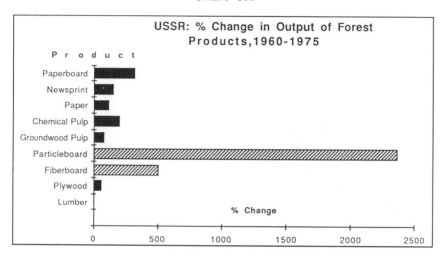

Chart 5.2

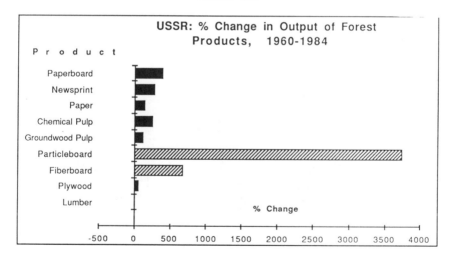

Chart 5.3

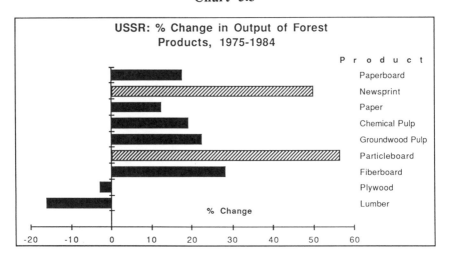

Chart 5.4

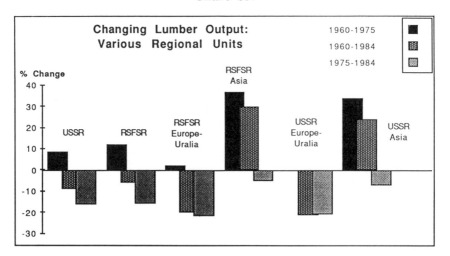

A COMPARISON WITH OTHER WORLD REGIONS

Despite the large size of its forest resource in terms of actual growing stock, the Soviet Union is relatively underdeveloped, except for production of lumber, in the comprehensive processing of timber and the output of forest commodities demanded by other major industrial societies. The USSR continues to supplement critical domestic shortages of some products with imports, particularly from Finland. Investment in wood-processing is enhanced by importing technology from Western countries and by joint-investment projects inside the USSR with some of its CMEA partners.

The Soviet Union has over one-fifth of the world's forested land (22.4 percent); over one-half of its coniferous standing timber (53.4 percent); and a modest, but important share of its deciduous growing stock (7.7 percent) (Vorob'yev *et al.*, 1984, p. 116). In comparison, North America (Canada and the United States) comprises approximately one-sixth of the world's forested land (17.1 percent), less than one-quarter of its coniferous timber (23.4 percent) and a share of deciduous timber similar to the USSR (6.5 percent). Despite its large share of coniferous timber and forested land, the USSR, however, still has a disproportionately small forest-products sector, dominated by lumber, rather than more technologically comprehensive products. Although other wood-processing industries have registered impressive production gains during the past quarter century, the structure of Soviet wood-processing still indicates that the recovery of processed items per unit of input is lower than in other major producers such as those in North America and Europe.

In order to place the USSR's wood-processing industries in perspective, the authors suggest that a simple ratio-comparison of these industries with similar ones in North America may help the reader gain an appreciation of the USSR's stage of development. Given Soviet planners' desire to bring the structure of their wood-processing sector more in line with that of North America and Europe (discussed by Petrov *et al.*, 1986, pp. 73-86), such international comparison may also indicate which sectors and regions may continue to receive important investment in the future. The ratio-comparison is facilitated by reference to international data compiled by Vorob'yev *et al.*, (1984, various pages, including pp. 122-23) for the year 1980.

North America produces 1.5 times more industrial timber than the USSR, but harvests 1.7 times more commercial roundwood. This reflects the USSR's significant level of fuelwood production (fuelwood comprises 1 percent of Soviet energy consumption) despite its large supplies of oil, gas, and coal. In lumber (including sleepers), however, North American production exceeds that of the USSR only by 1.2 times, despite the large consumption of lumber in the former for framehousing. In some more technologically advanced products, however, the difference between North America and the USSR is large. North American output of plywood exceeds that of the USSR by 9.4 times, of chemical pulp by 8 times, of groundwood pulp by 6 times, and of paper and paperboard together by 8.6 times. In composition boards, however, the difference is not great: North American production of fiberboard exceeds that in the Soviet Union by 2.8 times, and in particleboard by only 1.6 times.

The USSR produces more industrial timber than Europe, but slightly less commercial roundwood. It surpasses Europe in output of lumber but not in production of other processed items. European production, in turn, exceeds that of North America only in the output of particleboard (by 3.1 times). European particleboard output, however, exceeds that of the USSR by 5.1 times, and, in fact, three-fifths of world particleboard production originates in Europe. Production of fiberboard in Europe is 1.1 times greater than that in North America but 3.2 times that of the USSR.

These imbalances between the USSR and North America or Europe comprise a very important context for understanding many of the subjects identified in this book. The Soviet structure is deemed adverse by the country's own critics whose remedies are steadily bringing about change in the product and spatial structure of that country's forest industries. Lumber production continues to decline. More and more emphasis is being placed on the substitution of wood waste, refuse, and fuelwood for commercial roundwood. Output of composition boards has become significant in the USSR. The import of raw materials such as wood pulp and of processing equipment to sustain important new industries seems to have become an established practice. Strong attention is being paid to the need to reduce average length haul of roundwood in order to reduce transportation inefficiencies, and many aspects of timber harvesting and handling are being mechanized to enhance efficency and rates of material recovery. A world perspective on the Soviet wood-processing industry strongly suggests that future sectoral developments will seek to emulate leading world regions. Changes to the product mix and processing methods will, in turn, strongly affect types of roundwood or substitutes consumed, and thereby will directly influence regional patterns of production.

INDUSTRIAL STRUCTURE

The contribution of the forest-products sector to the Soviet industrial structure is relatively modest,approximately 5 percent of gross output (Dienes, 1983, p. 234). In regions like the Northwest, East Siberia, and the Far East, it comprises approximately 12 to 14 percent of regional gross output; in others such as the Southwest, Baltics, and Volgo-Vyatka, this sector accounts for between 6 and 9 percent of regional gross output. In no region is the sector dominant. Its importance in the East rests with timber and sawn lumber; in the Northwest these items are supplemented with pulp, paper, and paperboard. Although the origin of any forest product or export commodity may favor particular regions, many timber and wood-processing regions also have other important industries such as fuels and minerals (Northwest, Urals, Siberia, and the Far East) or machine building (Northwest, Urals, and Western Siberia). These other industries also place heavy burdens on available transportation routes, particularly the railways, and may outcompete the forest-products sector for available rolling stock. Although their annual total weight moved by rail is less than that of other major Soviet commodities, forest products have consistently accounted for the greatest average length of haul of any major commodity group. Furthermore, until comparable data on this feature ceased to be published in the 1970s, the average length of rail haul of forest products continued to increase while the average length of rail hauls over 1000 km for all other commodities showed significant decreases (*Narodnoye Khozyaystvo SSSR v 1970 godu*, 1971, p. 432). This transportation factor with its associated bottlenecks, particularly in the East, probably partially underlies the increasing preference for some forms of industrial development in western or border regions of the European USSR associated with foreign trade (Dienes, 1983), particularly with CMEA countries. The European-Uralian "factor" identified throughout this book thus may receive additional stimuli from sectors of the Soviet economy unrelated to growing environment and silviculture and may further reduce the "natural" utility or economic viability of eastern forests and associated developments.

REGIONAL CHANGE OF FOUR MAJOR INDUSTRIES

Four major groups of forest products comprise over 80 percent of the nation's wood-processing. Regional production data on minor products and items which are consumed in relatively unprocessed form are not formally published but have been discussed in a recent book by Timofeyev (1980, pp. 142-95). Some of these industries are identified in Table 5.1 for 1975, but data are insufficient to proffer reliable estimates for 1984. Previous estimates by Barr (1983, p. 418) for 1990 now appear to be rather tenuous. We can suggest, however, to what extent the regional supply and demand for timber among major regions coincides, and the degree to which a few major regions traditionally supplying almost all the timber deficits may likely sustain their relative shares in the near future. A mix-and-share analysis evaluates the changing macro regional structure of the major forest products, particularly the extent to which some of these industries have grown in the peripheral heavily forested regions, while others have continued to develop in traditional processing regions.

Among Soviet regions, however, changes in the output of the four forest products for which data are available have been rather spectacular and not as favorable to RSFSR Asian regions as many statements would have us believe. Many of the supporting tables identify changes in output for major regions and for some of the important provincial (oblast, kray, ASSR) units associated with each product. Lumber production over the entire period (Table 5.4 and Chart 5.4) has clearly increased significantly east of the Urals, except in the most recent period, when it declined there. Important shortages of sawlogs in the European-Uralian zone have hurt that region's sawmilling industry. Nevertheless, for the period 1960-1975, the output of lumber in the European-Uralian zone of the RSFSR actually increase, although recent declines are rather dramatic. The sawmilling industry in Europe-Uralia is clearly undergoing a major decline, even in regions with large traditional shares of national production, and it is declining as well east of the Urals except in a few important regions of activity such as Tyumen oblast and Yakut ASSR.

Growth of plywood (Table 5.5 and Chart 5.5) continued east and west of the Urals throughout much of the last quarter century, although since 1975 production east of the Urals continued to increase while in Europe-Uralia it

Table 5.4
Regional Change in Lumber Production

Lumber Output, 1960, 1975, 1984 (Thousands of cu. m)
Change by Period (%)

	1960	% of Total	1975	% of Total	1984	% of Total	1960-1975	1960-1984	1975-1984
USSR	105,556	100.0	114,511	100.0	95,902	100.0	8.5	-9.1	-16.3
RSFSR	83,568	79.2	93,513	81.7	78,650	82.0	11.9	-5.9	-15.9
Northwest	16,622	15.7	18,530	16.2	15,109	15.8	11.5	-9.1	-18.5
Archangel	6,411	6.1	7,120	6.2	5,413	5.6	11.1	-15.6	-24.0
Center	9,909	9.4	9,657	8.4	8,059	8.4	-2.5	-18.7	-16.5
Volgo-Vyatka	8,392	8.0	8,197	7.2	6,072	6.3	-2.3	-27.6	-25.9
Kirov	3,313	3.1	3,902	3.4	3,050	3.2	17.8	-7.9	-21.8
Black Earth	1,241	1.2	1,085	0.9	893	0.9	-12.6	-28.0	-17.7
Volga Littoral	7,640	7.2	6,705	5.9	4,513	4.7	-12.2	-40.9	-32.7
North Caucasus	2,887	2.7	2,956	2.6	1,890	2.0	2.4	-34.5	-36.1
Urals	12,758	12.1	13,450	11.7	10,910	11.4	5.4	-14.5	-18.9
Perm	3,280	3.1	3,657	3.2	3,131	3.3	11.5	-4.5	-14.4
Sverdlovsk	6,122	5.8	6,337	5.5	5,100	5.3	3.5	-16.7	-19.5
RSFSR Europe-Uralia	59,449	56.3	60,580	52.9	47,446	49.5	1.9	-20.2	-21.7
Western Siberia	7,237	6.9	8,790	7.7	8,728	9.1	21.5	20.6	-0.7
Omsk	686	0.6	998	0.9	1,006	1.0	45.5	46.6	0.8
Tomsk	1,241	1.2	1,943	1.7	1,601	1.7	56.6	29.0	-17.6
Tyumen	1,092	1.0	2,118	1.8	2,652	2.8	94.0	142.9	25.2
Eastern Siberia	11,585	11.0	17,339	15.1	16,137	16.8	49.7	39.3	-6.9
Chita	731	0.7	1,136	1.0	1,166	1.2	55.4	59.5	2.6
Irkutsk	5,010	4.7	7,691	6.7	7,131	7.4	53.5	42.3	-7.3
Krasnoyarsk	4,750	4.5	6,858	6.0	6,438	6.7	44.4	35.5	-6.1
Far East	5,089	4.8	6,580	5.7	6,195	6.5	29.3	21.7	-5.9
Khabarovsk	1,634	1.5	2,389	2.1	2,106	2.2	46.2	28.9	-11.8
Maritime	1,394	1.3	1,703	1.5	1,526	1.6	22.2	9.5	-10.4
(South)	4,306	4.1	5,559	4.9	4,971	5.2	29.1	15.4	-10.6
Yakut	443	0.4	582	0.5	767	0.8	31.4	73.1	31.8
(North)	783	0.7	1,021	0.9	1,224	1.3	30.4	56.3	19.9
RSFSR Asia	23,911	22.7	32,709	28.6	31,060	32.4	36.8	29.9	-5.0
Belorussia	3,023	2.9	3,171	2.8	3,031	3.2	4.9	0.3	-4.4
Baltics	3,021	2.9	2,893	2.5	2,492	2.6	-4.2	-17.5	-13.9
West	3,229	3.1	3,117	2.7	2,636	2.7	-3.5	-18.4	-15.4
Southwest	10,977	10.4	10,005	8.7	7,995	8.3	-8.9	-27.2	-20.1
Caucasus	1,497	1.4	1,036	0.9	925	1.0	-30.8	-38.2	-10.7
USSR Europe-Uralia	75,152	71.2	74,738	65.3	59,002	61.5	-0.6	-21.5	-21.1
Central Asia	3,470	3.3	3,893	3.4	2,809	2.9	12.2	-19.0	-27.8
USSR Asia	27,381	25.9	36,602	32.0	33,869	35.3	33.7	23.7	-7.5

Source: 1960 and 1984 RSFSR data - *Narodnoye Khozyaystvo RSFSR v 1984 godu* (1985, pp. 82-83); other data - *Narodnoye Khozyaystvo SSSR v 1984 godu* (1985, p. 188). 1975 RSFSR data - *Narodnoye Khozyaystvo RSFSR v 1975 godu* (1976, pp. 90-91); other data - *Narodnoye Khozyaystvo SSSR v 1975 godu* (1976, p. 274).

Table 5.5
Regional Change in Plywood Production

Plywood Output, 1960, 1975, 1984 (Thousands of cu. m)
Change by Period (%)

	1960	% of Total	1975	% of Total	1984	% of Total	1960-1975	1960-1984	1975-1984
USSR	1,354	100.0	2,199	100.0	2,132	100.0	62.4	57.5	-3.1
RSFSR	900	66.5	1,559	70.9	1,526	71.6	73.2	69.6	-2.1
Northwest	236	17.4	417	19.0	390	18.3	77.1	65.3	-6.7
Karelian	23	1.7	40	1.8	28	1.3	74.9	21.6	-30.4
Leningrad	98	7.2	140	6.4	88	4.1	43.5	-9.4	-36.9
Center	213	15.8	360	16.4	291	13.7	68.8	36.4	-19.2
Bryansk	14	1.1	48	2.2	40	1.9	237.1	181.8	-16.4
Kalinin	42	3.1	75	3.4	51	2.4	79.6	22.1	-32.0
Kaluga	4	0.3	17	0.8	15	0.7	293.2	247.7	-11.6
Kostroma	99	7.3	128	5.8	104	4.9	29.9	5.3	-19.0
Moscow	2	0.1	18	0.8	20	1.0	982.4	1,094.1	10.3
Vladimir	44	3.3	55	2.5	48	2.2	25.4	8.2	-13.7
Yaroslavl	8	0.6	11	0.5	9	0.4	37.0	7.4	-21.6
Volgo-Vyatka	64	4.7	92	4.2	92	4.3	44.2	44.0	-0.1
Gorki	8	0.6	19	0.9	14	0.7	128.9	72.3	-24.7
Kirov	55	4.1	73	3.3	78	3.6	31.8	40.1	6.3
Black Earth		0.0				0.0			
Volga Littoral	189	13.9	239	10.9	201	9.4	26.4	6.3	-16.0
Bashkir	85	6.3	109	4.9	101	4.8	27.3	19.0	-6.5
Penza	24	1.7	26	1.2	27	1.3	10.6	14.8	3.8
Tatar	80	5.9	94	4.3	60	2.8	17.3	-25.3	-36.2
Ulyanovsk		0.0	10	0.5	12	0.6			19.4
North Caucasus	4	0.3	53	2.4	68	3.2	1,408.6	1,834.3	28.2
Krasnodar	3	0.2	52	2.4	68	3.2	1,574.2	2,083.9	30.4
Urals	108	8.0	233	10.6	237	11.1	115.0	118.9	1.8
Perm	41	3.0	115	5.2	120	5.6	180.7	192.7	4.3
Sverdlovsk	67	5.0	118	5.4	117	5.5	74.9	74.0	-0.5
RSFSR Europe-Uralia	814	60.1	1,394	63.4	1,278	59.9	71.3	57.1	-8.3
Western Siberia	38	2.8	68	3.1	49	2.3	79.3	28.1	-28.6
Altay	6	0.4	25	1.1	11	0.5	320.3	93.2	-54.0
Omsk		0.0	15	0.7	18	0.8			19.9
Tyumen	32	2.4	29	1.3	20	0.9	-10.2	-38.2	-31.1
Eastern Siberia	17	1.3	50	2.3	160	7.5	190.2	826.6	219.3
Irkutsk	17	1.3	50	2.3	160	7.5	190.2	826.6	219.3
Far East	31	2.3	47	2.1	39	1.8	50.3	25.5	-16.5
Khabarovsk	6	0.4	16	0.7	13	0.6	178.9	128.1	-18.2
Maritime	25	1.9	31	1.4	26	1.2	21.3	2.4	-15.6
(South)	31	2.3	47	2.1	39	1.8	50.3	25.5	-16.5
RSFSR Asia	86	6.4	165	7.5	248	11.6	91.1	187.0	50.2
Belorussia	170	12.6	230	10.5	220	10.3	35.2	29.4	-4.3
Baltics	171	12.6	198	9.0	195	9.1	15.5	13.8	-1.5
West	341	25.2	428	19.5	415	19.5	25.3	21.6	-3.0
Southwest	104	7.7	205	9.3	183	8.6	96.7	76.1	-10.5
Caucasus	9	0.6	8	0.4	8	0.4	-10.3	-10.3	0.0
USSR Europe-Uralia	1,268	93.6	2,034	92.5	1,884	88.4	60.5	48.6	-7.4
Central Asia		0.0		0.0		0.0			
USSR Asia	86	6.4	165	7.5	248	11.6	91.1	187.0	50.2

Source: 1960 and 1984 data - *Narodnoye Khozyaystvo RSFSR v 1984 godu* (1985, p. 84); and *Narodnoye Khozyaystvo SSSR v 1984 godu* (1985, p. 188). 1975 data - Barr (1983).

Chart 5.5

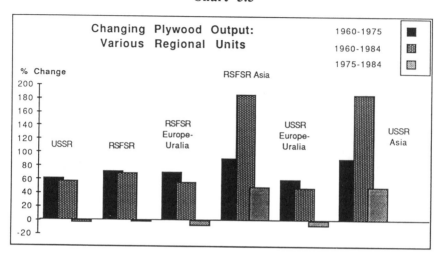

Chart 5.6

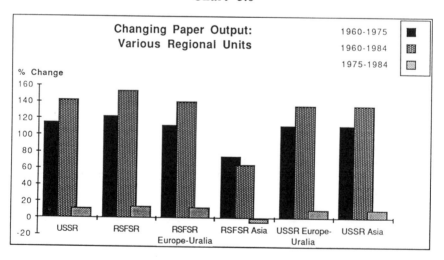

declined. Supplies of peeler and saw logs are clearly inadequate in much of Europe-Uralia, and the length of rail haul associated with roundwood movement, although continuing to increase, probably has reached a level where some plywood and sawmilling facilities in Europe-Uralia will have to be shut down or converted to other uses, including those compatible with various deciduous species and the utilization of wood chips. Most regions within Europe-Uralia registered important decreases in plywood production during the past decade, although output increased in a few regions such as Moscow and Ulyanovsk oblasts, and Krasnodar kray. Conversely, although aggregate output east of the Urals was positive, some jurisdictions sharply declined in their levels of plywood production.

Lumber and plywood production are usually thought of as raw-material-oriented because they are direct consumers of roundwood. The extent to which these two industries are more clearly associated with major eastern harvesting regions is reinforced by shortages of local timber supply and a growing reluctance to continue with long rail hauls or incur still greater hauls. Paper and paperboard, however, can have elements of raw-material and market orientation depending on the specific nature of their final product. Hence, much of the growth of these two industries during the past quarter century (Tables 5.6 and 5.7 and Charts 5.6 and 5.7) has occurred in Europe-Uralia. In the case of paper, growth in this zone has exceeded that east of the Urals; furthermore, in the period 1975-1984, the relative and absolute output of paper east of the Urals declined, probably due to supply, technological and managerial problems at plants in the three major Asian paper regions - Sakhalin oblast and Krasnoyarsk and Khabarovsk krays. In addition, the USSR continues to focus European-Uralian paper investment in a few regions, such as the Karelian ASSR, and Archangel, Gorki, and Perm oblasts. Some of these regions are well endowed with timber, and others including Leningrad city and oblast, are accessible to imported pulp supplies, particularly from Finland.

Paperboard and paper production in certain cases can utilize pulp directly while it is still in liquid form or as a "pure" raw material which has been shipped considerable distance. While newsprint made from groundwood pulp is usually spatially contiguous with the pulp producer, many fine paper grades blend pulps from different sources or supplement them with other materials. In such cases, interregional shipment of pulp is preferable because it is less fragile than paper and paperboard, and very little is lost during manufacturing. Major Soviet paperboard mills, like those producing newsprint, also tend to be relatively large (discussed by North and Solecki, 1977, p. 298). Hence the commissioning of new paperboard units such as those in Archangel, Gorki, Moscow, Tula, Astrakhan, Perm, or Irkutsk oblasts, or Krasnoyarsk and Khabarovsk krays represents a substantial increment, but has relatively little effect on the spatial distribution of the entire industry because investment is occurring simultaneously both in Europe-Uralia and in Asia.

Paper and paperboard production also attest to a locational constraint which plays a major role in Soviet decision making and industrial production given the central administration of the country's economy. Considerable investment in pulp, paper and paperboard was obtained as a result of Soviet expansion between 1939 and 1945. Plants in Karelian ASSR, Estonia, Latvia, and Lithuania, and

Table 5.6
Regional Change in Paper Production

Paper Output, 1960, 1975, 1984 (Thousands of Tons)
Change by Period (%)

	1960	% of Total	1975	% of Total	1984	% of Total	1960-1975	1960-1984	1975-1984
USSR	2,420.8	100.0	5,215.0	100.0	5,861.7	100.0	115.4	142.1	12.4
RSFSR	1,940.8	80.2	4,317.5	82.8	4,916.7	83.9	122.5	153.3	13.9
Northwest	671.8	27.8	1,874.6	35.9	2,474.4	42.2	179.0	268.3	32.0
Archangel	37.9	1.6	319.8	6.1	378.1	6.5	743.8	897.6	18.2
Karelian	256.4	10.6	876.6	16.8	1,197.6	20.4	241.9	367.1	36.6
Komi		0.0	163.5	3.1	315.7	5.4			93.1
Vologda	104.2	4.3	130.2	2.5	137.7	2.3	25.0	32.1	5.8
Leningrad	194.5	8.0	291.7	5.6	370.6	6.3	50.0	90.5	27.0
Novgorod	78.8	3.3	92.8	1.8	74.7	1.3	17.8	-5.2	-19.5
Center	3.1	0.1	5.8	0.1	6.4	0.1	87.1	106.5	10.3
Kostroma	3.1	0.1	5.8	0.1	6.4	0.1	87.1	106.5	10.3
Volgo-Vyatka	259.3	10.7	592.4	11.4	606.0	10.3	128.5	133.7	2.3
Gorki	191.6	7.9	465.9	8.9	484.8	8.3	143.2	153.0	4.1
Kirov	15.1	0.6	43.1	0.8	45.5	0.8	185.4	201.3	5.6
Mari	52.6	2.2	83.4	1.6	75.7	1.3	58.6	43.9	-9.2
Black Earth	7.6	0.3	14.4	0.3	7.2	0.1	89.5	-5.3	-50.0
Kursk	7.6	0.3	14.4	0.3	7.2	0.1	89.5	-5.3	-50.0
Volga Littoral	40.0	1.7	79.8	1.5	76.3	1.3	99.5	90.8	-4.4
Bashkir	6.3	0.3	27.6	0.5	19.5	0.3	338.1	209.5	-29.3
Penza	28.7	1.2	45.9	0.9	54.5	0.9	59.9	89.9	18.7
Ulyanovsk	5.0	0.2	6.3	0.1	2.3	0.0	26.0	-54.0	-63.5
North Caucasus	22.7	0.9	33.0	0.6	28.6	0.5	45.4	26.0	-13.3
Rostov	22.7	0.9	33.0	0.6	28.6	0.5	45.4	26.0	-13.3
Urals	507.1	20.9	1,027.9	19.7	1,033.4	17.6	102.7	103.8	0.5
Perm	459.5	19.0	948.6	18.2	957.9	16.3	106.4	108.5	1.0
Sverdlovsk	47.6	2.0	79.3	1.5	75.5	1.3	66.6	58.6	-4.8
RSFSR Europe-Uralia	1,511.6	62.4	3,627.9	69.6	4,232.3	72.2	140.0	180.0	16.7
Western Siberia	1.4	0.1	1.8	0.0	2.2	0.0	28.6	57.1	22.2
Novosibirsk	1.4	0.1	1.8	0.0	2.2	0.0	28.6	57.1	22.2
Eastern Siberia	9.9	0.4	133.3	2.6	119.3	2.0	1,246.5	1,105.1	-10.5
Irkutsk		0.0	13.8	0.3	12.1	0.2			-12.3
Krasnoyarsk	9.9	0.4	119.5	2.3	107.2	1.8	1,107.1	982.8	-10.3
Far East	197.0	8.1	229.0	4.4	221.5	3.8	16.2	12.4	-3.3
Amur		0.0	4.3	0.1	3.6	0.1			-16.3
Khabarovsk	7.5	0.3	9.0	0.2	9.2	0.2	20.0	22.7	2.2
Sakhalin	189.5	7.8	215.7	4.1	208.7	3.6	13.8	10.1	-3.2
(South)	197.0	8.1	229.0	4.4	221.5	3.8	16.2	12.4	-3.3
RSFSR Asia	208.3	8.6	364.1	7.0	343.0	5.9	74.8	64.7	-5.8
Belorussia	69.3	2.9	178.0	3.4	198.0	3.4	156.9	185.7	11.2
Baltics	220.1	9.1	396.0	7.6	379.0	6.5	79.9	72.2	-4.3
Kaliningrad	107.7	4.4	139.0	2.7	145.6	2.5	29.1	35.2	4.7
West	397.1	16.4	713.0	13.7	722.6	12.3	79.6	82.0	1.3
Southwest	147.4	6.1	235.0	4.5	283.0	4.8	59.4	92.0	20.4
Caucasus	33.7	1.4	44.1	0.8	55.0	0.9	30.9	63.2	24.7
USSR Europe-Uralia	2,089.8	86.3	4,620.0	88.6	5,292.9	90.3	121.1	153.3	14.6
Central Asia	9.5	0.4	44.4	0.9	30.0	0.5	367.4	215.8	-32.4
USSR Asia	217.8	9.0	408.5	7.8	373.0	6.4	87.6	71.3	-8.7

Source: Barr (1970, 1983); *Narodnoye Khozyaystvo RSFSR v 1984 godu* (1985, p. 85); and *Narodnoye Khozyaystvo SSSR v 1984 godu* (1985, p. 189).

Table 5.7
Regional Change in Paperboard Production

Paperboard Output, 1960, 1975, 1984 (Thousands of Tons)
Change by Period (%)

	1960	% of Total	1975	% of Total	1984	% of Total	1960-1975	1960-1984	1975-1984
USSR	806.1	100.0	3,369.5	100.0	3,965.0	100.0	318.0	3,91.9	17.7
RSFSR	490.5	60.8	2,513.9	74.6	2,814.5	71.0	412.5	473.8	12.0
Northwest	141.8	17.6	775.3	23.0	952.5	24.0	446.8	571.7	22.9
Archangel		0.0	561.1	16.7	582.9	14.7			3.9
Karelian	18.7	2.3	40.6	1.2	52.0	1.3	117.1	178.1	28.1
Komi		0.0	36.5	1.1	5.1	0.1			-86.0
Vologda	9.5	1.2	11.1	0.3	11.4	0.3	16.8	20.0	2.7
Leningrad	113.6	14.1	126.0	3.7	301.1	7.6	10.9	165.1	139.0
Center	98.1	12.2	447.5	13.3	445.9	11.2	356.2	354.5	-0.4
Bryansk	23.3	2.9	27.7	0.8	42.7	1.1	18.9	83.3	54.2
Kalinin	7.2	0.9	8.8	0.3	17.9	0.5	22.2	148.6	103.4
Kaluga	1.9	0.2	3.2	0.1	2.3	0.1	68.4	21.1	-28.1
Moscow	36.0	4.5	179.7	5.3	164.0	4.1	399.2	355.6	-8.7
Ryazan		0.0	47.6	1.4	47.1	1.2			-1.1
Smolensk		0.0	21.1	0.6	20.6	0.5			-2.4
Tula	4.3	0.5	123.1	3.7	115.2	2.9	2,762.8	2,579.1	-6.4
Vladimir	15.3	1.9	25.3	0.8	27.6	0.7	65.4	80.4	9.1
Yaroslavl	10.1	1.3	11.0	0.3	8.5	0.2	8.9	-15.8	-22.7
Volgo-Vyatka	77.8	9.7	170.7	5.1	160.4	4.0	119.4	106.2	-6.0
Gorki	41.9	5.2	123.6	3.7	115.0	2.9	195.0	174.5	-7.0
Kirov	6.5	0.8	24.2	0.7	21.6	0.5	272.3	232.3	-10.7
Mari	29.4	3.6	22.9	0.7	23.8	0.6	-22.1	-19.0	3.9
Black Earth	1.7	0.2	2.7	0.1	0.0	0.0	58.8	-100.0	
Volga Littoral	48.0	6.0	214.1	6.4	239.2	6.0	346.0	398.3	11.7
Astrakhan		0.0	107.7	3.2	107.5	2.7			-0.2
Bashkir		0.0	18.6	0.6	52.3	1.3			181.2
Kuybyshev	30.3	3.8	32.3	1.0	33.0	0.8	6.6	8.9	2.2
Saratov	1.9	0.2	10.4	0.3	3.7	0.1	447.4	94.7	-64.4
Tatar	8.5	1.1	15.5	0.5	12.2	0.3	82.4	43.5	-21.3
Ulyanovsk	7.3	0.9	29.6	0.9	30.5	0.8	305.5	317.8	3.0
North Caucasus	30.8	3.8	109.9	3.3	105.2	2.7	256.8	241.6	-4.3
Krasnodar	23.2	2.9	102.6	3.0	101.3	2.6	342.2	336.6	-1.3
Rostov	7.6	0.9	7.3	0.2	3.9	0.1	-3.9	-48.7	-46.6
Urals	18.1	2.2	136.5	4.1	143.9	3.6	654.1	695.0	5.4
Perm	6.4	0.8	119.2	3.5	129.8	3.3	1,762.5	1,928.1	8.9
Sverdlovsk	11.7	1.5	17.3	0.5	14.1	0.4	47.9	20.5	-18.5
RSFSR Europe-Uralia	416.3	51.6	1,856.7	55.1	2,047.1	51.6	346.0	391.7	10.3
Western Siberia	0.0	18.1	0.5	32.4	0.8			79.0	
Altay		0.0		0.0	15.5	0.4			
Kemerovo		0.0	18.1	0.5	16.9	0.4			-6.6
Eastern Siberia	3.4	0.4	393.9	11.7	469.1	11.8	11,485.3	13,697.1	19.1
Buryat		0.0	25.2	0.7	114.0	2.9			352.4
Irkutsk	1.0	0.1	215.7	6.4	219.2	5.5	21,470.0	21,820.0	1.6
Krasnoyarsk	2.4	0.3	153.0	4.5	135.9	3.4	6,275.0	5,562.5	-11.2
Far East	29.5	3.7	133.7	4.0	168.7	4.3	353.2	471.9	26.2
Khabarovsk	10.4	1.3	42.9	1.3	97.5	2.5	312.5	837.5	127.3
Sakhalin	19.1	2.4	90.8	2.7	71.2	1.8	375.4	272.8	-21.6
(South)	29.5	3.7	133.7	4.0	168.7	4.3	353.2	471.9	26.2
RSFSR Asia	32.9	4.1	545.7	16.2	670.2	16.9	1,558.7	1,937.1	22.8
Belorussia	32.3	4.0	145.9	4.3	216.0	5.4	351.7	568.7	48.0
Baltics	58.7	7.3	149.0	4.4	169.1	4.3	153.8	188.1	13.5
Kaliningrad	30.5	3.8	44.2	1.3	33.2	0.8	44.9	8.9	-24.9
West	121.5	15.1	339.1	10.1	418.3	10.5	179.1	244.3	23.4
Southwest	213.8	26.5	362.2	10.7	510.0	12.9	69.4	138.5	40.8
Caucasus	2.8	0.3	67.3	2.0	58.6	1.5	2,303.6	1,992.9	-12.9
USSR Europe-Uralia	754.4	93.6	2,625.3	77.9	3,034.0	76.5	248.0	302.2	15.6
Central Asia	8.0	1.0	131.2	3.9	196.8	5.0	1,540.0	2,360.0	50.0
USSR Asia	40.9	5.1	676.9	20.1	867.0	21.9	1,555.0	2,019.8	28.1

Source: Barr (1970, 1983); *Narodnoye Khozyaystvo RSFSR v 1984 godu* (1985, p. 86);
Narodnoye Khozyaystvo Estonskoy SSR v 1984 godu (1985, p. 55).

Chart 5.7

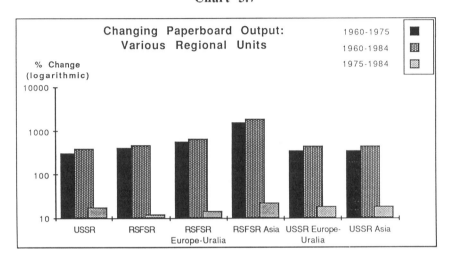

Chart 5.8

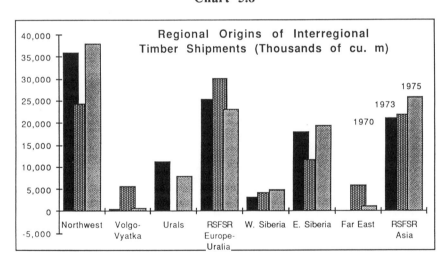

Kaliningrad and Sakhalin oblasts (discussed in Barr, 1971, and Eronen, 1984) represented a "free" investment to the paper- and investment-starved USSR which could be operated successfully by subsidizing the length of haul of raw material, or the allocation of market pulp from distant regions if necessary. Having control over operating costs of such facilities, the Soviet government can make their locations viable through appropriate transport and operating policies, while diverting investment capital to other sectors or to forest-product investments in other regions. Such existing plants also represent a form of locational inertia which, when equipment must be replaced, offers a lower-cost alternative than complete closure of the facility. At present, the USSR is seeking to intensify the regeneration of timber in Europe-Uralia specifically for the pulp and paper industry, thereby clearly attesting to the locational inertia which these industries exert.

The four industries for which 1984 regional production data have been published represent a roundwood equivalent of nearly 186 million cu. m (Table 5.8), or approximately four-fifths of the output of the USSR's basic wood-processing industries as shown in Table 5.1. (Table 5.1 omits paper and paperboard because these products are secondary manufactures which consume various primary pulp inputs.) During the past quarter century their regional location has continued to favor the European-Uralian zone of the RSFSR, although in 1984 that region comprised 52.5 percent of their output, compared with 56.9 percent in 1960. This is remarkable stability considering the major shifts in production which are frequently attributed to the forest-product sector. The Asian RSFSR, however, now has 28.6 percent of these industries' aggregate production compared with 21.5 percent in 1960; much of this shift occurred, however, not at the expense of European-Uralian Russia, but because of decreases in other European areas of the USSR. The northern forested region stretching from the Northwest to the Urals dominates the European-Uralian zone, whereas the most important Asian forest products region is Eastern Siberia. In these four major industries, however, the total European-Uralian zone of the USSR accounts for two-thirds of their output, although a small relative decline of 6.7 percent is noticeable between 1960 and 1984 (Table 5.8).

Production of lumber dominates every major Soviet region, although a few provinces such as Kaliningrad oblast (Tables 5.9 to 5.11) reflect the influence of other locational processes. In general, however, recent investments in forest industries other than sawmilling, and the general decline in output of sawn timber have influenced the regional product shares of most regions. Lumber nevertheless is still the dominant industry. The overall size of the forest products sector as measured by these four industries, however, has declined since 1975 (Table 5.12), mainly due to decreases in lumber output. Even the Asian RSFSR which registered over a 40 percent increase from 1960 to 1975, and from 1960 to 1984, saw virtually no growth between 1975 and 1984.

If the four industries analyzed here are representative of the Soviet wood-processing industry, as we suggest, then that industry displays far more regional inertia than previously believed. Press reports of specific projects and the commissioning of giant projects such as Ust'-Ilimsk and Bratsk can mislead us into believing that the Soviet forest-products sector is indeed shifting rapidly away from its traditional European-Uralian base. The data strongly suggest that

Table 5.8
Total Roundwood-equivalent Production, 1960, 1975, 1984
(Thousands of cu. m[r])

	1960	% of Total	1975	% of Total	1984	% of Total
USSR	175,871	100.0	205,376	100.0	185,793	100.0
RSFSR	138,534	78.8	166,775	81.2	151,465	81.5
Northwest	28,729	16.3	37,117	18.1	34,903	18.8
Center	16,460	9.4	17,292	8.4	15,079	8.1
Volgo-Vyatka	14,090	8.0	15,145	7.4	12,331	6.6
Black Earth	1,938	1.1	1,721	0.8	1,470	0.8
Volga Littoral	12,567	7.1	11,681	5.7	8,451	4.5
North Caucasus	4,579	2.6	5,008	2.4	3,497	1.9
Urals	21,641	12.3	24,956	12.2	21,804	11.7
RSFSR Europe-Uralia	100,005	56.9	112,921	55.0	97,533	52.5
Western Siberia	11,270	6.4	13,848	6.7	14,392	7.7
Eastern Siberia	17,933	10.2	27,917	13.6	27,675	14.9
Far East	8,613	4.9	11,227	5.5	11,112	6.0
RSFSR Asia	37,815	21.5	52,993	25.8	53,179	28.6
Belorussia	5,466	3.1	6,413	3.1	6,440	3.5
Baltics	5,992	3.4	6,586	3.2	6,007	3.2
Kaliningrad	714	0.4	860	0.4	752	0.4
West	7,516	4.3	8,976	4.4	8,289	4.5
Southwest	18,047	10.3	17,869	0.9	1,788	1.0
USSR Europe-Uralia	128,014	72.8	141,153	68.7	122,742	66.1
Central Asia	5,387	3.1	6,347	3.1	4,961	2.7
USSR Asia	43,202	24.6	59,340	28.9	58,140	31.3

Table 5.9
Regional Share of Production, 1960 (Roundwood Equivalents)
(% of Total)

	Lumber	Plywood	Paper	Paperboard	Total
USSR	92.4	2.4	4.4	0.7	100.0
RSFSR	92.9	2.1	4.5	0.6	100.0
Northwest	89.1	2.6	7.5	0.8	100.0
Center	92.7	4.1	2.2	1.0	100.0
Volgo-Vyatka	91.7	1.4	6.0	0.9	100.0
Black Earth	98.6	0.0	1.3	0.1	100.0
Volga Littoral	93.6	4.7	1.0	0.6	100.0
North Caucasus	97.1	0.2	1.6	1.1	100.0
Urals	90.8	1.6	7.5	0.1	100.0
RSFSR Europe-Uralia	91.5	2.6	5.2	0.7	100.0
Western Siberia	98.9	1.1	0.0	0.0	100.0
Eastern Siberia	99.5	0.3	0.2	0.0	100.0
Far East	91.0	1.1	7.3	0.5	100.0
RSFSR Asia	97.4	0.7	1.8	0.1	100.0
Belorussia	85.2	9.8	4.1	0.9	100.0
Baltics	77.6	9.0	11.8	1.6	100.0
Kaliningrad	44.9	0.0	48.3	6.8	100.0
West	66.2	14.3	16.9	2.6	100.0
Southwest	93.7	1.8	2.6	1.9	100.0
Caucasus	94.3	1.1	4.4	0.2	100.0
USSR Europe-Uralia	90.4	3.1	5.5	1.0	100.0
Central Asia	99.2	0.0	0.6	0.2	100.0
USSR Asia	97.6	0.6	1.6	0.2	100.0

Table 5.10
Regional Share of Production, 1975 (Roundwood Equivalents)
(% of Total)

	Lumber	Plywood	Paper	Paperboard	Total
USSR	85.9	3.4	8.1	2.6	100.0
RSFSR	86.4	3.0	8.3	2.4	100.0
Northwest	76.9	3.6	16.2	3.4	100.0
Center	86.0	6.6	3.2	4.2	100.0
Volgo-Vyatka	83.3	1.9	12.9	1.8	100.0
Black Earth	97.1	0.0	2.7	0.3	100.0
Volga Littoral	88.4	6.5	2.2	2.9	100.0
North Caucasus	90.9	3.3	2.1	3.7	100.0
Urals	83.0	2.9	13.2	0.9	100.0
RSFSR Europe-Uralia	82.6	3.9	10.8	2.7	100.0
Western Siberia	97.7	1.6	0.0	0.7	100.0
Eastern Siberia	95.6	0.6	1.5	2.3	100.0
Far East	90.3	1.3	6.5	1.9	100.0
RSFSR Asia	95.1	1.0	2.2	1.8	100.0
Belorussia	76.1	11.3	8.9	3.6	100.0
Baltics	67.6	9.5	19.2	3.6	100.0
Kaliningrad	40.1	0.0	51.7	8.2	100.0
West	53.5	15.1	25.4	6.0	100.0
Southwest	88.6	3.7	4.3	3.3	100.0
Caucasus	85.4	1.3	7.6	5.8	100.0
USSR Europe-Uralia	81.5	4.6	10.9	3.0	100.0
Central Asia	94.5	0.0	2.2	3.3	100.0
USSR Asia	95.0	0.9	2.2	1.9	100.0

Table 5.11
Regional Share of Production, 1984 (Roundwood Equivalents)
(% of Total)

	Lumber	Plywood	Paper	Paperboard	Total
USSR	83.6	2.9	10.1	3.4	100.0
RSFSR	84.1	2.5	10.4	3.0	100.0
Northwest	70.1	2.8	22.7	4.4	100.0
Center	86.6	4.8	3.8	4.8	100.0
Volgo-Vyatka	79.8	1.9	16.3	2.1	100.0
Black Earth	98.4	0.0	1.6	0.0	100.0
Volga Littoral	86.5	5.9	3.0	4.5	100.0
North Caucasus	87.6	4.8	2.6	5.0	100.0
Urals	81.1	2.7	15.2	1.1	100.0
RSFSR Europe-Uralia	78.8	3.3	14.5	3.4	100.0
Western Siberia	98.2	0.8	0.0	0.9	100.0
Eastern Siberia	94.5	1.4	1.4	2.7	100.0
Far East	90.3	0.9	6.4	2.4	100.0
RSFSR Asia	94.6	1.2	2.1	2.2	100.0
Belorussia	76.2	8.5	9.8	5.4	100.0
Baltics	67.2	8.1	20.2	4.5	100.0
Kaliningrad	31.0	0.0	61.9	7.1	100.0
West	51.5	12.5	27.9	8.1	100.0
Southwest	85.6	3.0	6.0	5.4	100.0
Caucasus	83.8	1.1	9.8	5.2	100.0
USSR Europe-Uralia	77.9	3.8	14.3	4.0	100.0
Central Asia	91.7	0.0	1.9	6.3	100.0
USSR Asia	94.4	1.1	2.1	2.5	100.0

Table 5.12
Change in Regional Distribution   of Production
(Roundwood Equivalents)
(Thousands of cu. m[r] and %)

	1960-1975	%	1960-1984	%	1975-1984	%
USSR	29,505	16.8	9,921	5.6	-19,584	-9.5
RSFSR	28,241	20.4	12,931	9.3	-15,310	-9.2
Northwest	8,388	29.2	6,174	21.5	-2,215	-6.0
Center	832	5.1	-1,382	-8.4	-2,213	-12.8
Volgo-Vyatka	1,055	7.5	-1,759	-12.5	-2,814	-18.6
Black Earth	-217	-11.2	-468	-24.2	-252	-14.6
Volga Littoral	-886	-7.1	-4,116	-32.8	-3,230	-27.7
North Caucasus	429	9.4	-1,083	-23.6	-1,512	-30.2
Urals	3,315	15.3	163	0.8	-3,152	-12.6
RSFSR Europe-Uralia	12,916	12.9	-2,471	-2.5	-15,388	-13.6
Western Siberia	2,578	22.9	3,122	27.7	544	3.9
Eastern Siberia	9,985	55.7	9,742	54.3	-242	-0.9
Far East	2,615	30.4	2,499	29.0	-115	-1.0
RSFSR Asia	15,178	40.1	15,364	40.6	186	0.4
Belorussia	947	17.3	973	17.8	26	0.4
Baltics	594	9.9	16	0.3	-578	-8.8
Kaliningrad	147	20.6	39	5.4	-108	-12.6
West	1,460	19.4	773	10.3	-687	-7.7
Southwest	-661	-3.7	-2,916	-16.2	-2,255	-13.0
Caucasus	-576	-23.6	-657	-26.9	-81	-4.3
USSR Europe-Uralia	3,139	10.3	-5,272	-4.1	-18,411	-13.0
Central Asia	960	17.8	-426	-7.9	-1,386	-21.8
USSR Asia	16,138	37.4	14,938	34.6	-1,200	-2.0

such a shift is not occurring. Although many more forest products now emanate from the East than 25 years ago, their relative contribution has been consistently offset by enhanced output in Europe-Uralia. As of 1985, relatively and absolutely more roundwood originates in Asian RSFSR than in previous years but the forest-manufacturing sector in the USSR has not shifted accordingly. The combination of locational inertia and a command economy ensures that the maintenance of output at existing sites to fulfill planned output priorities dominate the spatial structure of the Soviet wood-processing industry. The basic dilemma facing those who would overcome the "geographical scissors" problem in the Soviet forest product sector has been cogently lamented by *Izvestiya* (*Current Digest of the Soviet Press* [hereafter abbreviated *CDSP*], vol. 29 [26], pp. 8-9), as follows:

> The efforts of lumbermen and wood processors alone cannot eliminate or even minimize the wasteful shipment of timber in the form of logs. Pulp and paper production, hydrolysis, and other methods of chemically processing timber need to be developed more rapidly in areas where timber is harvested. . . . The siting of enterprises for the chemical processing of timber does not always correspond to the availability of timber resources. A blatant example of this is West Siberia. In this vast area, where many of our timber resources are concentrated, there is not yet a single pulp-and-paper industry enterprise. [When this statement was made about West Siberia in 1977, a small paper mill annually was producing 2.4 thousand tons of paper in Novosibirsk Oblast; in the paperboard sector, Kemerovo Oblast produced 18.4 thousand tons that year, and Omsk Oblast 41.1 thousand tons (*Narodnoye Khozyaystvo RSFSR v 1978 godu,* 1979, pp. 67-68)(authors' note).]

After noting the problems in ministerial organization which had then long delayed construction of a LPK at Asino in Tomsk oblast (Western Siberia), the authors of the same article concluded:

> Meanwhile, the USSR Ministry of the Pulp-and-Paper Industry is expanding its production facilities in the Karelian Autonomous Republic, Arkhangelsk and Gorky Provinces and certain other regions where timber harvesting either remains at former levels or is declining. Is this a rational use of capital investments? After all, either now or in the very near future, timber for these developing enterprises will have to be shipped in from West Siberia or from other more distant timber regions. It would seem that some of the capital investments for the chemical processing of timber should be shifted to areas where timber harvesting is developing more rapidly - to West Siberia and other eastern regions.

TIMBER SUPPLY AND DEMAND AMONG MAJOR REGIONS

Our ability to assess the origin and quality of roundwood has been severely limited since 1975 because of the ban on publishing regional logging data. A fairly recent analysis of this subject by Vorob'yev *et al.* (1979) actually used data from 1973, and then only referred to timber administered by a division of the chief national procurement agency for timber (Tables 5.13 and 5.14). Those data, however, when compiled from numerous tables throughout that book, confirm the importance of a few taiga forests in the European north, the Urals, and accessible Siberia. The data also describe the product mix of regional timber consumption and harvest. All the major forested regions can support structural and fiber needs, but the product mix in European-Uralian regions is more diverse and clearly reflects a wider range of manufacturing facilities. Presumably, the total surplus of 13,294 thousand cu. m reflects roundwood for export. The European-Uralian region, however, is not shown to be a timber deficit area (Table 5.15) although some major regions are deficient in certain types of roundwood. The West, Southwest, and Caucasus are deficient in overall timber demands, but the European-Uralian zone, no matter how configured, always indicates a surplus of supply over demand. This would probably not be true if exports were subtracted from constituent subregions.

The European-Uralian RSFSR is a significant shipper to itself and to other European Soviet regions (Table 5.16). The general European-Uralian direction of flow is from North and East to West, Southwest, and South; Asian RSFSR flows move west and south. Europe mainly supplies itself, but Asia supplies both Asia and Europe. Both major areas in the RSFSR provide wood for export. The spatial patterns of these flow patterns are confirmed by solutions to the transportation problem of linear programming for various years (Barr, 1970, 1983; Barr and Smillie, 1972) which clearly indicate the regional export function of the European North (previous analyses by Barr separated it from the Northwest, although the data in Table 5.16 of this chapter simply refer to the entire region as the Northwest), the Urals, and Eastern Siberia. The Northwest, the Urals, and Eastern Siberia have been the three major regions traditionally covering the timber deficits throughout the nation's wood-processing regions. Their contribution is likely to remain dominant in the near future, although the ability of the Urals to offset other regions' deficits is declining. In terms of the European-Uralian versus Siberia dichotomy, however, the 1975 estimate (Table 5.17 and Chart 5.8) clearly shows that the balance has now shifted in favor of Siberia and suggests that the length of haul of interregional timber shipments may, despite Soviet plans to the contrary, actually increase in forthcoming decades. The traditional dominance of European-Uralian timber reflected both overcutting in accessible European-Uralian forests and the large amount of mature industrial roundwood previously available for harvest in that region's forests.

The actual data provided by Vorob'yev *et al.* (1979) indicate that the interregional movement of timber in 1973, for example, was not as simple or straightforward as estimated by Barr for 1970 and 1975 (Table 5.17). The estimates for 1970 and 1975, however, are net regional balances, whereas those in Table 5.16 are gross because the major regions engage in subregional exchange of timber within themselves and also receive timber from unspecified other sources. Even the net estimates for 1973, however, reveal a greater-than-predicted shipment from the Volgo-Vyatka and Far Eastern regions, probably because overcutting has been permitted in the former, and because many forests

Table 5.13

Volume and Mix of Consumed Timber

(Thousands of cu. m[s])[a]

	Total	Saw Logs	Peeler Logs	Pulp-wood	Pit Props	Con-struction Timber	Other Timber	Fuel-wood
USSR	289,270	116,423	7,397	18,814	15,964	21,207	49,815	59,650
RSFSR	230,910	99,239	5,123	17,180	6,899	11,152	43,038	48,279
Northwest	56,830	23,274	1,177	6,964	840	1,778	13,008	9,789
Center	21,238	10,246	1,192	222	750	941	3,068	4,819
Volgo-Vyatka	19,352	8,944	284	1,852	14	731	3,083	4,444
Black Earth	1,959	758	16		32	558	118	477
Volga Littoral	14,059	6,074	722		65	1,278	2,753	3,167
North Caucasus	5,728	2,069	328		627	722	1,136	846
Urals	35,115	14,904	695	3,326	1,204	1,270	5,926	7,790
RSFSR Europe-Uralia	154,281	66,269	4,414	12,364	3,532	7,278	29,092	31,332
Western Siberia	17,995	7,796	268		2,088	1,130	3,015	3,698
Eastern Siberia	36,066	16,351	197	2,743	302	959	9,369	6,145
Far East	22,568	8,823	244	2,073	977	1,785	1,562	7,104
RSFSR Asia	76,629	32,970	709	4,816	3,367	3,874	13,946	16,947
Belorussia	6,349	2,473	600	54	1	818	1,122	1,281
Baltics	8,117	2,413	702	1030	75	992	1,202	1,703
West	14,466	4,886	1,302	1,084	76	1,810	2,324	2,984
Southwest	25,785	7,067	858	454	6,433	5,605	3,519	1,849
Caucasus	2,613	916	109	96	319	546	293	334
USSR Europe-Uralia	197,145	79,138	6,683	13,998	10,360	15,239	35,228	36,499
Central Asia	15,496	4,315	5		2,237	2,094	641	6,204
USSR Asia	92,125	37,285	714	4,816	5,604	5,968	14,587	23,151

[a]Refers to industrial timber administered by *Soyuzglavlesa* (a division of *Gossnab*) for 1973 (Vorob'yev *et al.*, 1979, p. 193).

Source: Compiled from Vorob'yev *et al.* (1979, various pages).

Table 5.14
Volume and Mix of Harvested Timber[a]
(Thousands of cu. m[s])

	Total	Saw Logs	Peeler Logs	Pulp-wood	Pit Props	Construction Timber	Other Timber	Fuel-wood
USSR	302,564	125,175	7,033	23,824	16,486	20,064	55,061	54,921
RSFSR	283,982	118,561	6,093	22,832	16,328	17,972	51,769	50,427
Northwest	81,325	29,461	1,405	11,623	6,018	6,213	15,576	11,029
Center	20,527	8,337	974	1,536	183	1,415	2,469	5,613
Volgo-Vyatka	24,978	10,248	832	1,484	1,198	2,272	4,192	4,752
Black Earth	604	177	15			166	92	154
Volga Littoral	6,271	2,328	194	50	10	768	991	1,930
North Caucasus	2,116	1,041	124			94	455	402
Urals	48,678	19,628	1,679	4,049	3,287	3,064	8,472	8,499
RSFSR Europe-Uralia	184,499	71,220	5,223	18,742	10,696	13,992	32,247	32,379
Western Siberia	22,463	10,200	432	2,663	2,001	1,574	3,545	4,711
Eastern Siberia	47,720	24,140	282	1,427	2,360	1,559	10,379	6,337
Far East	29,300	13,001	156		1,271	847	5,598	7,000
RSFSR Asia	99,483	47,341	870	4,090	5,632	3,980	19,522	18,048
Belorussia	4,770	1,558	463	83	98	560	845	1,163
Baltics	5,617	1,508	179	591	60	787	823	1,669
West	10,387	3,066	642	674	158	1,347	1,668	2,832
Southwest	5,920	2,334	265	280		737	1,576	728
Caucasus	664	300	33	38		6	45	242
USSR Europe-Uralia	201,470	76,920	6,163	19,734	10,854	16,082	35,536	36,181
Central Asia	1,611	914				2	3	692
USSR Asia	101,094	48,255	870	4,090	5,632	3,982	19,525	18,740

[a]Refers to Industrial Timber administered by Soyuzglavlesa (a division of Gossnab) for 1973 (Vorob'yev et al. 1979, p. 193).

Source: Compiled from Vorob'yev et al. (1979, various pages).

Table 5.15
Regional Surplus or Deficit in Mix of Harvested Timber
(Thousands of cu. m[s])
(Table 5.14 minus Table 5.13)

	Total	Saw Logs	Peeler Logs	Pulp-wood	Pit Props	Con-struction Timber	Other Timber	Fuel-wood
USSR	13,294	8,752	-364	5,010	522	-1,143	5,246	-4,729
RSFSR	53,072	19,322	970	5,652	9,429	6,820	8,731	2,148
Northwest	24,495	6,187	228	4,659	5,178	4,435	2,568	1,240
Center	-711	-1,909	-218	1,314	-567	474	-599	794
Volgo-Vyatka	5,626	1,304	548	-368	1,184	1,541	1,109	308
Black Earth	-1,355	-581	-1	0	-32	-392	-26	-323
Volga Littoral	-7,788	-3,746	-528	50	-55	-510	-1,762	-1,237
North Caucasus	-3,612	-1,028	-204	0	-627	-628	-681	-444
Urals	13,563	4,724	984	723	2,083	1,794	2,546	709
RSFSR Europe-Uralia	30,218	4,951	809	6,378	7,164	6,714	3,155	1,047
Western Siberia	4,468	2,404	164	0	-87	444	530	1,013
Eastern Siberia	11,654	7,789	85	-80	2,058	600	1,010	192
Far East	6,732	4,178	-88	-646	294	-938	4,036	-104
RSFSR Asia	22,854	14,371	161	-726	2,265	106	5,576	1,101
Belorussia	-1,579	-915	-137	29	97	-258	-277	-118
Baltics	-2,500	-905	-523	-439	-15	-205	-379	-34
West	-4,079	-1,820	-660	-410	82	-463	-656	-152
Southwest	-19,865	-4,733	-593	-174	-6,433	-4,868	-1,943	-1,121
Caucasus	-1,949	-616	-76	-58	-319	-540	-248	-92
USSR Europe-Uralia	4,325	-2,218	-520	5,736	494	843	308	-318
Central Asia	-13,885	-3,401	-5	0	-2,237	-2,092	-638	-5,512
USSR Asia	8,969	10,970	156	-726	28	-1,986	4,938	-4,411

[a]Refers to industrial timber administered by *Soyuzglavlesa* (a division of *Gossnab*) for 1973 (Vorob'yev *et al.* (1979, p. 193).

Source: Compiled from Vorob'yev *et al.* (1979, various pages).

Table 5.16
Selected Major Directions of Timber Flows
(Millions of cu. m)

Region	Receives	Ships	Destination
RSFSR			
Northwest	1.1	25.6	Ukraine (9.7), Center (3.1), Kaliningrad (1.8), Belorussia (1.1)
Center	5.9	5.2	Ukraine (1.3), Volgo-Vyatka (1.1)
Volgo-Vyatka	2.5	8.2	Ukraine (2.3), Center (1.8), Volga Littoral (0.9)
Black Earth	1.4	0.1	Ukraine, Belorussia (n.s.)[a]
Volga Littoral	8.2	0.4	Ukraine (.1), North Caucasus (0.1), Kazakhstan (0.1)
North Caucasus	3.7	0.1	n.s.
Urals	1.7	15.2	Ukraine (3.1), Volga Littoral (6.0), North Caucasus (1.8)
RSFSR Europe-Uralia	24.5	54.7	
Western Siberia	2.1	6.5	Ukraine (0.9), Kazakhstan (1.9), Urals (1.1)
Eastern Siberia	0.2	11.9	Ukraine, Kazakhstan, Central Asia, Volga Littoral, North Caucasus, export (n.s.)
Far East	0.0	6.0	Ukraine, Kazakhstan, others (n.s.)
RSFSR Asia	2.3	24.4	
Belorussia	1.8	0.3	Ukraine, Kaliningrad (n.s.)
Baltics	2.6	0.0	
West (including Kaliningrad)	4.4	0.3	
West and RSFSR Europe-Uralia	28.9	55.0	
Southwest	18.6	0.0	
Caucasus	1.9	0.0	
Southern Non-RSFSR Europe	20.5	0.0	
USSR Europe-Uralia	49.4	55.0	
Central Asia (excluding Kazakhstan)	3.4	0.0	
USSR Asia	5.7	24.4	

[a]N.s. = not specified.

Source: Vorob'yev *et al.* (1979, various pages).

Table 5.17
Comparison of Optimal Shipments[a] of Roundwood,
1970 and 1975, with 1973 Actual[b] Flows
(Thousands of cu. m[r])

	1970	%	1973	%	1975	%
Northwest	35,917	52.0	24,500	46.7	37,980	52.4
Volgo-Vyatka	667	1.0	5,700	10.9	714	1.0
Urals	11,258	16.3	135	0.3	7,954	11.0
Western Siberia	3,198	4.6	4,400	8.4	5,021	6.9
Eastern Siberia	18,118	26.2	11,700	22.3	19,563	27.0
Far East	-70	-0.1	6,000	11.4	1,305	1.8
Total Surplus These 6 Major Regions	69,088	100.0	52,435	100.0	72,537	100.0
RSFSR Europe-Uralia	25,475	54.5	30,200	57.7	23,351	47.4
RSFSR Asia	21,246	45.5	22,100	42.3	25,889	52.6
Total Surplus Europe-Uralia and Asia	46,721	100.0	52,300	100.0	49,240	100.0

[a]Recalculated from Barr (1983).

[b]Compiled fromVorob'yev *et al.* (1979, various pages).

in the latter contain extensive volumes of mature and overmature timber being harvested for reasons not associated with transportation efficiency. The actual flows in Table 5.16 probably also reflect cross hauls arising from institutional priorities and heterogeneity of species demand (i.e., similar to that shown in Tables 5.13 and 5.14). Earlier analyses by Barr (1970) and others have suggested that, in general, a high correspondence exists between actual and optimal aggregate flows, but that discrepancies are to be expected due to important variations in species of timber shipped, product designation, and institutional ownership or control of shipments. (The locational significance of these factors, particularly for Europe-Uralia, is succinctly discussed in relation to the pulp and paper industry by Anuchin [1986, pp. 104-107].) So-called departmentalism transcends economic priorities which might be expected to play a more dominant role in other countries. Thus, in 1964, for example, Barr (1970, p. 83) noted that the optimal pattern was 20 percent cheaper than the actual pattern when shipments among oblasts, krays, and ASSRs were assessed. To be truly valid, however, linear programming analyses must incorporate differences in type of roundwood, something which simply could not be achieved in previous estimates by Barr and which, unfortunately, is still impossible.

MIX-AND-SHARE ANALYSIS

Although we can demonstrate through roundwood equivalents how the basic structure of Soviet wood-processing has changed since 1960, we must use some "explanatory" technique to identify the major similarities and differences between regional and national change. How, for example, can we account for a decline of 9.5 percent in national production between 1975 and 1984 compared with an increase of total wood-processing in Asian RSFSR of 0.4 percent? One technique, mix-and-share analysis (m&s) (Bendavid, 1974, pp. 82-93) considers regional change relative to national change to be the net result of three "effects": (1) the regional impact of *total national change* (can be growth or decline but is usually termed growth (+ or -), (2) the regional *industry mix* compared with the national industrial structure, and (3) the changing *regional shares* of total national activity in each industry. M&s accounts for regional change by identifying the components of change according to the following formula:

$$R \; = \; N \; + M \; + S$$

where (Tables 5.18 and 5.19)

R = net actual change in regional activity
N = national growth effect
M = industry mix effect
S = regional-shares effect

In Western advanced industrial countries, m&s could utilize criteria such as employment, value added during manufacturing, or selling value of factory shipments to assess changing regional output relative to national change for a given time period. Such tools are not available in the USSR. The authors instead use roundwood equivalents to ensure comparability among the four major forest product industries and to obtain a total which can be manipulated regionally and nationally. The analysis covers three time periods: 1960-1975, 1960-1984, and 1975-1984. Six regions of the USSR are examined: the RSFSR; the European-Uralian RSFSR, including the Northwest and the Urals; and the Asian RSFSR, including Eastern Siberia. Because these are the most important timber-producing and wood-processing regions of the USSR, the authors felt that identification of major changes in them would ensure identification of the most important structural and regional changes in the Soviet forest industries. If Bendavid's (1974, pp. 91-92) suggestion that m&s "will always yield greater insights when performed for several shorter periods rather than for a single, longer, time span" is true, the most reliance can be placed on the period 1975-1984, and the least on that for 1960-1984. The reversal in fortunes of lumber alone during the longest time period suggests that Bendavid's statement has particular relevance for Soviet wood-processing.

Calculation of the three effects for the six regions is summarized for each region according to absolute numbers (Table 5.18) or percentages (Table 5.19). Let us illustrate the utility of m&s with a discussion of lumber in Eastern Siberia for 1975-1984. If regional lumber output had changed at the national total rate of change (**national growth effect**) in wood-processing, output in Eastern Siberia would have shown a decline of 2,547,000 cu. m. Instead, regional lumber output decreased by only 560,000 cu. m. The difference between the two figures is the **net relative change** to be accounted for (1,987,000 cu. m). This **net relative change** can be accounted for by two factors. First, the national lumber sector declined more than the decline in total wood-processing. Hence lumber output decreased as a proportion of total national wood-processing. A larger share of Eastern Siberian production was accounted for by lumber, however, than in the national total (95.6 percent compared with 85.9 percent). The larger share of regional than national employment in lumber (**industry mix effect**) means that Eastern Siberia was more strongly affected by a drop in lumber output than the nation and was responsible for a decline of 631,000 cu. m. However, during this period the region's share (**regional shares effect**) of lumber output increased from 13.6 percent to 14.9 percent. This **regional shares effect** of +2,619,000 cu. m helped to offset the impact of the **industry mix effect** (-631,000) and the **national growth effect** (−2,547,000). Consequently the actual decline (figures are rounded in the calculations) was only -560,000 cu. m (-2,547,000 -631,000 +2,619,000).

If we stay with Eastern Siberia to examine the impact of the three effects on other industries in the region, the regional shares effect is seen to be relatively strong both in plywood and in the change in total regional wood-processing. The regional shares effect was negative for paper and almost of no significance either way for paperboard. The same types of negative and positive influences of the three effects are observed for production changes in each sector of the Asian RSFSR (Table 5.18).

Change in each wood-processing industry and total wood-processing in the RSFSR between 1975 and 1984 corresponds closely to that of the USSR because of the relative contribution of the RSFSR to national output. In all

Table 5.18
Mix-and-Share: Summary of 3 Effects, Selected Regions
(Thousands of cu. m[r])

Shift[a]/Effect[b]	Total	Lumber	Plywood	Paper	Paperboard
RSFSR					
1960-1975					
R	28,241	15,315	2,083	7,605	3,237
N	23,274	21,621	478	1,043	132
M	-883	-10,672	1,298	6,127	2,364
S	5,851	4,367	307	435	742
1960-1984					
R	12,931	-1,282	971	9,523	3,718
N	7,813	7,258	160	350	44
M	-910	-12,956	538	8,477	3,031
S	6,027	4,416	273	695	643
1975-1984					
R	-15,310	-16,597	-1,111	1,917	481
N	-15,910	-13,739	-470	-1,318	-384
M	41	-3,406	-679	3,031	1,094
S	559	547	37	205	-230
RSFSR Europe-Uralia					
1960-1975					
R	12,916	1,742	1,834	7,007	2,334
N	16,801	15,381	432	873	115
M	769	-7,592	1,174	5,129	2,058
S	-4,653	-6,047	228	1,004	161
1960-1984					
R	-2,471	-14,689	624	8,971	2,623
N	5,640	5,164	145	293	39
M	1,006	-9,217	487	7,097	2,639
S	-9,118	-10,636	-7	1,580	-55
1975-1984					
R	-15,388	-16,431	-1,210	1,964	289
N	-10,773	-8,900	-420	-1,164	-288
M	686	-2,206	-607	2,678	821
S	-5,301	-5,324	-183	451	-244
Northwest					
1960-1975					
R	8,388	2,938	574	3,849	1,027
N	4,826	4,300	125	361	40
M	1,050	-2,123	340	2,121	712
S	2,512	761	109	1,367	275
1960-1984					
R	6,174	-1,121	229	5,768	1,298
N	1,620	1,444	42	121	13
M	1,411	-2,577	141	2,934	913
S	3,142	12	46	2,713	372
1975-1984					
R	-2,215	-4,060	-345	1,919	271
N	-3,541	-2,722	-126	-572	-121
M	803	-675	-182	1,316	344
S	523	-662	-37	1,176	47

Shift[a]/Effect[b]	Total	Lumber	Plywood	Paper	Paperboard
Urals					
1960-1975					
R	3,315	1,066	393	1,667	189
N	3,636	3,301	57	273	5
M	215	-1,629	156	1,601	87
S	-536	-606	180	-207	97
1960-1984					
R	163	-1,973	251	1,684	201
N	1,221	1,108	19	92	2
M	414	-1,978	65	2,215	112
S	-1,471	-1,103	166	-622	88
1975-1984					
R	-3,152	-3,039	-143	18	12
N	-2,381	-1,976	-70	-314	-21
M	190	-490	-101	722	59
S	-961	-573	29	-390	-27
RSFSR Asia					
1960-1975					
R	15,178	13,549	249	499	882
N	6,353	6,186	46	112	9
M	-2,113	-3,054	125	658	159
S	10,938	10,416	78	-271	714
1960-1984					
R	15,364	13,494	347	431	1,092
N	2,133	2,077	15	38	3
M	-2,542	-3,707	52	910	203
S	15,773	15,125	280	-516	885
1975-1984					
R	186	-55	98	-68	210
N	-5,056	-4,805	-50	-111	-89
M	-753	-1,191	-72	256	254
S	5,995	5,942	220	-212	45
Eastern Siberia					
1960-1975					
R	9,985	8,861	104	395	625
N	3,013	2,997	9	5	1
M	-1,407	-1,480	25	31	16
S	8,379	7,343	70	358	607
1960-1984					
R	9,742	8,301	346	350	745
N	1,011	1,006	3	2	0
M	-1,722	-1,796	10	43	21
S	10,452	9,091	333	305	724
1975-1984					
R	-242	-560	242	-45	120
N	-2,663	-2,547	-15	-41	-60
M	-388	-631	-22	94	171
S	2,809	2,619	279	-98	9

[a]R = net actual change in regional activity.

[b]N = national growth effect; M = industry mix effect; S = regional shares effect.

Table 5.19
Mix-and-Share: % Share of 3 Effects, Selected Regions
(% of Change in Each Industry by Time Period)

Shift[a]/Effect[b]	Total	Lumber	Plywood	Paper	Paperboard
RSFSR					
1960-1975					
R	100.0	100.0	100.0	100.0	100.0
N	82.4	141.2	22.9	13.7	4.1
M	-3.1	-69.7	62.3	80.6	73.0
S	20.7	28.5	14.7	5.7	22.9
1960-1984					
R	100.0	100.0	100.0	100.0	100.0
N	60.4	-566.3	16.5	3.7	1.2
M	-7.0	1,010.9	55.4	89.0	81.5
S	46.6	-344.6	28.1	7.3	17.3
1975-1984					
R	100.0	100.0	100.0	100.0	100.0
N	103.9	82.8	42.3	-68.7	-79.8
M	-0.3	20.5	61.1	158.1	227.5
S	-3.7	-3.3	-3.3	10.7	-47.8
RSFSR Europe-Uralia					
1960-1975					
R	100.0	100.0	100.0	100.0	100.0
N	130.1	883.1	23.5	12.5	4.9
M	6.0	-435.9	64.0	73.2	88.2
S	-36.0	-347.2	12.5	14.3	6.9
1960-1984					
R	100.0	1,146.0	64.3	94.2	70.5
N	-228.2	-402.9	14.9	3.1	1.0
M	-40.7	719.1	50.1	74.5	71.0
S	368.9	829.8	-0.8	16.6	-1.5
1975-1984					
R	100.0	100.0	100.0	100.0	100.0
N	70.0	54.2	34.7	-59.3	-99.7
M	-4.5	13.4	50.2	136.3	284.4
S	34.4	32.4	15.1	23.0	-84.7
Northwest					
1960-1975					
R	100.0	100.0	100.0	100.0	100.0
N	57.5	146.4	21.8	9.4	3.9
M	12.5	-72.2	59.2	55.1	69.3
S	29.9	25.9	19.0	35.5	26.8
1960-1984					
R	100.0	100.0	100.0	100.0	100.0
N	26.2	-128.8	18.3	2.1	1.0
M	22.9	229.8	61.5	50.9	70.3
S	50.9	-1.1	20.1	47.0	28.6
1975-1984					
R	100.0	100.0	100.0	100.0	100.0
N	159.9	67.1	36.5	-29.8	-44.5
M	-36.3	16.6	52.7	68.6	127.0
S	-23.6	16.3	10.9	61.3	17.5

Shift[a]/Effect[b]	Total	Lumber	Plywood	Paper	Paperboard
Urals					
1960-1975					
R	100.0	100.0	100.0	100.0	100.0
N	109.7	309.7	14.6	16.4	2.6
M	6.5	-152.9	39.7	96.1	46.0
S	-16.2	-56.8	45.7	-12.4	51.4
1960-1984					
R	100.0	100.0	100.0	100.0	100.0
N	749.5	-56.2	7.7	5.4	0.8
M	254.0	100.2	25.9	131.5	55.6
S	-903.5	55.9	66.4	-37.0	43.6
1975-1984					
R	100.0	100.0	100.0	100.0	100.0
N	75.5	65.0	49.1	-1,782.9	-176.0
M	-6.0	16.1	70.9	4,099.7	501.9
S	30.5	18.9	-20.0	-2,216.7	-225.9
RSFSR Asia					
1960-1975					
R	100.0	100.0	100.0	100.0	100.0
N	41.9	45.7	18.4	22.5	1.0
M	-13.9	-22.5	50.1	131.9	18.0
S	72.1	76.9	31.4	-54.4	81.0
1960-1984					
R	100.0	100.0	100.0	100.0	100.0
N	13.9	15.4	4.4	8.7	0.3
M	-16.5	-27.5	14.9	211.1	18.6
S	102.7	112.1	80.7	-119.8	81.1
1975-1984					
R	100.0	100.0	100.0	100.0	100.0
N	-2,717.7	8,791.6	-50.6	164.6	-42.5
M	-404.9	2,179.3	-73.1	-378.5	121.1
S	3,222.6	-10,870.8	223.8	313.9	21.4
Eastern Siberia					
1960-1975					
R	100.0	100.0	100.0	100.0	100.0
N	30.2	33.8	8.8	1.3	0.1
M	-14.1	-16.7	24.0	7.9	2.6
S	83.9	82.9	67.2	90.7	97.2
1960-1984					
R	100.0	100.0	100.0	100.0	100.0
N	10.4	12.1	0.9	0.5	0.0
M	-17.7	-21.6	3.0	12.4	2.8
S	107.3	109.5	96.1	87.1	97.1
1975-1984					
R	100.0	100.0	100.0	100.0	100.0
N	1,098.4	454.8	-6.3	90.8	-50.0
M	160.1	112.7	-9.0	-208.9	142.5
S	-1,158.5	-467.5	115.3	218.0	7.5

[a]R = net actual change in regional activity.

[b]N = national growth effect; M = industry mix effect; S = regional shares effect.

cases, the national growth effect in the RSFSR exerted a negative influence on wood-processing, although the industry mix effect in the case of paper and paperboard was able to ensure positive change in actual output for the period. Actual change in the European-Uralian RSFSR, corresponds closely to that for the entire RSFSR but the regional shares effect is strongly negative, particularly in lumber and total output, and moderately negative in plywood and paperboard. This confirms the general declining importance of total wood-processing and some sectors in RSFSR Europe-Uralia with the strong exception of paper which is gaining in importance (particularly in the Northwest). This pattern contrasts sharply with the changes identified for RSFSR Asia above and in Table 15.18. Eastern Siberia and the Northwest stand in sharp contrast to each other, particularly in the changing relative fortunes of lumber and paper.

M&s analysis, particularly for the time periods 1960-1975, and 1975-1984, strongly confirms the growing polarity of wood-processing in major regions of the RSFSR, and the essential differences between Europe and Asia in the sectors of importance. Asia with its greater availability of structural and peeler timber is developing a strong profile in lumber and plywood manufacture. Europe with a large volume of fiber material; important existing investment in pulp, paper, and paperboard; and more effective access to secondary manufacturers is strengthening its fiber-based forest sectors. Overall, however, the wood-processing industry is shifting eastward, particularly as the regional shares effect in the most important processing industry, lumber (including sleepers), continues to exert a powerful influence on Asian RSFSR regions such as Eastern Siberia.

TRANSPORTATION

Transportation costs and modes of transport are important but problematic in the movement of roundwood and products in the USSR. The following analysis consequently pays special attention to the structure of rail tariffs and the movement of roundwood by inland waterways. Soviet planners are alarmed by the continuing rise of average length of haul of forest-sector products on the railways associated with the growth of processing in peripheral regions and the continuing localization of demand in the European-Uralian heartland. Roundwood continues to move by water, but the drift floating of logs is steadily being replaced by rafting and use of bulk carriers to reduce timber losses during transport and to reduce the fouling of river bottoms and spawning grounds by sunken logs. Improved technology is enhancing the tree-length movement of logs out of the forests to the major transshipment points and the chipping of substandard trees and related items in the forest for truck and rail shipment to processors.

Transportation has been a key element in the industrial development of the USSR and of its predecessor, the Russian Empire. The basis of transportation has been the railway, although in recent years efficient water (river and ocean), air, and pipeline transport has facilitated the industrial maturation of the Soviet economy. The Eleventh Five-Year Plan (1981-1985), for example, called for an increase of nearly 20 percent in ton-kilometers incurred in river transport, 15 percent on railways, and 9 percent in maritime transport (Shiyanskaya, 1985, p.

721). Nevertheless, Sagers and Green (1985, p. 306) note that railways continue to bear most of the Soviet freight burden despite inadequate levels of government investment: between 1950 and 1983, rail freight traffic grew almost six times "without commensurate increases in capital and labor resources. Recently, however, the railroads have begun to falter from the increasing strain."

The timber and wood-processing industries rely heavily on rail and water transport for interregional movement of materials and commodities. It is hard to imagine any industrial sector more widely distributed over the surface of the USSR, particularly the RSFSR, than timber harvesting and wood-processing. Tying these activities together and to markets necessitates the appropriate use of rivers, railways, and some ocean routes, especially for reaching export markets not served by rail connections with the USSR. In 1974, for example, 284 million tons of timber and wood products were transported in the USSR (Glotov, 1977, p. 123). The largest share was moved by rail (64 percent); lesser amounts were shipped by river (31 percent) and sea (5 percent). These shipments represented 5.3 percent of total shipments by rail, 19.5 percent of those on rivers, and 6.4 percent of those by maritime transport.

The basic dilemma, however, in Soviet movement of timber and wood products is related to the large distances between resources and consumers, or between places of material origin and ultimate utilization (Anuchin's [1986, p.166] "geographical scissors" syndrome). Furthermore, this problem is compounded by the absence of railways in many forests and by the short river navigation season. Many of the rivers on which timber and other products move flow northward, so that their mouths thaw late in the spring and transportation along the Arctic coast is problematic for much of the year.

RAILWAYS

Many of the railways used to move timber and wood products intersect the rivers in the southern taiga. Recent years have witnessed the construction of many feeder lines from the rail network north into specific regions. The most notable recent lateral connection which may eventually serve to promote the harvesting of peripheral timber is the BAM railway extending over 3100 km from the Lena River in Eastern Siberia to the Tatar Strait on the Pacific Coast of the Far East. A northern line currently under construction (AYAM) will connect the BAM at Tynda to Berkakit, Tomot, and Yakutsk. The first part of this line, initially called the little BAM with a terminus at Berkakit, will ensure access to the forests of Southern Yakutia, thereby repeating a pattern of northern connectors previously established in the Northwest, Urals, Western Siberia, and Eastern Siberia for at least half a century (Archangel-Karpogory, Mikun'-Koslan, Ivdel'-Sergino, Tyumen-Tobol'sk-Surgut, Asino-Belyy Yar, Achinsk-Abalakovo, Reshoty-Boguchany, Khrebtovaya-Ust'-Ilimsk, etc.).

New railways, however, have added length to the haul of timber and wood-products, particularly as the largest share of rail freight (Glotov, 1977, p. 124; Mel'nikov *et al.,* 1977, p. 5) comprises roundwood (68 percent in 1974). Consequently, although only a modest proportion of all rail freight, timber and wood products constituted nearly 10 percent of the freight turnover on Soviet railways in 1974. Glotov (1977, p. 131) notes that the BAM, plus the line from

BAM on the Transsiberian railway through Tynda to Berkakit, will add 3512 km to the rail network. This will provide access to 1.2 to 1.4 billion cu. m of timber with an annual potential cut of 12 to 16 million cu. m. Mel'nikov *et al.* (1977, pp. 5-6) state that new Siberian northern railways caused the average length of rail haul of timber and wood-products to increase from 1645 km in 1975 to 1780 km by 1976. They confidently added, however, that future shifts in wood-processing will obviate the long-haul movement of roundwood, the main culprit in the continuing rise of the length of haul. We suspect, however, that most of this timber and that from the BAM service area will move in round or sawn form for some time because construction of associated processors has not yet been undertaken, and construction periods for major projects in many Soviet industries frequently require between 10 and 20 years![1]

Although the length of haul for most other bulky commodities has declined with the advent of pipelines, electrical transmission systems, and preshipment beneficiation of ores, the length of haul of timber and forest products continues to rise despite the additional costs to the national economy. Although processing is increasing in heavily forested regions and many wood-manufacturing activities are declining in lightly forested areas, sawnwood, pit props, and even fuelwood must nevertheless be shipped long distances to meet market demand. In 1950, this average length of haul was 998 km; it reached 1387 km in 1960 and 1647 km in 1970, after which it seemed to remain approximately the same until the mid-1970s when figures on this matter ceased to be published (Glotov, 1977, p. 124). In recent years, however, water transport of timber and wood products has been neglected in favor of greater land-based movement (trucks and railways). In 1984, the average length of rail haul exceeded 1800 km, thereby exceeding that of any other major commodity in the USSR (Borisovets, 1985, p. 3). The average length of haul of timber by truck increased from 31.2 km in 1970 to 45 km in 1984 (Borisovets, 1985, p. 3). Consequently, interregional movement of forest products (not yet a truck phenomenon) continues to increase more rapidly than total freight shipments.

By 1977, the share of timber and wood products in total interregional rail shipments reached 20 percent compared to only 13.7 percent in 1959 (Glotov, 1977, p. 125). The greater availability of trucks in the 1970s and 1980s and their ability to operate year-long is obviously ensuring their substitution for water movement in reaching the sites of initial processing, rail terminals, or water-oriented mills, particularly in Europe-Uralia. At the Bratsk LPK in Eastern Siberia, however, trucks in 1984 delivered 25.5 percent of the raw material (down from 31 percent in 1975) and railways, 24 percent (up from 21 percent in 1975), while water transport comprised 50.5 percent (up from 48 percent in 1975) (Petrov *et al.*, 1986, p. 43). The greater use of water and rail at Bratsk probably reflects the ruinous actions of nomadic loggers in the complex's local resource base and the need to supplement the plant's attendant supply shortfalls by longer distance movement of wood generally inappropriate anywhere for trucks. Nevertheless, in 1984, half of all items shipped in the USSR by *Minlesbumprom* moved by rail (Prokhorenko, 1986, p. 5).

Some of this increase is inevitable given the role of timber and wood products in any modern economy, and the greater utilization of many products as the Soviet economy has expanded since 1960. These movements simply are a fact of life for a large country with great distances between resources and markets (population). On the other hand, the country faces extreme congestion on many railways, especially on lines connecting the Center with the Volga Littoral, the Urals, Western Siberia, Central Asia, and the southern European USSR (*CDSP*, vol. 37 [48], p. 20). The USSR has many priorities for investment which cannot be met if funds are consumed by transportation and construction costs. Because of the structure of tariffs and product pricing, plus administrative rather than economic relations among suppliers and consumers, the economic system generates an uneconomic or "irrational" way of spatially matching supply and demand. Hence, the problem of increasing length of haul is not simply a function of geography, but a true drawback. We might expect, for example, to observe long hauls for certain commodities in the USSR because of the separation of materials and consumers, but under different economic circumstances we would not expect commodities such as saw logs to move thousands of kilometers by rail for conversion and attendant generation of wood waste).

Glotov (1977, pp. 125-26) observes that the movement of Krasnoyarsk lumber to Eastern European export markets involves a land haul of 5575 km just to the border point of Chop. Shipment of roundwood to European markets from Tyumen oblast, for example, entails distances of over 3600 km. In recent years, Finns (Eronen, personal communication, November 1985) have observed that Soviet roundwood rail shipments to them have originated at least 5000 km away. Traditional Northwest suppliers for Eastern European land-based exports like Archangel, Petrozavodsk, and Kotlas, which now face shortages of material supply, are situated only 2100 km to 2760 km away from similar export points (discussed extensively for all export points by Eronen, 1983). Similarly, cross hauls occur when demand in Siberia for impregnated sleepers, for example, can only be met with imports from the European USSR in which the treatment facilities are located (Glotov, 1977, p. 125). Approximately three-quarters of Soviet sleepers, however, are produced in Eastern Siberia and the Far East (Timofeyev, 1980, p. 142). In other cases, insufficient investments have been made in Siberia to convert roundwood before it is shipped to the North Caucasus, Caucasus, Volga Littoral, or Central Asia. In 1975, for example, Eastern Siberia and the Far East shipped in total at least 5.4 million cu. m of roundwood to these four regions (Glotov, 1977, p. 125).

WATER TRANSPORT

Transportation of timber and wood products in the USSR by inland waterways may be declining in relative importance. Economic advantages of movement by water or rail are increasingly turning in favor of rail, particularly with the decline in drift (or loose) floating (*molevoy lesosplav*) of timber on Soviet rivers. Glotov claims that drift floating never has been particularly well suited to movement of deciduous species, larch, or fuelwood (presumably due to sinking or mixing of product designations with most species of commercial roundwood). Movement of timber on inland waterways decreased between 1965 and 1975 from 77 million to 68 million tons (Glotov, 1977, p. 129). At the same time as Soviet conservationists have succeeded in reducing freshwater pollution and despoilation of fishing rivers from sunken timber and related materials, the railways and trucking systems have increased their ability to handle tree-length logs, and industry has become increasingly oriented toward total use of delivered roundwood. For example, the Bratsk LPK in 1984 received half of its timber in the form of tree-length logs, whereas in 1975 the share of this form of roundwood delivery comprised only 17 percent (Petrov *et al.*, 1986, p. 43). Between 1965 and 1975 in the then Ministry of Timber and Woodworking, delivery of timber to processing enterprises by river rafting diminished from 49 to 39 percent, while that by railway increased from 27 percent to 33 percent. Timber shipped directly to consumers, presumably by truck, grew from 24 to 28 percent (Glotov, 1977, p. 129).

On the other hand, inland water transport of timber and forest products is far from being finished. In 1980, rafting of timber still comprised 53.4 million tons, a drop from 71.8 million in 1970 (Tonyaev, 1984, p. 59). Movement by inland water craft, however, during the same period decreased from 19.4 million tons only to 17.8 million tons. Thus, although considerable timber and wood products still move by river, the decline in rafting is much more pronounced than by water craft. Presumably some of this decline has also been effected by the greater availability and use of trucks to move timber relatively short distances.

Nevertheless, many statements in forestry journals suggest that inland water movement will continue, but in the form of various types of bundled raft and on water craft. In 1979, for example, between 40 and 43 percent of timber was moved by water with an average length of haul of about 550 km (the author does not differentiate between river and maritime transport) (Gendel', 1982, p. 5). In Karelia, for example, in 1970, 7.1 million cu. m of timber were rafted by water (*lesosplav* ; this appears to include timber moved by water craft) but only 4.0 million cu. m in 1980. In each case some 0.2 million cu. m seem to have been lost (Gendel', 1982, p. 7). Drift floating decreased from 94 percent of shipments in 1970 to 70 percent in 1980. Rafting (*plotovoy lesosplav*) increased from 5.5 percent to 25.5 percent, and movement by water craft grew from 0.5 percent to 4.7 percent. These last two items are surprisingly small given Soviet desire to eliminate drift floating of timber. Nevertheless, they are a start in the right direction. Gendel' (1982, p. 7) states that water transport of timber in the future will be continued and will not decline in the general share of delivered timber. Some of the decline in timber shipped by water could be attributed to the decline of timber harvesting in Karelia, but appropriate data are not available. Nevertheless, the decline of 2 million cu. m in harvest between 1970 and 1975, for example, agrees with the 2 million cu. m decline in river shipments between the same two dates. Deliveries in 1980 of timber in Karelia by drift floating, however, comprised 11 percent of total waterborne deliveries (some 60 percent of deliveries are not by water: approximately 27 percent are by truck directly to the consumer, and 33 percent are by railway [Gendel', 1982, p. 9]); rafting comprised 63 percent and water craft, 26 percent. Drift floating had comprised 32 percent of deliveries in 1970, and water craft 17 percent. If the Karelian example is representative of some major changes in the river movement of timber, water craft are gradually being substituted for rafting, but drift floating is still practiced to a surprising extent.

USSR *Minlesbumprom* in 1983 had 150 sorting-raft-forming booming grounds, which handled 41 percent of the 69 million cu. m timber rafted during 1983 (Burdin and Yevdokimov, 1985, p. 75). Presumably these same figures suggest that 59 percent of the total timber rafted in that year moved by other means such as water craft and drift floating. Borisovets (1986, p. 3) states that *Minlesbumprom* rafted 350 million cu. m of roundwood during the Eleventh Five-Year Plan, during which the share of drift floating declined from 52.3 percent in 1981 to 46.4 percent in 1985. Movement by water craft during the same period increased from 7.9 percent to 8.8 percent, and that by rafting from 38.4 percent to 44.8 percent (1.4 percent is unaccounted for in the 1981 total).

Drift floating still appears to be extensively practiced in taiga regions lacking an effective network of logging roads or logging railways, such as the Northern Dvina Basin, supplying Archangel. With a five-month drift-floating period, this form of movement is used to gather timber from tributaries of the Northern Dvina. When logs reach the main river itself, they are gathered into bundles, assembled into rafts, and towed to Archangel. Each year, however, 2.5 percent of the timber dispatched is lost through breakage in transit, sinking, or scattering along the shore or in shallow water during drift floating (Pankratov, 1985, p. 28). Recovery of this timber is becoming an important part of the Northern Dvina rafting authority's activities: in the Eleventh Five-Year Plan (1980-1985), it planned to recover 573,000 cu. m, although examples from constituent enterprises suggest that two-fifths of the recovered wood may only be suitable for fuel.

Recovery of sunken logs in the Northwest is probably largely motivated by the shortages of roundwood in the region. In Karelia, for example, due to extended overcutting of mature timber, loggers are now limited to the allowable cut which itself is insufficient to meet the continuing growth of demand for raw material within the region (Sankin and Simakov, 1985, p. 6).

TARIFFS

Sagers and Green (1985, p. 307) observe that "it is uncertain what role freight rates play in determining the pattern of traffic movement in the Soviet context." Movement of commodities among suppliers and producers is determined by central administration, not by the purchasers themselves. Yet, as Sagers and Green note, Soviet administrators seem to expect freight rates to affect the movement of commodities. Of particular interest to the present analysis is whether the structure of freight rates, including the taper effect common in the West and in the USSR, has any true influence on the length of haul or on the movement of raw materials instead of finished goods. Sagers and Green (1985, p. 313) demonstrate that "on a cumulative basis, they [total transport charges per ton] are a monotonically increasing, step-wise function of distance." They (p. 321) also demonstrate that Soviet freight rates incorporate some notion of the "value of service as well as the cost of service." Thus we should expect higher rates for higher value commodities, and we should expect a greater influence of long hauls than short ones in the delivered value of commodities. Nevertheless, to encourage shippers to move commodities off the railways, relatively high rates are set on both long and short hauls. According to this reasoning, then, the

Soviet freight rate schedule has become more neutral than previously (Barr, 1970, pp. 95-109) and "no longer specifically favors longer hauls, particular regions, or individual commodities as much as it did in the past" (Sagers and Green, 1985, p. 321).

Sagers and Green conclude, therefore, that economic or behavioral factors other than the rate schedule likely influence the continuing growth of length of haul on Soviet railways. These factors include the location of resources (raw materials) and the adherence to centrally imposed performance goals such as the total ton-kilometers plan. Despite the influence of such other factors, Soviet transport costs, regardless of structure, become part of the planned costs of meeting the state plan for delivery of commodities or products. Regardless of shipping cost, the products will move if included in the plan. The tariff structure seems to us not to be a deterrent because it has relevance only to planners, not shippers or purchasers. In that sense, those charged with overall administration or planning of the economy seem to have a tool more useful for choosing among various plans than for actually allocating commodity movement.

The astonishing characteristic of Soviet rail freight rates, however, is that they do not distinguish between shipping 10 tons of roundwood and 10 tons of lumber, although the former loses almost half its weight during conversion into lumber. Approximately two-thirds is lost during conversion into plywood, and approximately 84 percent during production of chemical pulp. The rate for shipment of roundwood, however, is only 14 percent cheaper per ton than shipping plywood, but is virtually the same as shipping chemical pulp. The tariff structure, while perhaps apparently neutral in some ways, actually seeks to encourage shipment of lumber instead of roundwood (or shipment of plywood, pulp, or other products). The freight rates are clearly indicating to Soviet processors of roundwood that locations minimizing the shipment of eventual waste (i.e., facilitating weight loss as close as possible to the harvest site) are desirable economically. Even if all material were recovered from each ton of roundwood arriving at its destination, the country would still lose money because approximately one-quarter of each cubic meter of roundwood comprises water. Lumber is dried before shipment and its moisture is removed (discussed in Barr, 1970, pp. 92-109).

Because railways receive the same revenue whether lumber or roundwood is hauled, and because shippers' and consumers' profitability is not affected by transport costs, the loser is the national economy as a whole. Thus, the tariff structure emits strong signals of spatial preference for the location of wood-processing, but these messages are aimed at an abstract entity rather than at the profit margins of specific enterprises.

We conclude, therefore, that Soviet freight rates do not have an independent influence on the location of production or the shipment of commodities. Once the output, shipment, and consumption of roundwood has been established by planners, and directives have been issued to various enterprises, the freight rates have no further meaning. We must assume that freight rates are taken into account when linkages are established between suppliers and consumers, but obviously transportation costs alone even during planning are overridden by other considerations. Given unlimited investment capital and an effective means of moving labor among locations, the Soviet Union would not ship roundwood long distances by rail (shipments of perhaps a few hundred kilometers might occur where necessary to support the scale economies of a large processor, for example).

Locational inertia in the form of existing investment, and administered economic relations instead of market-dictated operational profitability, ensure that processing sites remain in place long after their initial raw material locations have become exhausted. We surmise from many accounts in the Soviet media that the most important industrial goal is to achieve production targets consistently. The economic system, not the railways, thus subsidize locational inefficiencies by permitting uneconomic linkages to exist among suppliers and consumers. Presumably these subsidies in turn are weighed against the cost of establishing new mills in peripheral regions, constructing new cities and infrastructure, and securing labor in a labor-deficient national economy with inhospitable peripheral regional environments. The freight rate structure alone is a powerful indicator of how planners truly favor a raw-material orientation for primary processing (i.e., operations involving initial conversion of roundwood or raw timber materials) but are forced nevertheless to permit continuing flows of roundwood over long distances in the name of pragmatism or expediency.

TRENDS AND PLANS

The Soviet Union is continuing to derive more processed products from each cubic meter of industrial roundwood harvested, primarily through development of technologically advanced forest-product sectors and greater recovery of waste materials. Some wood-processing industries are growing significantly in Asia, while others are expanding in European market areas or relatively close to them in the Northwest's taiga. European-Uralian areas are increasingly short of timber, however, but Asian harvesting activities are becoming more distant from European consumers. Furthermore, problems in the management of Siberian forests and delays in comprehensive use of newly accessible stands in the Far East mean that even the peripheral resource does not guarantee adequate levels of timber supply.

The Twelfth Five-Year Plan, which commenced in 1986, offers important insights into the probable future development of Soviet wood-processing. The basic goals of this new planning endeavor permit us to gauge the extent to which total and regional levels of product output may conform to those of the recent past. Its goals have significance for the degree to which the timber reserves of Siberia and the Far East, and the coniferous plantations and deciduous forests of the European-Uralian zone, can influence the spatial orientation and structural development of Soviet industrial forest utilization.

The plan stresses efficiency (intensification) in use and replenishment of the resource. Better supervision of resource utilization is demanded, and more nonforested forestry land (regeneration backlog) is proposed. Among proposals to develop zonal systems in forestry (presumably to take advantage of particular species and growing conditions), the plan also intends "to develop a permanent raw-material base for the pulp and paper industry in the European-Urals zone" (*CDSP*, vol. 37 [48], p. 19). The plan proposes a reduction in the unit consumption of timber in construction by 10 to 12 percent (*CDSP*, vol. 37 [46], p. 13). Both these items if achieved would reduce interregional shipments of timber because they are large consumers of roundwood.

In wood-processing, the plan envisages greater recovery of product per unit of raw material and more effective reforestation, logging, and sawmilling. Proposals for restructuring the national economy involve the improvement in the efficiency of organizational links among associated enterprises, less departmentalism, and a unified functional national economy (*CDSP*, vol. 37 [41], pp. 1-5, 17). All units of *Minlesbumprom* were directed to adopt the operating measures of the new "economic experiment" by 1 January 1987 (Edel', 1986, p. 3; *Narodnoye Khozyaystvo SSSR v 1984 godu*, 1985, p. 130). This change applies to forestry and wood-processing both in timber-deficient regions and in major European and Siberian taiga regions because management problems have become severe (Medvedev, 1986, p. 3). The new plan proposes priority development of chemical and chemical-mechanical processing of timber in logging regions (discussed in detail by Nikol'skiy, 1986). It proposes by 1990 to increase the annual output of pulp by 15 to 18 percent, paper by 11 to 15 percent, fiberboard by 17 to 20 percent, and paperboard and particleboard by approximately 30 percent (*CDSP*, vol. 37 [47], p. 24; pulp and paper developments are described in "Razvitiye Otrasli Puti Uskoreniya," 1986). It foresees an increase of 70 percent by 1990 in the production of paperboard packing containers and a greatly expanded output of printing, writing, and packaging papers and wallpaper. (The future of pulp and paper is assessed in Chernovol [1984], Podkovyrin [1984], "Proizvodstvo Tovarov Narodnogo Potrebleniya. Opyt. Problemy. Perspectivy," [1984], and Shchukin [1984].)

The plan specifies that the share of deciduous species in wood-processing by 1990 increase to between 65 and 70 million cu. m and the utilization of wood waste reach between 70 and 75 million cu. m (assessed for pulp and paper in "Za Povysheniye Effektivnosti Ispol'zovaniya Drevesiny i yeye Otkhodov v Tsellyulozno-Bumazhnoy Promyshlennosti," [1985]). The FAO (1986, p. 77) estimates that 59 million cu. m of coniferous timber were produced in 1984. The average substitution of waste and other recovered materials per annum during the Eleventh Five-Year Plan was 70 million cu. m, which presumably included the recycling of waste paper (Busygin, 1986, p. 1). A more detailed outline of the new plan, however, states (Busygin, 1986, p. 2) that the annual increment of other materials substituting roundwood will be 18 million cu. m, which suggests that the total is 90 million cu. m over five years. The difference between this total and that for wood waste, 15 to 20 million cu. m (roundwood equivalent) is probably accounted for by waste paper (described in Veselov, 1985). The average annual output of roundwood is expected to be only 3.5 to 4 million cu. m (Busygin, 1986, p. 2).

The plan envisages stepped-up development of productive forces in Siberia and the Far East, including improvements in fulfilling output targets and in providing comprehensive infrastructure for settlements and industry. On the other hand, the plan states that "resource conservation will become a decisive source of satisfying the growth of the national economy's requirements for fuel, energy, and raw and other materials." (*CDSP*, vol. 37 [44, supplement], pp. 9-10). Although not specifying which regions are to receive additional investment, the general tenor of the plan as well as numerous statements by individual authors suggest that output of timber and lumber will continue to grow in Asia, and that pulp, paper, and paperboard will continue to grow in the European-Uralian zone, despite the present adverse situation in timber supply. Thus, the mix-and-share analysis of change between 1975 and 1984 presented above in this chapter appears to be a strong indicator of what may continue to transpire regionally between 1986 and 1990.

CONCLUSIONS

Chapter 5 has identified the present structure of wood-processing industries in the USSR and many of the trends or proposals likely to influence its composition in the near future. The Soviet Union continues to seek greater efficiencies in product recovery from each unit of raw material, and appears on the threshold of adopting operational procedures to deal more appropriately with the resource and sector mix of its major regions. The chapter has demonstrated that, because of material shortages in Europe-Uralia, and increasingly unacceptable long hauls in the westward and southward movement of timber, greater efficiency will have to be achieved in the regional utilization of roundwood. Although the freight rate structure corresponds in many ways to that of other countries, the rates convey no economic messages to individual enterprises and are of utility principally in planning, including the planning of suboptimal alternatives. Railways continue to dominate the movement of timber and wood products, and seem likely to incur more traffic at the expense of the interior waterways of the USSR because of technological change. The new Five-Year plan proposes greater output of those commodities which have received priority investment during the past quarter century, and seems to recognize that continued development of wood-processing in the USSR cannot proceed simply on the basis of overcutting in Europe-Uralia or greater use of Asian forests. By stipulating the formation of a sustained output of roundwood from European-Uralian forests for the pulp and paper industry, the new plan clearly implies that differential strategies in regional industrial management have finally been accepted in the USSR, at least in the forestry sector.

NOTES

1. Discussed by Premier Ryzhkov in *CDSP* (1986, vol. 38 [12], pp. 10–11). An editorial in *Izvestiya* previously cited similar lengths of time required to commission new facilities (*CDSP*, 1984, vol. 36 [47], pp. 20-21).

6
Forests and Society

Forests have long been an integral part of Russian society and history. In his book, *The Russians*, Hedrick Smith noted (1976, pp. 115-16),

> Russians have a passion for their countryside. City people, like American urbanites, revel in roughing it at some rented peasant cabin. . . . The sun playing through a stand of birches or the coolness of the majestic pines casts a spell.

The use of forests for recreation thus appears to be an increasingly important part of Soviet leisure activities, judging by the statistics on the growth in outdoor recreation in the USSR. Data are less available on nonindustrial utilization of forests and, therefore, economic value is more difficult to measure, but the "social" role of forests is nevertheless an important function. Nonindustrial uses of forests include recreation (resting, hiking, camping, birdwatching, fishing, hunting); food gathering (fruit, nuts, mushrooms, game, fish); and environmental enhancement (biosphere protection, pollution reduction, soil and water conservation).

RECREATION AND PRESERVATION

As noted in Chapter 4, forests in the USSR are divided into three basic groups. Group 3, comprising over three-quarters of the country's forests, are designated for commercial use. Group 1 forests are those given the highest degree of protection, with cutting allowed only for maintenance of the health of the stand, as specified in Article 15 of Soviet forest law (Reymers and Shtil'mark, 1978, p. 63). This forest group may be broken down by classification of use, as well as by regional share, and species mix (Table 6.1; see also Table 3.4). Group 1 forests are designated for green belts; recreational and food uses; protection strips along roads, fields, and water bodies; and soil management. Their species composition (Table 6.1) corresponds to the mix of species within each region's overall forest stand. Thus 12 percent of the Group 1 forests in the European RSFSR are shade tolerant-hardwood species (STHS) such as oak; 28 percent are shade-intolerant hardwoods (SIHS) such as birch; and the remaining 60 percent are conifers. Forests in Group 1 play a large role not only in conservation of forests and environments, but also in recreation and increasingly in food supply.

Group 2 forests (Table 3.4) have a mixed industrial and preservation function. Although more utilization is allowed for commercial purposes than in Group 1 forests, such harvesting is supposed to be limited in scope. Watershed preservation and other environmental protection roles are a main function of Group 2 forests. Overcutting, however, has reduced the amount of timber in Group 2 forests.

Table 6.1
Group 1 Forests by Union Republic and Species Mix
(% of Total Group 1 Forest in Each Area)

	Conifers				STHS			SIHS[a]
	Total	Pine	Spruce	Larch	Total	Oak	Beech	Total
USSR	63.6	19.1	14.3	21.0	10.5	2.5	1.9	25.9
USSR Europe-Uralia	52.7	30.2	21.3	0.3	19.0	4.6	5.0	28.3
USSR Asia	70.0	12.6	10.2	32.8	5.5	1.3		24.5
RSFSR	67.9	18.1	15.1	24.1	6.0	1.8	0.4	26.1
RSFSR Europe-Uralia	60.0	29.9	24.4	0.4	11.9	2.5	1.3	28.1
RSFSR Asia	73.6	12.4	10.7	35.5	3.2	1.4		23.2
Belorussia	72.7	62.3	10.4	<0.1	5.4	5.0		21.9
Estonia	74.2	54.4	19.6	0.1	0.7	0.5		25.1
Latvia	73.0	58.0	15.0	<0.1	0.6	0.3		26.4
Lithuania	72.7	56.4	16.2	0.1	2.7	1.6		24.6
Ukraine	39.8	30.4	9.1	.01	51.5	21.3	8.6	9.7
Moldavia	0.2	0.2			91.2	21.8	0.1	8.6
Georgia	19.1	3.7	15.4		67.4	6.5	49.7	13.5
Armenia	2.8	1.4			90.5	23.9	35.0	6.7
Azerbaydzhan	<0.1	<0.1			88.1	24.2	31.5	11.9
Uzbekistan	24.0				28.1			47.9
Kirgizia	34.3	0.4	17.8	0.2	6.0	<0.1		59.7
Tadzhikistan	34.5				17.4			48.1
Turkmenistan	45.2				8.7			46.1
Kazakhstan	23.1	19.2	3.4	0.3	39.4	<0.1		37.5

[a]Also includes a category, others.

Source: Compiled from Vorob'yev et al. (1979, p. 37).

HUMAN SIGNIFICANCE OF SOVIET FORESTS

Although this book focuses on the industrial and commercial forests of Group 3, one of its recurrent themes - the potential significance of the European-Uralian forests for intensive management and utilization - must be viewed in relation to other important functions associated with this resource. The Soviet Union is an urban nation whose residential accommodation is primarily concentrated in multistoried apartments. Urban and exurban Group 1 forests, therefore, perform an important recreational venue for millions of Soviet citizens, particulary in the European USSR (Table 3.4) where the country's population is concentrated.

In the European USSR, nearly one-third of the population at any one time (depending on the season and time of week) may utilize the forests (urban and rural) for recreation (Tarasov, 1986, p. 21). The average annual recreational use of European USSR forests is estimated (1974-1981) at approximately 11 billion hours per year; each inhabitant of this area spends an average of 71 hours per year enjoying the forest (Tarasov, 1986, p. 21). In Estonia, for example, over 70 percent of the population lives in cities and place important demands on the republic's forests and lakes. Over 40 percent of Estonia is forest covered, but Group 1 forests comprise 28 percent of the general forested area. Forests designated "recreational" comprise 17 percent of the forested land and surround all populated places with over 1000 people and are particularly significant in the industrial-urban northern part of the republic, which has three-quarters of such forests (Margus, 1983, p. 35). These forests are a major part of Soviet social and cultural policy because they facilitate organized and individual tourism within the context of local and regional public transportation, and state medical-psychological recuperation in various sanitoria and other institutions.

This recreational-psychological function is performed simultaneously with many of these forests' environmental and conservation functions. If we again cite the Estonian example, we observe that nearly one-half of the Group 1 forests have a general conservation and economic designation (for social rather than industrial purposes). Parks and soil protection each comprise one-sixth of this group, shelterbelts along roads comprise one-quarter, and nature preserves comprise 5 percent. These forests thus reflect many of the policies, programs and priorities of Soviet society in which considerable amounts of money are expended to control environmental degradation. With the rising use of private automobiles, pressure on all Group 1 forests is increasing, particularly as the country has been developing a comprehensive network of all-weather roads. Greater demands on the environment are also affecting Group 2 forests. Consequently, as more intensive harvesting occurs within these two groups in the accessible European-Uralian area (the allowable cut of conifers has increased in these two groups in Europe-Uralia since 1976 [Petrov *et al.*, 1986, pp. 208-9]), we might expect some opposition by the millions of urbanites whose lives they normally complement. Nevertheless, shortages of resources for eastern development are increasingly placing demands on the "protection" forests of European USSR, and we may expect in the future that more comprehensive attempts will be made to extract timber from Group 1 and 2 forests, despite their important environmental protection designations.

Soviet research attests to the importance of recreational use of the country's forests. *Gosleskhoz*, for example, held an all-union meeting in Moscow in May 1985 to discuss problems of recreational use of forests (Elanov, 1985, p. 76). The meeting was in response to growing pressure on Soviet forests for leisure activities, particularly in forest preserves near urban centers. A 1980 study done on the Novosibirsk area, for example, found that 150,000 to 170,000 people left Novosibirsk on weekends or holidays to utilize the forests within one to two hours drive from the city. Some type of recreational facility is found at 136 different places within this zone. Each hectare of forest thus was used on the average by over 50 people (Bekh, 1985, p. 31). A study conducted on the 3600 ha Valaam Island archipelago, an area of architectural and historical preserves in Lake Ladoga, showed that in 1967, 450 people visited the islands. By 1970, this number grew to 20,000, while in 1979, it reached 130,000 (Kuchko and Krutov, 1986, p. 44).

Although heaviest use appears to coincide with forest zones near urbanized areas, even remote regions receive visitors. Sapozhnikov (1983, pp. 112-24) has argued that along the BAM service zone, forests need to be preserved now for future recreational needs. Of the 5 million ha of forests estimated to be under the influence of the BAM, almost 3 million ha are in reserves, 1.3 million ha in nature parks, and 634,000 ha in protected hunting grounds.

Soviet planners have been addressing the issue of preservation versus recreation for land set aside from commercial uses. One of the main features of the system of preserved lands in the USSR is the *zapovednik*, or reserve. The USSR in 1984 listed 147 reserves and hunting reserves totaling 14.8 million ha (*Narodnoye Khozyaystvo SSSR v 1984 godu*, 1985, p. 401). The exact number of *zapovedniki* in existence is hard to estimate because Soviet data do not always specify *when* an area comes under legal definition as a reserve. A large share of the existing reserves is located in forested zones. Of the 107 reserves listed by Philip Pryde in 1977, approximately 70 percent were found in taiga, mixed forests, forest-steppe, or mountain environments (Pryde, 1977, p. 174). Dora Fischer listed 142 reserves, game reserves, and national parks in 1981, with 78 percent located in forested or mountain areas of the USSR (Fischer, 1981, pp. 500-22). The total number of reserves had risen to 147 by 1984 (*Narodnoye Khozyaystvo SSSR v 1984 godu*, 1985, p. 401), but the forested share of reserves may have diminished slightly in the 1980s because new *zapovedniki* added recently have included large areas of tundra (i.e., Wrangel Island and Taymyr, both in Northern Siberia).

Eight Soviet reserves have been accorded *biosphere* status under the UNESCO "Man and the Biosphere" program. Other categories of preserved land include hunting preserves, monuments of nature, *zakazniki* (short-term reserves), and national parks (Braden, 1986b). The designation of national parks (12 were listed for 1984 with a total of 752 thousand ha [*Narodnoye Khozyaystvo SSSR v 1984 godu*, 1985, p. 401]) is a recognition of the struggle between recreational use of preserved lands and conservation goals. In a concession to tourist pressures, national parks are multipurpose: they allow visitors, although acknowledging that wilderness preservation may be jeopardized.

Soviet scientists are beginning to document the impact of human visitors on reserves and on Group 1 forests. In the Valaam Islands (noted above), Kuchko and Krutov (1986, p. 45) estimate that only 1 to 3 percent of the traumas suffered by trees in the area was due to controlled cutting hazards, while 5 to 12 percent was due to recreational use. They determined furthermore that incidences of diseased trees were 20 to 30 percent greater in areas used heavily by visitors; such areas also had smaller numbers of trees and a smaller amount of tree growth. In the case of the forests surrounding Novosibirsk, researchers documented poorer soil conditions, disappearance of undergrowth, reduction in number of trees, and diminished numbers of wildlife, particularly in popular recreational areas (Bekh, 1985, p. 32).

As a result of such findings, Dyrenkov (1983, p. 25) has proposed a four-stage system to measure forest damage:

Stage I: *Little disruption* - paths and areas trampled underfoot are not more than 10 percent of total area; trees distributed evenly with growth throughout the forest; all types of plants normal for that forest biome are present.

Stage II: *Disturbed* - paths and trampled areas comprise 10 to 25 percent of total; sharp drop in rate of tree growth; increased invasion by plants requiring more light; drop in weight of needles on conifers by 10 percent compared with Stage I; 15 percent of bird nests are disturbed.

Stage III: *Strongly disturbed* - paths and trampled areas represent 60 percent of total; few juvenile trees; weight of conifer needles is down by 12 to 15 percent over Stage I; some plants retreat to "island" groups only; 16 to 30 percent of bird nests are disturbed.

Stage IV: *Degraded* - paths and trampled areas comprise over 60 percent of total area; young trees are completely absent; weight of needles is down 45 percent over Stage I; more than 30 percent of bird nests are disturbed.

Using his four stages to examine certain forests, Dyrenkov concludes that some degradation of forests is inevitable with recreation use, but recognition of Stage II should serve as a signal that a stand of timber needs to be accorded a more protected status and allowed to regenerate. Dyrenkov (1983, p. 32) also argues that an example of degradation exists in the northwest RSFSR, a region which has suffered from overutilization for recreation and requires recultivation of strongly disturbed stands.

The RSFSR has about 80 percent of the Soviet forests available for recreational use (Vorob'yev *et al.*, 1979) (Table 6.2). Two percent of the "recreationally significant" forests fall into the category for "health-resorts/sanitoria," and the remainder of the RSFSR's recreational forest is designated as green zone. The estimates by Vorob'yev *et al.* indicate that approximately 13.4 million ha of forest land is thus available for recreational use in the RSFSR. If Group 1 forests comprise about 16 percent (Table 3.4) of total state forest area, and if total forest area in 1983 was estimated at 811 million ha (Table 4.3), then recreationally significant forests amount to 1.6 percent of total USSR forest lands, and 10 percent of the country's Group 1

Table 6.2

Group 1 Forests of Environmental and Recreational Significance (Forested Area, Thousands of ha)

	Protective Zones Along Roads	Resort Forests	Greenbelts Total	Managed Forests
USSR	3,169	620	12,782	9,599
USSR Europe-Uralia	2,495	515	9,595	6,713
USSR Asia	674	105	3,187	2,886
RSFSR	2,171	232	10,661	8,143
Northwest	808	15	1,512	1,357
Center	219	2	2,334	1,408
Volgo-Vyatka	108	28	524	391
Black Earth	11		237	125
Volga Littoral	64	20	891	589
North Caucasus	24	56	278	201
Urals	275	7	1,708	1,206
RSFSR Europe-Uralia	1,518	128	7,604	5,329
Western Siberia	138	22	631	558
Eastern Siberia	244	53	1,327	1,209
Far East	271	29	1,099	1,047
RSFSR Asia	653	104	3,057	2,814
Belorussia	655	33	496	431
Estonia	54	4	126	78
Latvia	41	5	146	26
Lithuania	44	21	261	229
Ukraine	172	32	661	572
Moldavia	3		44	32
Georgia	6	286	226	
Armenia	1	3	13	13
Azerbaydzhan	1	3	18	3
Uzbekistan	1		4	
Kirgizia		1	16	16
Tadzhikistan			2	2
Turkmenistan	2		3	
Kazakhstan	18		105	54

Source: Compiled from Vorob'yev *et al.* (1979, pp. 104, 109).

forests. This estimate varies regionally (estimates for Estonia are described earlier in this chapter).

Several scientists have argued for a better integration of recreational activities and forest preservation and planning in urban zones. Dyrenkov terms this approach "urban forestry" in the green belts around cities. Bekh (1985, p. 32) recognizes a shortage of recreational forest land in the area around Novosibirsk and a need to manage existing land effectively. He proposes that the type of general exurban forest management plan developed for Novosibirsk in 1979 could be adopted elsewhere in the USSR.

Another example of urban forestry based on integrated-use plans is the green belt of Moscow. The protected land zone around Moscow includes 172 thousand ha with a general stocking density of 42 percent (Ponomarenko, 1985, p. 28). Its administration involves many agencies, and the system includes 12 forest-parks, a historic *zapovednik* (Gorki Leninskiy *zapovednik*), and a national park (*Losiniy ostrov*). The forests have a carrying load of 110 people per ha, or 90 sq. m of forestland per Moscow resident. Maintenance cost for the area is 6.5 million rubles per year. The area's administrative plan includes allowance for maintenance cutting, control of poaching, plant protection, facilities maintenance, and supervision of scientific research. A recent additional function has been the organization of "health routes" through the forests for exercise and sport (Ponomarenko, 1985, pp. 28-29).

The maintenance of such programs within the goal of preserving forestland from severe degradation requires the establishment of clear norms for utilization. Biologist L. P. Rysin (1983, p. 10) of the USSR Academy of Sciences has recommended that carrying capacity be established for recreational use of various forest types: inner city parks could handle 50 people per ha; exurban forest parks 10 to 20 people per ha; and forests outside urban zones, 5 to 10 people per ha. Usage thus becomes less intensive with increasing distance from urban centers. We suggest that the issue of recreational competition for forest resources will intensify in the USSR with increases in leisure time and population mobility.

FOOD PROVISION BY FORESTS

The 1980s have placed an additional demand by officials on Soviet forests unrelated to the provision of industrial fiber, although this "new" activity has been part of the country's formal social structure for centuries. Increasing urbanization during the past 25 years has removed many people from the countryside and hence from self-sufficiency in food production. Furthermore, many rural residents now purchase food from state enterprises as its processing has become more prevalent. Because the general supply of food, however, has not kept pace with these rising demands, the government has recently integrated forest items into its major food programs. Some Group 1 forests already have had a designation (Table 3.4) clearly related to food supply.

Throughout all Soviet forests, however, the variety and size of food and other nutrients is significant. Vorob'yev (1982, pp. 36-39) reports that over 100 species of fruits, berries, and nuts, and 200 varieties of edible mushrooms are available for human consumption; many also have medicinal and commercial utility. (Mushroom gathering is both a recreational activity dear to the hearts of many Soviet people and a serious source of food.) Use of the forest for food takes on an even greater significance when thousands of species of bush and grass are included. Vorob'yev identifies 2500 types of forest plants which are available for medicinal use, including at least 600 species which are used in the pharmaceutical industry. Over 6 million ha of fruit and berry land are included in the USSR state forest reserve. If fully utilized, their estimated harvest could exceed 5 million tons of edible products, including 1 million tons of seeds and stonefruits. Items harvested from this land have already contributed significantly to the Soviet diet and have comprised an important share of organized raw and processed food production during recent five-year plans (Vorob'yev, 1982, p. 38). These so-called "minor produce" (UNIDO, 1983, p. 14) activities include haymaking; cattle grazing; beekeeping; harvesting of mushrooms, fruits, nuts, berries, and herbs; hunting; and medicinal research and product derivation.

The VNIILM (All-Union Scientific-Research Institute of Silviculture and Forestry Mechanization) estimates (Anuchin, 1986, pp. 232-33) that the state forest reserve currently provides the USSR with the following amounts (thousands of tons) of these items (figures in parentheses pertain to Europe-Uralia):

All fruits and berries	167.3	(145.1)
Cranberries and cowberries	22.9	(20.3)
Honey	40.1	(21.7)
Birch juice	42.7	(41.9)
Mushrooms	31.7	(28.7)
Nuts	10.5	(3.2)
Medicinal herbs, grasses and related raw materials	15.7	(11.8)
Hay	338.3	(232.7)

Other, more specialized, food products are derived from forest land. Consumption of birch juice has long been important to Russian culture because it is regarded as a type of health drink. Production requires large trees of not less than 20 cm diameter. One mature tree can produce an average of 100 liters every season, and 1 ha of birch trees can yield 20 to 30 tons of juice per year. Honey production is also associated with forests, particularly with basswood and willows. One hectare of basswood can produce 500 kg of honey in a season; over 50 percent of the apiary output associated with basswood forests originates in the Volga Littoral (Vorob'yev *et al.*, 1979, p. 70). Although we have emphasized the importance of the extensive forests of the RSFSR to industrial activity, some southern regions of the USSR contribute significantly to the nonindustrial use of forests. Forest-deficient Central Asia and the Caucasus, for example, play a much larger role in providing forest foods than in the industrial exploitation of forests (Table 6.3).

Table 6.3
Wild Nut and Fruit Harvest from Soviet Forests

Item	Area	Major Regions
	Thousands of ha	% of Total Production
Walnuts (including Manchurian walnuts)	74	RSFSR (35%; Far East comprises 20% of national total), Kirgizia (35%)
Pistachios	57	Turkmenistan (44%), Kirgizia (32%),
Almonds	9	Uzbekistan (44%)
Chestnuts	90	Georgia (53%), North Caucasus (45%)
Beechnuts	2,500	Georgia (40%), North Caucasus (26%), Ukraine (21%)
Hornbeam	791	North Caucasus (29%), Azerbaydzhan (24%), Ukraine (19%), Georgia (19%)
Apples	38	Kazakhstan (34%), Kirgizia (34%)
Pears	23	North Caucasus (87%)
Apricots	9	Central Asia (almost 100%)
Olives (Russian)	26	Kazakhstan (58%)
Mulberries	3	Azerbaydzhan (67%)
Persimmons	1	Azerbaydzhan (almost 100%)

Source: Compiled from Vorob'yev *et al.* (1979, p. 69).

Table 6.4
Distribution of Pasturelands in the State Forest Reserve

	% of USSR Total
USSR	100.0
USSR Europe-Uralia	32.8
USSR Asia	67.2
RSFSR	86.1
RSFSR Europe-Uralia	27.0
USSR Asia	59.1
Belorussia	1.5
Ukraine	1.9
Kazakhstan	7.7
(All other republics comprise <1%)	

Source: Compiled from Vorob'yev *et al.* (1979, p. 69).

Most Soviet pasture lands, however, are located in the RSFSR (Table 6.4). This land, part of the state forest fund, provides a source of feed for cattle in Group 2 and 3 forests. Together with other sources of forest foods, pasturelands provide a major increment to Soviet food supply, particularly in the provision of meat. The Twelfth Five-Year Plan envisages an increase in the direct contribution of forest lands to food output: between 1985 and 1986 alone, the plan foresees a 2 percent increase in food output from forested areas. Commercial forests also play an indirect role in agricultural output as suppliers of materials to farming activities. The Twelfth Five-Year Plan, for example, seeks an increase in production of packing crates for collective and state farms ("Sotsialisticheskiye Obyazatel'stva Kollektivov Predpriyatiy i Organizatsiy Lesnogo Khozyaystva na 1986 godu," 1986, p. 4).

OTHER NONINDUSTRIAL USES OF THE FOREST

In addition to their production by the wood chemicals industry, resinous materials tapped directly from trees provide another use for some forests. Fir balsa, stone pine aromatic resin, and pine resin are produced. Fifteen million ha of pine, mainly in the RSFSR, are available for tapping pitch and, of these stands, 50 percent are in Eastern Siberia, 15 percent in Western Siberia, and 25 percent in the Northwest (Vorob'yev *et al.*, 1979, pp. 61-62).

Finally, the USSR recognizes the utility of forest stands for environmental enhancement. The role of the Soviet forests in biospheric protection is significant in view of the large areal extent of forest lands, and their contribution to the world's oxygen-carbon dioxide cycle is frequently discussed by Soviet scientists. The local microclimatic role played by trees is also apparent: trees along roads absorb atmospheric pollutants, with a belt of trees 50m to 70 m wide taking most of the harmful emissions from automobile traffic. Group 1 forests include a category (Table 3.4) of protective forest belts along roads, but their total is less than half of 1 percent of all Soviet forests; Vorob'yev *et al.* (1979, p. 105) estimate that 10 ha to 14 ha of forest would be required per 1 km of road to ensure adequate pollution abatement. The USSR reported 773 thousand km of paved roads for 1983 (*Narodnoye Khozyaystvo SSSR v 1983 g.*, 1984, p. 326). Thus, even the lesser estimate of 10 ha per km of road would require a minimum of 7.7 million ha of protective forests along major roads to attain the pollution abatement goal of Group 1 forests. Only 3.2 million ha of trees, representing 0.4 percent of the 811 million ha of state forest lands, are now set aside for this purpose (Table 3.4). We are tempted to conclude that an insufficient amount of forest land is dedicated to pollution abatement, but such a conclusion is tenuous given our difficulty in determining whether some Group 1 trees are multipurpose, and our limited knowledge of spatial variation in automobile traffic.

CONCLUSIONS

Several factors emerge from discussion of the nonindustrial use of forests in the USSR. First, while the RSFSR dominates industrial use of forests, other union republics play significant roles in nonindustrial use. The forests of the Caucasus and Central Asia appear to be more significant in some food production than in their industrial output. Second, demands on food supply in the USSR indicate that forests will take an increasing share of the duties in supplementing the fare on Soviet tables. Third, recreation continues to place a major demand on forests, but this role often conflicts with the objectives of environmental preservation.

The Twelfth Five-Year Plan (1986-1990) calls for better use of existing capacity in industry. As Shabad (1986, p. 1) has reported, "This aspect of economic strategy has been interpreted as a turning away from the comprehensive development of Siberia toward the European part of the USSR." If the new plan thus envisions continued urbanization in populated areas, then a further recreational and perhaps nutritional burden will be placed on forests surrounding European-Uralian cities.

To meet this challenge, the State Committee on Science and Technology has called for more research on recreational problems. *Gosleskhoz* itself is required to formulate a scheme of rules for recreational use of forests, including key aspects of planning, financing, and conservation (Elanov, 1985, p. 77). As with all industrial societies, the USSR faces problems reconciling multipurpose use of forests.

In general, therefore, the USSR's forests play an important secondary production role in society not associated with the principal and intermediate harvest of timber, although these uses can conflict. Given the country's dependence on supplementary sources of food and related items, the utilization of forests and forested areas could impose an important limitation on the use of European-Uralian forest land for logging, particularly because many of the secondary usages are spatially extensive. Multifaceted pressures on the forest resource, particularly in accessible regions, means that overall usage will intensify in forthcoming decades and that attempts will be made to gain the greatest possible yield from all aspects of the forest. Although it is still premature to estimate the consequences of such developments, we might expect that more intensive usage of given regional forests could be associated with reforestation and silviculture and a rise in the importance of thinning or intermediate cuts. Greater intensity thus seems to presage greater utility for accessible forests, particularly in Europe-Uralia, and a shift of investment funds to projects having the promise of multiple payoffs in food, recreation, timber, and fiber.

Given the strong contribution to Russian traditions made by the forest, assurance of a continued supply of forest land for cultural needs should thus perhaps be considered of equal importance with its fulfillment of commercial demands. A scenario of "forests without trees" would not only be disastrous for Soviet wood industries, but could also be a blow to the Russian spirit.

7
Forests and International Trade

Chapter 7 assesses the role of forest products in Soviet foreign trade. First the relative importance of the USSR in world forest product trade is discussed, and then major trends in Soviet forest product exports and imports are examined. The institutional structure of foreign trade is described briefly in order to place the control of trade within the broader Soviet economic and administrative structure. Because this general structure involves many regional considerations, the chapter proceeds to examine regional influences on trade in forests products, particularly on exports, first in relation to domestic regions, and then as part of a discussion of prices in foreign markets. The chapter concludes with a summary assessment of prospects for future Soviet behavior in international forest-product trade.

THE USSR AND THE WORLD

Given the size of its forests, the USSR is not a correspondingly major player in world forest product trade. The Soviet Union in 1984 accounted for 5 percent of world forest-product exports and 1.8 percent of world imports (FAO, 1986, pp. 344-47). Western Europe's exports in this sector exceed those of the USSR by 8 times; those of North America exceed the USSR's by near 7 times. Forest-product exports from the USA are 2.2 times, and those from Canada 4.4 times, greater than those from the USSR.

As an importer of forest products, however, the USSR is surpassed by many countries and areas, particularly those in Western Europe and North America. Western European imports exceeded those of the USSR in 1984 by 26 times, and those of North America by 12 times (this amount is almost equally split between the USA and Canada). USSR imports of forest products comprise approximately one-half those of China.

THE ROLE OF FOREST PRODUCTS IN FOREIGN TRADE

Forest-product exports have not generated substantial earnings for the USSR, but they have followed patterns typical of Soviet raw material exports. Forest products have not risen above a 7 percent share of the value of exports, and actually peaked in 1965 (Table 7.1). Despite the overall small role of forest products in trade, however, they have been significant in bilateral relations with some countries. In 1984, for example, forests products comprised 26.4 percent of the FTR (foreign trade ruble) value of Soviet exports to Japan.[1]

To put forest products trade in perspective, a brief summary of Soviet foreign trade might be useful: the USSR's partners in CMEA account for 52 percent of the country's trade;[2] other communist countries raise the total for the socialist

Table 7.1
Forest Products: Share of Export Earnings, 1960-1984
(Selected Years)

Year	% of USSR Export Earnings
1960	5.5
1965	7.2
1970	6.5
1975	4.0
1980	3.8
1981	3.1
1982	2.5
1983	2.6
1984	2.6

Source: *Vneshnyaya Torgovlya SSSR* (various years).

Table 7.2
USSR Forest Product Exports, 1960-1984
(Thousands of Rubles)

Product	1960	1965	1970	1975	1980	1984
Logs	55,074	161,977	254,330	464,604	614,790	538,916
Plywood	13,250	21,683	32,506	58,533	79,248	83,438
Lumber	164,527	253,363	267,352	253,978	783,787	765,322
Pulp	22,594	29,641	54,461	77,552	220,722	315,884
Paper	17,431	28,673	64,952	113,022	171,605	230,843
Total	272,876	495,337	673,601	967,689	1,870,152	1,934,403
Share of Total USSR Exports (%)	5.5	7.2	6.5	4.0	3.8	2.6

Source: *Vneshnyaya Torgovlya* (various years).

block to nearly 58 percent. Developed capitalist economies account for 30 percent of the USSR's foreign trade, and the developing world comprises the remainder. Soviet foreign trade has grown over 6 times since 1970 and reached 140 billion rubles in 1984 (*Vneshnyaya Torgovlya SSSR v 1984 godu*, 1985, p. 6). Prior to World War II, foreign trade was negligible and totaled only 500 million rubles in 1938. Soviet exports (1984) are dominated by sales of fuel and energy (54 percent), machinery and transportation equipment (12 percent), and metallic ores and products (7 percent). (In the early 1970s, fuel and energy exports accounted for only one-sixth of total exports.) Soviet imports are dominated by machinery and transportation equipment (37 percent), and by food products and allied equipment (22 percent).

Timber, pulp and paper products comprised 2.8 percent of Soviet exports and 1.2 percent of imports in 1984 (*Vneshnyaya Torgovlya SSSR v 1984 godu*, 1985, p.18). In 1940 and as recently as 1970, these products comprised 6.5 percent of the country's exports. Their share of imports, however, was consistently about 2 percent until the 1980s.

In addition to the limited importance of forest products to overall Soviet trade, four other characteristics are of note:

1. Forest products show a dominance of primary product exports. This fact is typical of Soviet trade patterns, and does not appear to be diminishing. A reverse flow, i.e., import of forest products into the USSR, also occurs and may be a stronger pattern than is usually identified.

2. The geographic direction of forest product trade is mainly to Europe and Japan, although two recent large sales to China may indicate the beginning of a new pattern.

3. Soviet prices for exported forest products generally have been rising.

4. Supply constraints, increasing harvest of remote stands, apparent inability to shift to higher value-added exports, and the need for a technological breakthrough in the use of larch may be inhibiting growth of forest product exports.

Forest products thus appear to conform to the notion that Soviet foreign trade structure resembles that of an underdeveloped economy because it depends on raw-material exports.[3]

FOREST-PRODUCT EXPORTS

Forest products have not performed well in Soviet foreign trade (Tables 7.1 and 7.2). Total exports by value tend to comprise about 10 percent of the domestic value of all industrial output, which in 1984 comprised 779 billion rubles (*Narodnoye Khozyaystvo SSSR v 1984 godu*, 1985, p. 129); exports had a value of 74.4 billion rubles, 9.5 percent of output (*Vneshnyaya Torgovlya SSSR v 1984 godu*, 1985, p. 6). Forest products tend to be underrepresented in relation to the export-national output ratio for all industry; forest-product exports comprised only 6.5 percent of this sector's total ruble output in 1984.

In 1984, roundwood comprised one-quarter of forest-sector exports; pulp, paper, and paperboard together constitute 30 percent of this sector's exports and lumber accounts for just over one-third. The remainder consists of plywood, particleboard, and fiberboard. In 1940, exports of roundwood and lumber dominated the foreign sales from the forest-product sector, and foreign sales of Soviet timber exceeded those of lumber by a ratio of 1.3: 1.

Logs or roundwood exports, while comprising 26 to 27 percent of the total value of forest product exports (Table 7.2, Chart 7.1), nevertheless comprise only 5.5 percent of national output. At the same time, the USSR imported 249 cu. m of roundwood in 1984, less than 1 percent of national production.

Turnover in forest products, therefore, is not limited to exports alone. From 1960 through 1984, forest-product imports accounted for between 1.3 and 2 percent of all imports (Table 7.3). Imports, particularly of logs and lumber from Finland, Eastern Europe, and even the United States, account for much of the value of imported forest products. Imports from Europe suggest that regional domestic shortfalls in supply are countered with imports, usually from CMEA countries, or in the case of Finland, under long-term "soft-currency agreements" (Eronen, 1977).

Relatively low-value products tend to dominate forest-product exports (Table 7.2, Chart 7.2). For the nine years shown in Table 7.2, logs have ranged from a low of 20.2 percent (1960) of forest-product export (by ruble value) to a high of 48 percent in 1975, the peak harvest year.[4] Over the period shown, logs and lumber have usually made up at least 70 percent of exports in forest products, and the trend lines shown in Chart 7.2 confirm their dominance and the relative absence of high value-added products.

The Soviet Union exported 15.6 million cu. m of roundwood in 1984 (4 percent of total industrial removals, 5.5 percent of total commercial timber). These exports (Chart 7.1) consisted of saw logs (7.7 million cu. m), pulpwood (6.7 million cu. m), pitprops (0.54 million), and a variety of other unprocessed timber including construction timbers, matchwood, peeler logs, and sleepers.[5] By the 1980s, the share of exports comprised about one-eighth for paper and paperboard, one-sixth for pulp and plywood, and one-fifth for fiberboard. Between 1960 and 1984, the value of Soviet exports increased almost fifteenfold. Growth of forest-sector exports grew only eightfold, although some products such as pulp and paper increased their export value by 14 (pulp) and 13 (paper) times. The export of some forest products, however, such as fiberboard, particleboard, and paperboard was negligible or nonexistent in 1960, and the share of exports in national production does not exceed 15 percent for any major commodity (Chart 7.3).

The growth in export of forest-sector products during the past quarter century has thus not equaled the rate of growth of all Soviet exports. Particularly since the early 1970s, the USSR has benefited greatly from the rise of world energy prices, and from a major diversification in the products which it exports. Although they earn the country over 2 billion rubles of foreign exchange, annual exports of forest-sector products have a minor relative role in the country's total exports. On the other hand, with the collapse of world energy prices in late 1985, the relative importance of the forest-products sector may again increase toward the level it occupied at the start of the 1970s. If we remove the 54.4

Chart 7.1

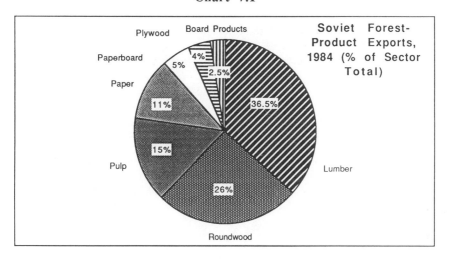

Chart 7.2

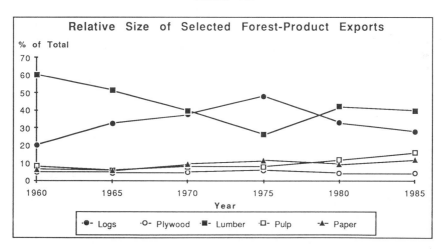

Table 7.3
USSR Imports of Forest Products, 1960-1984
(Selected Years)

Millions of Rubles

Product	1960	1965	1970	1975	1980	1984
Logs	2.7	0.9	2.7	16.5	29.1	20.3
Lumber	28.2	18.1	18.6	32.8	53.9	62.1
Pulp	12.8	32.9	48.6	91.3	89.0	86.4
Paper	15.6	31.3	84.6	236.2	369.6	307.5
Total of Above	59.3	83.2	154.5	376.7	541.6	476.3
As % of Total						
USSR Imports	1.2%	1.1%	1.5%	1.4%	1.2%	0.7%
Total Forest						
Product Imports	94.4	135.3	233.8	572.8	889.2	814.4
As % of Total						
USSR Imports	1.9%	1.9%	2.2%	2.1%	2.0%	1.2%
Total Imports	5,066.1	7,248.4	10,558.5	26,669.2	44,462.8	65,327.3

Source: *Vneshnyaya Torgovlya* (various years).

Chart 7.3

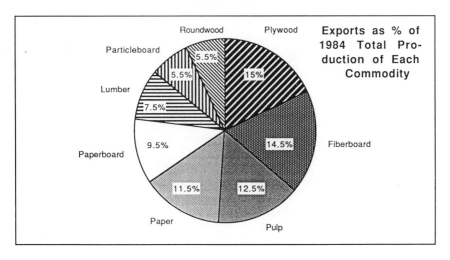

Chart 7.4

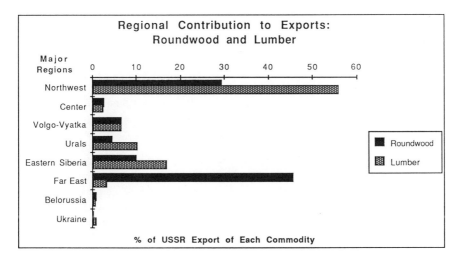

percent of Soviet export value contributed in 1984 by fuels and energy, and replace it with 11.5 percent of total as would have been the case if 1970 shares prevailed, the 1984 total export value does not equal 74.4 billion rubles, but 38.4 billion rubles. The forest-sector exports totaled 2.15 billion rubles in 1984, or 5.6 percent of our hypothetical, adjusted total exports.

FOREST-PRODUCT IMPORTS

The Soviet Union also has significant imports of forest products to supplement its domestic consumption of specific items, to obtain species of roundwood and veneer not available domestically, and to provide strategic markets for client states. Although Soviet forest-product imports are not directly germane to the utilization of that country's standing timber, we briefly examine several key aspects of wood and product imports here to demonstrate that, when in the USSR's strategic and economic interest, certain items are imported, even roundwood. Thus, if future regional shortages should occur in the USSR, it is not inconceivable that they may be offset in raw or processed form with imports. This already happens with grains and other food products and could occur in timber and wood-processing as well. Furthermore, the vast spatial extent of the USSR means that Soviet ships and railways used to import goods to certain regions could well offset severe transport costs on the long-distance domestic movement of similar products over congested railways.

The Soviet Union, for example, in 1984 imported 249 thousand cu. m of roundwood, of which 193 thousand cu. m were tropical woods otherwise unavailable for high-quality flooring, furniture, or other uses. In 1981, one-half of these imports by value were species for flooring, and one-quarter was single-sheet veneer. Peeler logs comprised most of the remainder. Some of these originated with CMEA members like Romania and Vietnam, others from such Third World countries as the Ivory Coast, Cameroon, the Congo, and Liberia (UNIDO, 1983, p. 54). The remainder, however, originated entirely in Mongolia and helped to offset the trade deficit (it purchases 2.6 times more than it sells to the USSR [*Vneshnyaya Torgovlya SSSR v 1984 godu,* 1985, pp. 221, 227]) the country has with the USSR. Presumably Soviet imports from Mongolia are utilized in adjacent oblasts of the RSFSR, and presumably they consist heavily of larch, which is utilized in relatively unprocessed form in the USSR (Mongolian timber and wood-processing have recently been discussed by Eronen, 1982a). The USSR purchased 207 thousand cu. m of deciduous lumber in 1984, primarily from Romania and to a lesser extent from Yugoslavia. It obtained 35 million sq. m of single-sheet veneer panels, mainly from six countries; approximately one-half originated from Yugoslavia, and a lesser amount from Romania. Soviet pulp purchases in 1984, although less than in 1983, nevertheless totaled 192 thousand tons, equivalent to one-fifth of pulp exports. These imports originated almost entirely in Scandinavia (93.4 percent) and in the USA (6.1 percent). Scandinavian imports of pulp can feed directly into Soviet mills with relatively easy ship access through the Baltic Sea or on the Soviet-gauge railway connecting Finland directly with Soviet consumers. (These imports, consisting mainly of dissolving pulp, are probably destined for manufacturing facilities outside of the pulp and paper industry in the chemical or chemical-product sectors.)

Finland's trading relationship with the USSR, however, is based on more than convenient proximity, the signing of long-term bilateral agreements, and has been nurtured by astute political behavior by both sides since Finnish war reparations ceased in the 1950s. Finnish sales to the USSR have profited by an environment of confidence and capability which the Finns probably first demonstrated during post-war relations. Furthermore, many of the mills in the Northwest were originally Finnish and in the convoluted world of politics their original loss may have offered a lever to the Finns for subsequent upgrading and rehabilitation when the original equipment needed to be replaced or repaired. Finland is the principal supplier to the USSR (1984) of paper (68 percent) and of paperboard (95 percent). The only major CMEA supplier of these products is the GDR, which supplied 8 percent of Soviet paper imports in 1984.

Soviet imports of paper and paperboard are high relative to exports: 84 percent for paper and 45 percent for paperboard. They suggest that the USSR is prepared to trade for special items and that it can include certain commodities in its bilateral CMEA and capitalist trading relations which take advantage of special foreign expertise, although theoretically the USSR could produce these items itself. Thus, in the country's imports, a significant share consists of manufactured paper and paperboard items such as napkins and disposable containers (USDA, 1983, p. 7). The USSR appears to have a comprehensive policy of assisting some developing countries of CMEA and of the Third World to develop wood-processing by exporting to them plant, equipment, and expertise. This cost is partially offset by payback or countertrade shipments of roundwood and products to the USSR. Such imports are also a means by which the USSR can circumvent the need to allocate hard currency to obtain these items on the world market, especially when the prices for some tropical hardwoods are unstable and when many other demands, particularly in technology, are made on the USSR's available currency and gold reserves.

Soviet discussions of this strategy and its wider integration within CMEA and between the Soviet bloc and the Third World (UNIDO, 1983, pp. 52-58) leave no doubt that more trade of this form could be expected if Soviet influence expands in Asia, Africa, and Central or Latin America. Furthermore, if sector-by-sector integration between the USSR and members of CMEA continues to grow, then such experience and confidence could also be expanded to additional client states and integrated into a broad strategy to relieve certain supply problems in the Soviet timber and wood-processing industries identified throughout this book.

ORGANIZATION OF FOREIGN TRADE

The foreign-trade sector of the Soviet economy has traditionally operated on a somewhat autonomous level from the domestic economy. A separate ruble price system is created for exported and imported items, and transactions traditionally have had to go through administrative organs called FTOs (foreign trade organizations). The two FTOs which have had the most influence on forest industries are *Exportles* [6] and *Prommashimport* (for machinery imports).

Western experts have argued that foreign trade serves as a balancing mechanism for the Soviet economy, and in the last several decades, has also provided a means for transferring Western technology into the USSR to provide a sorely needed increase in productivity (Bozek, 1979; Cooper, 1982; Goldman, 1983). Thus, along with the large-scale imports of grain from the United States and Argentina, imports of technology have increased the share of trade with the hard-currency nations of the West. In 1965, exports to the industrialized West made up 18 percent of Soviet exports; this figure reached 30 percent in 1981. Meanwhile, Soviet imports from the West grew from 20 percent to 34 percent for the same period (Cooper, 1982, p. 460). The growth of trade with the West has decreased slightly in the last several years, but an overall balance of payments deficit with the West persists. This deficit seems to indicate that one objective of the export sector of the Soviet economy is to develop Western markets. Forest products appear to be a likely commodity to sell in addition to other raw materials; therefore barter arrangements and compensation agreements have occurred in forest industries, particularly in pulp and paper. Two roadblocks, however, appear to have put a ceiling on expansion of wood exports to hard currency markets: supply constraints and locked-in. longer-term trade with the CMEA nations. The ability of the USSR to expand wood exports to Western countries is the main focus of our attention here.

The Ministry of Foreign Trade, *Gosplan,* and the FTOs, all traditionally responsible for foreign trade, serve as a sieve for materials flowing in and out of the USSR. They are often criticized because end users of imported technology are not necessarily privy to purchase decisions. The Ministry of Foreign Trade's grip on the international trade monopoly has been under severe attack in recent years as other organizations have started to exert greater influence on this sector of the Soviet economy.[7] Since the mid-1970s, foreign trade has undergone reorganizations to break down the division between outside markets and internal Soviet industrial consumers or sellers (Bozek, 1979, p. 518). The products themselves follow a path from enterprises to *Gossnab* (State Committee on Supply) and then to the FTOs. *Gossnab* compensates in domestic rubles, while the FTOs are paid in foreign currency. Thus, the enterprises themselves do not apparently benefit (at least in terms of the rubles received) from sales of their forest products abroad.

While trade is highly centralized, some regional trading operations are permitted. *Dalintorg* is the small-scale trading organization that deals with Soviet Far Eastern trade to Japan, and *Lenfintorg* conducts border trade with Finland. The emphasis on raw materials and consumer goods in these organizations, however, has very limited impact on forest-products trade. In 1975, a group of business and local government leaders from the state of Washington set up a trade fair in the Soviet Far East (Khabarovsk) to encourage transactions between Washington and Siberia, but were frustrated to discover that decisions were made in Moscow; the fair proved of small value in stimulating trade.[8]

One trend in Soviet foreign trade that emerged in the 1970s was the barter, or compensation agreement. In these arrangements, the USSR receives technology in exchange for exporting a share of output. Barter agreements have been significant in Soviet log, chip, and pulpwood sales to Japan. The Ust'-Ilimsk complex in Eastern Siberia received foreign machinery under compensation agreements with a variety of nations, including France (*Journal of the US-USSR Trade and Economic Council*, September-October 1979, p. 5). The USSR has preferred to conduct trade under the auspices of either bilateral umbrella agreements between itself and the government of another nation, or multinational agreements within organizations like CMEA. Long-term agreements, such as those which regulate trade between the USSR and Finland or Japan, and the ability to obtain credits at favorable rates for purchases of technology, also appear to be a priority goal of foreign trade planners.[9]

SOVIET REGIONS AND FOREIGN TRADE

Many problems in Soviet forest-product trade have a pronounced regional bias. Clearly some regions have been, and continue to be, more significant to Soviet timber exports and imports than others. In particular, present and impending shortages in Soviet timber have an important bearing on the ability of the country to continue its exports, and on sustaining its ability to provide adequate supplies of roundwood and primary manufactured inputs to numerous regional manufacturing plants as well as final consumers of wood-products. The major regional assessment of Soviet timber (Kanevskiy and Shaytanov, 1975), although slightly dated, nevertheless provides us with an interesting perspective on the past quarter century. It has also been utilized by two Canadian analysts (North and Solecki, 1977) as part of their assessment of the USSR's ability to sustain and promote growth in the timber and wood-processing industries. Eronen (1983) has succinctly described Soviet roundwood and sawn wood exports by focusing on the spatial linkages between foreign markets and Soviet suppliers via the USSR's major seaports and international railway nodes.

The Soviet Union continues to face two major dilemmas in its forest-product sector exports: (1) What should be the mix of processed to unprocessed timber in each region? (2) Which regions should sustain exports?

The method employed to assess the first question in the Soviet Union (Kanevskiy and Shaytanov, 1975, pp. 209-12) cannot provide an unequivocal solution. Although calling for greater processing of timber exported, especially from regions distant from foreign markets, Kanevskiy and Shaytanov recognize that forests adjacent to export ports and border crossings may be advantageously used to ship unprocessed materials. Presumably a significant share of such materials are then processed in neighboring countries which re-export them to the USSR. Policies affecting these patterns of trade are established within a much wider bundle of objectives than the mere sustained utilization of the actual growing stock. Policies serving balanced bilateral trade (Bradshaw, 1986) far outweigh the long-term concern for preservation of resources, although functionally they are linked.

The export of raw wood and the reimport of processed items frees the USSR to allocate investment capital in manufacturing to other sectors with a perceived higher economic return and strategic utility. It also permits that country to utilize many aspects of other nations' comparative locational and economic advantages. Finland, for example, is well placed to receive Soviet raw timber from the Northwest and to return processed goods to that regional market and to the Center. Once such flows are in place, however, administrative or institutional inertia seems to ensure that they are maintained even when adjacent forests can no longer supply enough raw timber. [10] The central administration of that country, however, means that railway shipments can be ordered and then subsidized with domestic currency in order that other, more important, foreign exchange objectives are met. It comes as no surprise that the average length of haul of roundwood in the USSR has steadily increased since the mid-1970s and now is approaching 2000 km (Chapter 5). Not surprisingly, therefore, Kanevskiy and Shaytanov conclude that simple economic criteria based on transfer and production costs cannot provide an adequate guide for the formation of appropriate regional export mix of timber and products. These exports simply should "comprise materials consisting of various degrees of processing" (Kanevskiy and Shaytanov, 1975, p. 212).

The answer to the second question appears to be a function of the regional location and production mix of existing logging and processing. Although our data base of regional shares in the export of various materials is regrettably limited, it reveals nevertheless that distinct regional biases exist. These probably reflect the timing of investment, access to railways and ports, and the mix of regional output. Many forest product enterprises, for example, appear to provide a share of their highest quality output for export. Although some timber and sawmilling enterprises are primarily engaged in the export trade due to the large size of this activity, the other products do not seem to be exported in sufficient size or in a consistent enough manner to warrant a special allocation of the entire enterprise to these activities. In special cases, such as the Ust'-Ilimsk complex, which was built in collaboration with specific members of CMEA in return for a share of its output being guaranteed as compensatory forest-product exports, mills have a high designated export component. Until the present time, individual enterprises normally have not established international market links; these are organized and administered through the Ministry of Foreign Trade, as noted above.

In the early 1970s, almost one-fifth of the lumber produced in 14 regions analyzed by Kanevskiy and Shaytanov (1975, p. 112) was destined for export. An important share of the lumber cut in 23 regions, however, is destined for foreign markets. This share constitutes one-half in Archangel oblast and Karelia ASSR; two-fifths in Krasnoyarsk kray, over one-quarter in Komi ASSR and Latvia; and about one-seventh in Vologda, Leningrad, Kalinin, Kirov, Perm, and Sverdlovsk oblasts. In some regions such as Archangel, Leningrad, Sverdlovsk, and Kirov oblasts, and Krasnoyarsk kray, the relative share increases by 6 to 10 percent if only lumber sawn in basic export-producing enterprises is considered. Roundwood export shares in the European-Uralian zone do not exceed 11 percent (except in Novgorod oblast with 14 percent), but in the Far East they comprise almost one-third, particularly in the Maritime kray (30.5 percent), Khabarovsk kray (39 percent), and Amur oblast (28 percent).

The share of exports in total output of each major commodity among exporting regions was 7 percent for roundwood (24 regions), 14 percent for plywood (18 regions), 6.5 percent for plywood (12 regions), and 27.5 percent for fiberboard (15 regions). Plywood export comprises about one-third of output in Kostroma; one-quarter in Komi and Kirov; one-fifth in Leningrad and Perm oblasts and Tatar ASSR; and at least over 10 percent in Karelia, and Bashkir ASSRs, Kalinin oblast, Krasnodar kray, and Latvia. Seventeen of the 18 plywood exporting regions identified by Kanevskiy and Shaytanov (1975) are in the European USSR. (Tyumen in Western Siberia exports 9 percent of its plywood output.)

The share of particleboard destined for export varies sharply among the twelve reporting regions (all in European-Uralian USSR). Almost one-half of the Bashkir ASSR's output is destined for export; the relative share is one-quarter in Kirov oblast, one-fifth in Lithuania, and over one-sixth in Sverdlovsk oblast. All regions but one exporting fiberboard are in Europe-Uralia. Fiberboard exports constitute nearly one-half of regional output in three regions, approximately two-fifths in five, and about one-quarter in three others. In all regions exporting this product, the export share is approximately one-tenth or greater. The only Soviet eastern region with fiberboard exports is Krasnoyarsk kray (over 40 percent).

The share exported of any commodity varies greatly among regions. For example, roundwood for export is highly significant in the Far East but not in Europe-Uralia. Lumber for export, however, has an opposite pattern and includes non-RSFSR European regions and a flow established during the First Five-Year Plan from the lower Yenisey toward the Northern Sea Route. Except for fiberboard produced in Krasnoyarsk kray, the share of sheet products destined for export clearly favors the accessible forested areas of Europe-Uralia. These patterns suggest that the regional origin of round, sawn, and sheet forest products exported is the result of a deliberate attempt by Soviet authorities to allocate the products of particular mills or groups of mills to the export market.

The relative shares of export-oriented production show less favor for heavily forested regions as we move from roundwood through lumber to the three sheet products. These products reflect greater applications of advanced technology to lower-quality roundwood and fiber; they have a greater capacity to utilize deciduous species, nondimensional roundwood, and wood waste. They seem to prefer market regions or those close to the market, and with one exception offer no justification for investment in eastern, peripheral regions. If these products, relatively new to the USSR, should increase in their overall share of domestic and export markets, then the justification for development of eastern forests would diminish even more.

The variations in shares of regional output destined for export markets attain further significance when we examine the contribution to national export made by a relatively few regions. The Northwest exports over half of all Soviet lumber (Table 7.4; Chart 7.4), and one of its oblasts, Archangel, accounts for one-third of the nation's exports. Krasnoyarsk in Eastern Siberia accounts for one-sixth, and Karelia for one-eighth. These are so-called traditional exporters in which long-established procedures and market destinations are invoked to sustain shipment patterns (Kanevskiy and Shaytanov, 1975, p. 111). Nearly half the nation's roundwood exports, however, originate in the Far East, particularly in the southern zone, which is "relatively" close to export ports in the Pacific.

Generally reliant on primary industries, this region conforms to the heartland-hinterland pattern of economic development in the USSR in which peripheral regions do not receive extensive investment in secondary industry. The Northwest also complies with this pattern. Although its processing sector is more extensively developed than in the Far East, the Northwest nevertheless comprises nearly one-third of the nation's roundwood exports. The comprehensive development of the forest-product sector in the Northwest, however, is reflected in its accounting for one-half the nation's exports of chemical pulp, paper, and paperboard, and nearly two-fifths of its fiberboard (Table 7.4 and Charts 7.5 and 7.6).

In plywood and particleboard, however, which utilize a greater share of hardwoods and waste-wood components, other regions are equally or more important to the export trade. The Center comprises one-quarter of the plywood exports, whereas the Northwest and the Urals account for one-fifth. The Ukraine supplies over one-quarter of the particleboard exports; the Urals, one-sixth; and the Volgo-Vyatka, Center, and Northwest each nearly one-tenth.

Exports from the Northwest are facilitated by the relatively short distances to Eastern and Western European markets, the major destination for most Soviet forest-sector exports, and by access to major ocean and river ports. The oceans of this region offer year-round or almost year-round ice-free conditions, and the major rivers and related canals permit combined river- and ocean-going craft to move timber directly from mills to foreign markets. The large timber and lumber port at Igarka on the Yenisey River ships to export markets by the Northern Sea Route. Igarka was established expressly for this purpose in 1929, and although the shipping season is only 3.5 to 4 months, the port is one of the largest forest-product exporters in the USSR. Other major export ports are Leningrad and Novorossiysk, and Pacific ports at Vanino (BAM access) and Vostochniy (Transsiberian port). Some border crossings facilitate direct rail export to adjacent members of CMEA. Sawmills in Karelia ASSR, and Sverdlovsk, Archangel, and Gorkiy oblasts export lumber through Leningrad. Enterprises in Perm, Kostroma, and Kirov oblasts, Komi ASSR, and Kansk in southern Krasnoyarsk kray export through Novorossiysk (Kanevskiy and Shaytanov, 1975, p. 114). Although all of these ports imply a related foreign service area, shipments to the Mediterranean, for example, are supplemented with materials moved through Leningrad, Archangel, and Igarka. Shipments from the Far East are mainly destined for Japan but may extend further afield to countries such as India in specific items such as paper (North and Solecki, 1977, p. 301).

These basic regional patterns of Soviet timber and wood-product exports are increasingly likely to be influenced by two important processes. The European-Uralian coniferous forests have undergone depredation and are increasingly unable to sustain present levels of harvesting. The BAM and AYAM railways in Eastern Siberia and the Far East are opening major portions of that region for logging, even though the principal regional forest species is larch. Although reforestation and better utilization of deciduous species in the former region would lessen the need for some logging investment in newly accessible eastern areas (discussed in Chapter 4), the extensive rail investment in the East motivated by multiple concerns other than forestry will probably be recovered in part by exports of timber. These investments also detract from the amount of

Table 7.4
Regional Origin of Exported Commodities
(% of Total Commodity Exported)

	Round wood	Lumber	Chemical Pulp	Paper/ Paper board	Plywood	Particle board	Fiber board
USSR	100.0	100.0	100.0	100.0	100.0	100.0	100.0
RSFSR	99.0	95.2	80.4	82.9	82.6	53.5	77.9
Northwest	29.5	55.9	52.2	52.8	21.1	8.8	37.2
Center	2.8	2.5			24.0	9.2	7.3
Volgo-Vyatka	6.6	6.5		11.9	6.3	9.3	8.2
Volga Littoral					8.5		
North Caucasus					1.9	9.5	
Urals	4.5	10.2	4.2	13.6	20.8	16.7	19.6
Eastern Siberia	10.0	16.8	12.6				5.6
Far East	45.6	3.3	11.4	4.6			
Belorussia	0.8	0.6			6.3	7.8	6.2
Latvia	1.4		0.3	6.7	1.4	2.2	
Lithuania			0.6		9.5	13.7	
Ukraine	0.2	0.8	2.6	0.3	3.2	27.8	
Unspecified	2.0	17.0	15.9	1.2			

Source: Compiled from Kanevskiy and Shaytanov (1975, pp. 110-11).

Chart 7.5

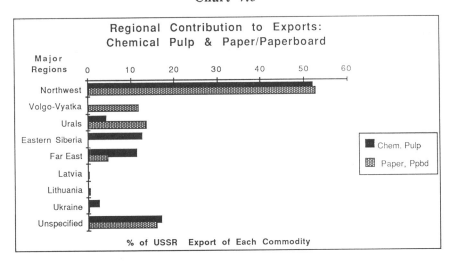

Chart 7.6

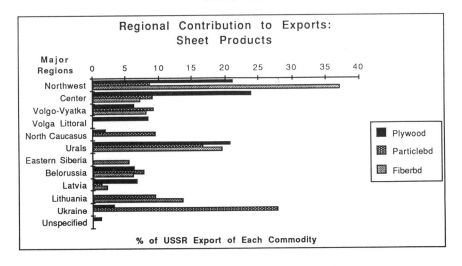

total national investment capital available for other projects such as European-Uralian reforestation and silviculture. The long rail distances to Soviet domestic and European timber markets and congestion on the major trunk rail lines will prevent large-scale shipments westward by rail.

The rate of eastern development of wood products is unlikely to ensure rapid utilization of these forests in processing. Furthermore, the westward shipment of many products would entail overloading the major rail lines, and foreign market opportunities in the Pacific have not been developed, other than Japan. Finally, the necessary expenditures to process eastern timber are not currently being made in Pacific Siberia, although various authors claimed in the 1970s that they would materialize. As Kanevskiy and Shaytanov (1975) note, increased logging in the Far East will only facilitate greater export to Japan and not resolve the general dilemmas facing Soviet timber and wood-product export unless export-dedicated processing facilities were built in the Far East. Nevertheless, given numerous developments since their analysis in 1975, we probably will witness, in the short term, greater export of roundwood, chips, and various forms of sawn timber from eastern ports, even if they are not destined solely for Pacific markets. Kanevskiy and Shaytanov (1975) state that forest-sector exports to Japan and the Pacific Basin should be generated from tributary districts east of and including Irkutsk oblast. Unfortunately, however, this basic assessment of Siberian forests sidesteps the problem of larch utilization and focuses mainly on the need to utilize major stands of pine, spruce, and fir, which are significant in the forests west of Lake Baykal. Ironically, despite the heavy emphasis paid to the BAM service area development since 1974, most of the suggestions for further expansion of the Soviet forest-product sector by Kanevskiy and Shaytanov (1975) focus on the Angara-Yenisey Basin, Tyumen oblast, and selected areas of the European North like Komi ASSR and the Pechora River Basin. Most of these would entail expansion of timber and wood-product port facilities on the Baltic and Black seas and improvements in lower Yenisey transshipment capacity.

Trade with Japan was intended by Kanevskiy and Shaytanov (1975) to justify considerable expansion of port facilities in the Far East but as Bradshaw (1986) has recently noted, the expectations have not been matched by reality. In the early 1970s, the Far East was unable to meet Japanese demand for roundwood, which in turn was supplemented with logs from other eastern regions at considerable loss in shipping costs to the USSR. Although Kanevskiy and Shaytanov (1975) do not attribute this shortcoming to the adverse species mix of many accessible Far Eastern forests, numerous reports, as discussed below, have alluded to Japanese reluctance to accept larch. In all likelihood, therefore, major coniferous logging regions of accessible Siberia and the European North will continue to be important in Soviet timber and lumber shipments in the foreseeable future. Nonlumber wood-product exports will probably continue for the remainder of this century to be met from European-Uralian regions, including those outside the RSFSR. Although we normally do not consider such regions to be well-forested, they nevertheless have well-managed forests supporting specific types of wood-processing like particleboard in the Ukraine.

TRENDS IN SOVIET FOREIGN TRADE

The goals motivating direction of Soviet trade and the ability of the Soviet Union to influence world markets are two issues which have been intensely debated in Western literature (Jensen, Shabad, and Wright, 1983). The first issue reflects the strength of Soviet ties to its CMEA trading partners and Soviet desire to expand balanced trade with hard-currency markets. The second issue pertains to the Soviet Union as price-taker or price-influencer in world commodity trade.

The regional direction of trade in forest-product exports from the USSR tends to correspond to those of most of its raw-material exports, although two traditional western markets outshine most others: Soviet lumber sales to Great Britain and log shipments to Japan. If all forest-product exports are examined in terms of that sector's share of *total* ruble value for the 1960-1984 period analyzed in this book (Chart 7.7), then a few patterns are revealed in direction and amount of trade. In exports to the West, the relative importance of forest products in export earnings has definitely been declining: in 1965, total forest product exports comprised 19.4 percent of such exports; but by 1984, they had diminished to 3.7 percent.[11] Forest products, however, still play a relatively larger role in exports to the West than to the CMEA European countries, where forest products have never accounted for more than 4 percent of Soviet exports.

A cross-product comparison of the same statistics (Table 7.5) shows that lumber, of all forest products traded with the West, has suffered most. Log exports have also diminished, but sales to Japan have supported the overall share to the West, and, as noted above, recent large sales to China have assisted the "Other" category. Thus, in 1984, Japan received almost 40 percent of Soviet exported logs; China took 12 percent; Eastern Europe, 18 percent; and Western Europe, 30 percent.

Lumber sales are concentrated in Europe, which comprised 81 percent of Soviet lumber exports in 1984 (38 percent to Eastern Europe and 43 percent to Western Europe). Outside of Europe, Egypt, Japan, and Syria are relatively small-scale purchasers of Soviet lumber.

Pulp sales likewise are concentrated in European markets: 60 percent of 1984 sales went to Eastern Europe and 26 percent to Western Europe (a complete reversal of the 1960 pattern in Europe). Cuba took about 5 percent of Soviet pulp exports.

Paper shows perhaps the most diverse and varying pattern. Europe, particularly Eastern Europe, dominates here too; its share has been increasing as that of Asian markets has declined. The Asian market share diminished by almost 50 percent over the 1960-1984 period.

The overall direction of trade in forest exports from the USSR appears to be westward to Europe, except for markets in Japan, and most recently, also in China. Some small amounts of Soviet wood products, such as birch plywood, have found their way into North American markets but do not contribute a significant share to overall exports. A few consistent "outliers" persist in Asian markets (newsprint sales to India), but the general Soviet penetration of Asian and Pacific markets has been weak.

Chart 7.7

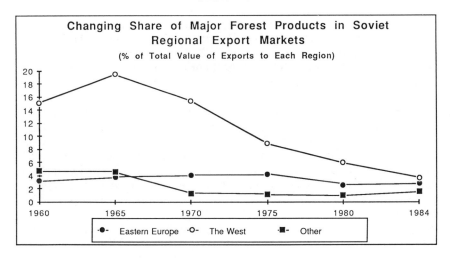

Chart 7.8

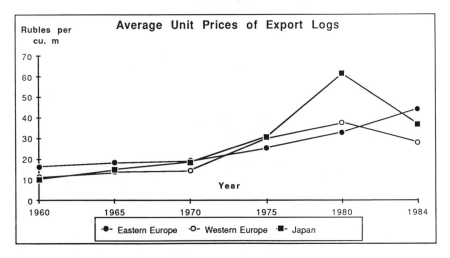

Table 7.5
Changing Importance of Four Major Forest Products in Total Soviet Export Trade (by World Region)

% of Total Exports, by Year

	1960	1965	1970	1975	1980	1984
Logs						
Eastern Europe	0.86	0.92	0.95	0.62	0.36	1.09
The West	3.10	6.85	8.52	5.66	3.02	2.03
Other	0.07	2.65	0.00	0.00	0.00	0.69
Lumber						
Eastern Europe	1.91	2.21	1.87	2.32	1.10	0.74
The West	10.40	11.28	6.34	2.88	2.49	1.32
Other	1.08	0.32	0.18	0.10	0.05	0.03
Pulp						
Eastern Europe	0.22	0.34	0.67	0.60	0.56	0.59
The West	1.44	1.03	0.44	0.24	0.40	0.32
Other	0.39	0.40	0.17	0.15	0.26	0.23
Paper						
Eastern Europe	0.19	0.35	0.58	0.67	0.57	0.44
The West	0.15	0.27	0.09	0.07	0.02	0.01
Other	3.14	1.13	1.01	0.86	0.65	0.69
These Four Products Together						
Eastern Europe	3.17	3.83	4.07	4.20	2.59	2.86
The West	15.09	19.43	15.38	8.85	5.92	3.68
Other	4.68	4.60	1.36	1.11	0.96	1.64

In the second major issue of concern here, how much does the Soviet Union influence world prices for forest products? Arthur Wright (1983) has noted that, in many markets, the Soviet Union is a price-taker, with the exception perhaps of certain strategic metals markets in which the country can exert a strong influence. Wright (1983, p. 619) concludes, however, that even in those markets, the USSR's ability to be manipulative may be exaggerated.

Comparison of Soviet export commodity price for CMEA and the West reveals some important patterns of Soviet behavior. CMEA (also called COMECON) full members consist of the USSR, Bulgaria, Cuba, Czechoslovakia, East Germany, Hungary, Mongolia, Poland, Romania, and Vietnam. As a type of customs union, prices for CMEA trade should show a different trend over time than those for hard-currency destinations. Whether the differential is to the benefit of the USSR depends on world prices and the length of bilateral agreements within CMEA. The USSR occasionally may be locked into unfavorable prices with its CMEA partners, and thereby suffers by being unable to take advantage of higher hard currency prices. On the other hand, CMEA can provide a cushion or a balancing mechanism for the USSR when world prices are unfavorable.

This adjustment-balancing exercise in prices may be assessed through examination of Soviet trade statistics for major forest commodities.[12] (The "price" term used here should more appropriately be called a "per-unit value.") The data reveal:

1.   A general upward trend in prices over time consistent with world price rises in raw materials. Logs and lumber, however, show more fluctuations than do pulp and paper exports.
2.   Changes in prices for Eastern European CMEA countries follow price rises for exports to the West, although at times they display a more steady trend line or have a slight lag (especially for lumber).

Prices of four commodities are examined here: logs, lumber, pulp, and paper.

LOGS

The average per-unit value of logs has risen from 12.19 foreign trade rubles (FTR) in 1960 to 32.65 FTR in 1984 (Table 7.6). The price rise for Eastern European CMEA nations has been steady (Chart 7.8) with Czechoslovakia paying the highest ruble prices within the bloc. Because Soviet foreign trade data do not differentiate by wood species, price variations among CMEA members are hard to ascertain. Type of wood (both in terms of species and commodity - raw logs versus pulpwood, for example) or terms of bilateral agreements may be important factors in explaining the variation.

FTR prices to Western Europe have tended to be lower than those to Eastern Europe (27.9 FTR per cu. m in 1984 versus 44.3 FTR for CMEA Europe), while FTR prices to Japan have been very favorable to the USSR, particularly with the large jump in price in 1980. Soviet roundwood (logs and pulpwood) sold to Japan, however, has been the lowest-value wood on the Japanese market (Chart 7.9). Given the direction of trade, prices may not relate to species. The

Table 7.6
Price of Soviet Log Exports by Region and Country

Rubles per cu. m

Country	1960[a]	1965	1970	1975	1980	1984
Bulgaria		19.3	20.7	29.0	31.3	48.6
Czechoslovakia	24.6	23.9	23.9	31.8	41.7	58.1
East Germany	4.0	13.7	13.6	17.3	26.1	35.4
Hungary	14.5	15.9	17.1	23.5	33.9	37.0
Poland	12.0	18.3	20.3	24.9	31.3	42.1
Eastern Europe (Total of Above)	16.3	18.2	19.1	25.3	32.8	44.3
Austria	11.0	8.0	12.6	31.0	31.4	24.2
Belgium	14.5	13.6	13.1	31.1		
Finland	8.9	10.9	10.2	21.2	21.4	23.4
France	8.4	13.4	13.0	32.8	34.9	
Great Britain	11.4	13.4	14.0	22.2	36.0	
Italy	12.1	13.6	10.8	28.8	34.6	25.0
Netherlands	15.2	18.0	13.7	35.2	35.8	
Norway	9.1	11.0	13.0			
West Berlin		22.0	30.0	38.0	69.1	39.1
West Germany	9.6	13.3	13.6	0.0		
Western Europe (Total of Above)	11.1	13.7	14.4	30.0	37.6	27.9
China	20.4	17.7				43.0
Japan	10.2	14.9	18.4	30.7	61.5	36.7
Average (of All Countries Above)	12.2	14.4	16.2	26.9	44.0	32.6

[a]Category 500, the three-digit classification for timber employed in Soviet foreign trade statistics published in annual volumes of *Vneshnyaya Torgovlya SSSR*, includes logs and *shpaly* (cross-ties or sleepers). Figures for all entries except *shpaly* are volume measures (cu. m); *shpaly* are reported as number of individual items. Entries for various subcomponents of this category employ a five-digit classification 500XX (e.g., 50001 represents sawlogs). Figures in the above table include all 500XX entries except *shpaly*.

Chart 7.9

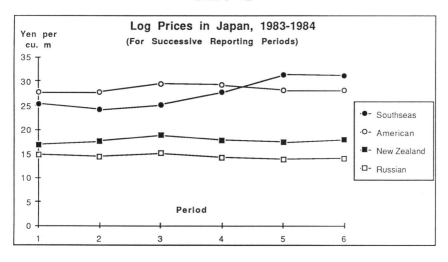

Chart 7.10

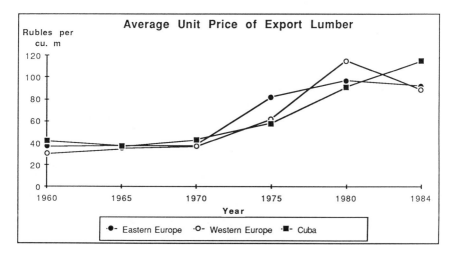

1984 sale of larch to China, for example, commanded a 43 FTR value per cu. m, equal or above the selling price of roundwood to Europe, which comprised species surely of more value than larch (the regional origin of exports to Europe is dominated by the Northwest [Chart 7.4], which is not a producer of larch).

Data series available from Japan showing prices in yen allow comparison of Soviet timber prices with those for logs from the United States, Southseas, and New Zealand (Chart 7.9). For three quarterly periods in each of 1983 and 1984, the *Japan Lumber Journal* reported that prices for Russian logs were the lowest among all Japanese log imports and had the least fluctuation. Longer-term agreements with Japan lock the Soviet Union into price ranges in a similar style to that of its trade with CMEA. The Japanese hard-currency market, purchases of technology by the USSR, and economic benefits for the Far East probably outweigh any unfavorable aspects of inflexibility in prices. The opportunity cost of Japanese sales is also much lower because logs originating in the Soviet Far East are almost entirely destined for markets in Japan or for some domestic long hauls. (The recent sales to China apparently consisted of wood that could not be marketed to Japan.)

The process for determining prices of Soviet roundwood exports to Japan occurs under the auspices of longer-term trade agreements, necessitating periodic meetings to set quarterly prices and quantities. Price discussions generally reflect not only a Soviet push which encourages Japan to purchase the maximum wood agreed to in the long-term general arrangements, but also frequent Japanese resistance due to poor markets in Japan. This tug-of-war, reported regularly in the *Japan Lumber Journal*, results in considerable price haggling by the Soviet Union. In some cases, the USSR has even agreed to a rebate system based on fluctuations in the yen-dollar exchange rate, thus abolishing the previous fixed exchange rate (*Japan Lumber Journal*, 15 January 1983, pp. 8-9).

LUMBER

Lumber prices (shown for the key study years in Table 7.7, but reported for 15 separate years in Chart 7.10) have been rising since 1960. Prices for Western Europe (Chart 7.10) have generally been more erratic than those for CMEA Europe, although the latter have taken jumps with a lag (usually of one year) after price rises in Western European markets. The 1983-1984 period showed a downward movement of lumber prices, but those to Western Europe began to rise again in 1984.

Because the European comparisons exclude the non-European members of CMEA, Chart 7.10 compares lumber prices for Western Europe with those to Cuba. Although Cuban prices also rise through the period, fluctuations are weaker than for Western Europe. The lower prices enjoyed by Cuba after 1972, however, disappeared in the early 1980s, and Cuba was locked into a higher price despite the drop in prices to Europe which occurred in 1983 and 1984.

Lumber prices in the Japanese market (in yen) for 1983 and 1984 (Chart 7.11) reflect the same steadiness as Soviet log prices as well as a lower value than that of other Japanese lumber imports.

Table 7.7
Unit Prices of Lumber Exports, 1960-1984
(Selected Years)

Average Ruble Price per cu. m

Country	1960[a]	1965	1970	1975	1980	1984
Bulgaria	38.7	39.2	38.6	73.8	95.6	126.7
Czechoslovakia	38.4	38.5	45.5	87.0	106.6	133.2
East Germany	36.7	38.5	38.6	83.6	95.6	111.8
Hungary	36.2	35.9	37.6	78.9	96.7	123.4
Poland	0.0	40.4	39.3	86.6	102.9	130.3
Rumania	0.0					135.1
Eastern Europe (Total of Above)	37.0	37.9	38.7	82.0	96.9	125.2
Belgium	34.0	39.5	37.5	50.0	123.0	88.5
Denmark	29.2	32.5	33.8	58.0	102.3	91.0
Finland	0.0	11.4	9.7			
France	33.0	38.2	37.8	63.0	124.0	87.0
Great Britain	30.1	35.0	35.5	64.0	127.9	92.8
Greece	33.1	33.1	38.2	70.0	121.0	91.4
Iceland	0.0		45.0		128.0	107.9
Ireland	0.0			54.0	128.0	92.8
Italy	30.9	31.0	35.5	54.0	117.0	91.0
Netherlands	29.8	35.9	37.9	63.0	121.0	78.7
Spain	36.6	40.4	30.5	62.0	127.7	91.2
Switzerland	0.0	27.6				
West Berlin	0.0	31.2			124.0	93.1
West Germany	30.9	34.0	36.8	60.0	111.0	86.3
Yugoslavia	0.0	41.5	39.1	77.4	112.9	112.1
Western Europe (Total of Above)	30.5	35.2	36.9	61.9	115.1	88.4
Total for Eastern and Western European Countries Above	32.7	36.3	37.3	72.3	110.5	91.0
Vietnam					43.6	126.4
Jordan		30.0	34.0		123.0	107.0
Iraq	30.6	30.8	48.4	90.0		
Iran	49.8	46.8	47.9	110.0	126.3	
Yemen Democratic Republic			29.3		86.4	
Kuwait		34.7	35.0		125.1	107.0
Lebanon	28.3	26.0	32.1	65.0	103.0	94.3
Saudi Arabia		30.0		63.0	113.4	105.4
Syria	33.3	33.0	36.9	88.0	140.0	125.2
Japan		26.3	33.2	42.1	96.0	52.0
Algeria	34.5	35.0	45.0		150.0	
Egypt	39.3	35.9	37.8	89.6	182.2	167.0
Libya	31.4	32.0	39.4		111.4	
Morocco	27.5	30.0	39.5		125.0	98.3
Cyprus	33.8	34.9	38.3			106.3
Tunisia	32.7	36.7	40.0	85.0	135.0	120.9
Somalia		31.7	54.1			
Sudan	32.5	32.0	52.0			
Cuba	41.8	37.0	43.0	58.0	91.0	114.4
Turkey	40.0					
Australia	40.8	23.9				
Total Non-European	33.0	34.5	37.7	72.5	112.6	96.5

[a]Averages for the regions Eastern Europe, Western Europe, Total Europe, and Total Non-European are computed by regional totals, not by the average prices of lumber exports to their individual constituent countries.

Chart 7.11

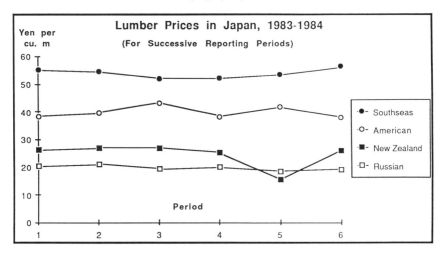

Chart 7.12

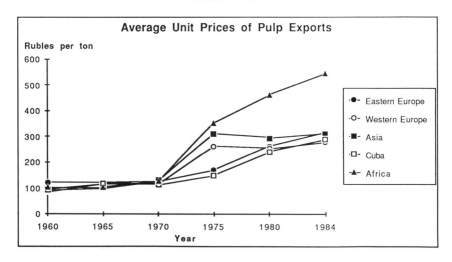

PULP

Pulp prices analyzed here (Table 7.8 and Chart 7.12) are a weighted average of sulphite and sulphate pulps, although the former tends to have a 10 to 15 percent higher value per unit. Egypt pays the highest ruble price for pulp (sulphate) of any country, while exports to Western Europe again tend to be lowest of all. CMEA Europe in 1975 enjoyed lower pulp prices than Western Europe, an advantage which has now disappeared, and Cuban prices appear to be subsidized by the rest of CMEA.

PAPER

Regional patterns for paper prices (Table 7.9) are most difficult to evaluate because of the variety in types of paper (per-unit value of newsprint, for example, is half that of most other exported papers), and because paper sales are geographically more wide-ranging than those for the other three commodities discussed above. Chart 7.13 (comparing four countries - three in CMEA and one in Western Europe) shows that traditional customers in Western Europe (France, Netherlands, and West Germany) have enjoyed lower paper prices than those in CMEA or among the lesser-developed countries. Pulp and paper prices in part are affected by the barter agreements made for the Siberian complexes. Cuba's paper imports from the USSR, however, consisted of approximately 40 percent newsprint in 1984, which lowered the apparent prices.

CMEA EUROPE AND THE WEST

Edward Hewett (1983, p. 657) concluded that the opportunity costs of Soviet exports to CMEA countries rose "dramatically" with the rise in world prices for raw materials. This may be more apparent for exports such as petroleum than for forest products, but evidence does suggest that the USSR would prefer to sell wood products for hard currency than for other forms of compensation.

Comparison of forest-product export shares (by quantity) within CMEA Europe, and among major countries and regions served by the USSR, shows that

1. Log purchases within Eastern Europe for 1960 and 1984 reveal that Hungary continues to play a dominant role, and that Romania has not yet emerged as a Soviet market (Charts 7.14 and 7.15).

2. Non-East European shares have become more consolidated since 1960, with strong growth in purchases by Japan, China (recently), and Finland (Charts 7.16 and 7.17).

3. Eastern Europe dominated log exports by quantity share in 1960 (Chart 7.18), but the onset of large sales to Japan by about 1965 started to shift the proportions. Western Europe's share is between that of Eastern Europe and Japan.

4. Log exports play a relatively greater role in trade to the West (Table 7.10) than to CMEA Europe. This is consistent with the overall pattern for forest

Table 7.8
Unit Prices of Pulp Exports, 1960-1984
(Selected Years)

Average Ruble Price per Ton

Country	1960	1965	1970	1975	1980	1984
Bulgaria	143.5	148.4	118.7	161.1	219.9	306.5
Czechoslovakia	0.0	110.2	124.4	182.3	255.8	331.7
East Germany	99.7	105.8	127.2	180.3	261.5	314.8
Hungary	119.8	124.1	118.1	167.3	246.6	302.4
Poland	0.0	0.0	126.0	165.4	260.0	308.4
Rumania	0.0	0.0	143.0		332.0	329.0
Eastern Europe (Total of Above)	121.0	122.1	126.2	171.3	262.6	315.5
Yugoslavia	0.0	0.0	0.0	299.0	321.4	0.0
Austria	95.0	0.0	0.0		298.9	286.2
Belgium	60.9	0.0	0.0		0.0	0.0
France	77.0	98.5	116.6	251.9	274.5	291.6
Great Britain	87.5	106.7	118.1	259.9	274.3	277.5
Greece	93.7	0.0	0.0		0.0	0.0
Italy	85.5	106.2	118.2	252.6	297.3	266.2
Netherlands	0.0	190.8	0.0		0.0	0.0
West Germany	90.9	108.0	110.4	240.8	28.3	285.2
Western Europe (Total of Above)	84.8	119.3	116.6	261.5	252.3	280.0
Sri Lanka	111.7	89.0	135.5	355.1	0.0	0.0
India	69.7	110.1	0.0		0.0	0.0
Japan	0.0	0.0	125.4	266.0	0.0	0.0
Thailand	0.0	0.0	0.0		293.2	0.0
Turkey	0.0	0.0	0.0		0.0	311.6
Asia (Total of Above)	90.7	99.5	130.5	310.6	293.2	311.6
Cuba	93.3	115.7	112.7	150.3	241.6	287.7
Egypt	114.6	104.7	127.1	353.3	461.5	544.0
Morocco	90.9	0.0	0.0		0.0	0.0
Africa (Total of Above Two)	102.7	104.7	127.1	353.3	461.5	544.0

Table 7.9
Unit Prices of Paper Exports, 1960-1984
(Selected Years)

Rubles per Ton

Country	1960	1965	1970	1975	1980	1984
Bulgaria	159.9	164.2	146.5	179.7	269.0	350.8
Czechoslovakia	581.7	408.7	105.8	214.4	325.2	444.6
East Germany	135.8	148.0	141.0	178.6	258.6	322.3
Hungary	124.9	138.5	134.9	161.7	272.1	343.9
Poland			132.7	172.5	257.7	361.1
Rumania			123.1	160.0	208.1	307.4
Eastern Europe (Total of Above)	250.6	214.8	130.7	177.8	265.1	355.0
Yugoslavia	114.3	121.2	83.8	172.7	591.7	382.3
Albania	132.0					
Austria				153.4		
Belgium	94.3	101.7	102.3	229.3	283.1	
France	115.5		79.4	238.8	253.3	186.7
Greece	107.1					
Netherlands	103.1		70.0	182.3	180.0	150.0
Sweden		206.8				
W. Germany			114.3	164.9	199.7	137.1
Western Europe[a] (Total of Above)	111.0	143.2	90.0	190.2	301.6	214.0
Afghanistan	160.0	213.3	208.6	372.4	348.5	446.5
Mongolia	214.4	196.8	185.5	185.9	273.9	391.8
Cambodia	148.0	206.9				
Sri Lanka		105.0		336.5		
India	128.1	113.4	121.9	275.7	278.3	351.2
Indonesia	120.4	117.3	107.0			
Iran	140.0	147.8	119.5	286.8	308.3	
Iraq	122.5	120.0				
Japan			111.3			
Laos					358.0	
North Korea	194.2	211.7	231.6	184.0	262.1	315.4
Pakistan						230.7
Thailand	120.3	98.8	99.2		305.8	186.7
Turkey	116.0		121.1		279.8	
Vietnam		187.1	1530.0	118.0	201.9	456.1
Asia (Total of Above)	146.4	156.2	283.6	251.3	282.3	342.0
Cuba	130.5	136.2	136.8	169.4	234.6	318.5
Argentina	112.5	105.4				
Nicaragua				300.1		384.9
Egypt	156.4	136.6	124.5	317.6	437.0	459.8
Tunisia		100.0	114.3			

[a]Yugoslavia and Albania are included in Western Europe here.

Chart 7.13

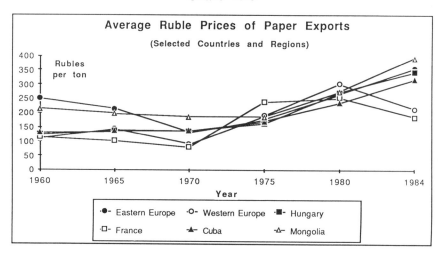

Chart 7.14

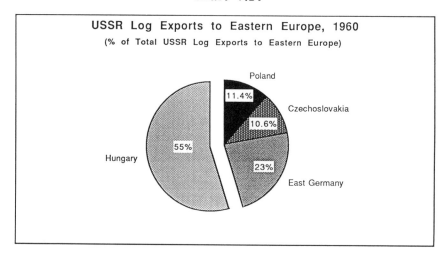

Chart 7.15

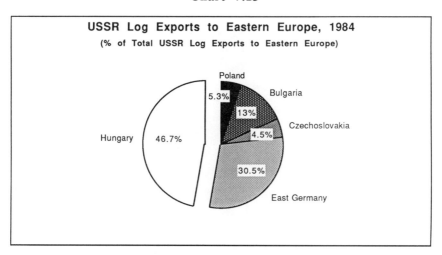

Chart 7.16

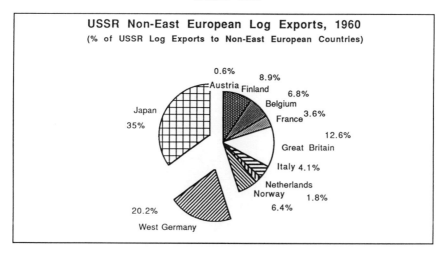

Chart 7.17

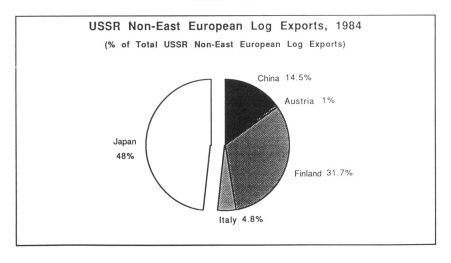

Chart 7.18

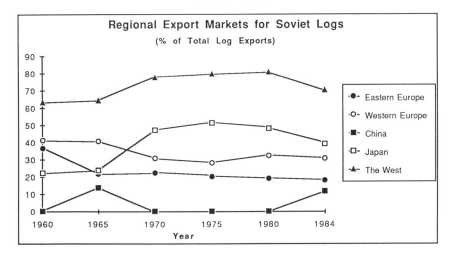

Table 7.10
USSR Log Exports by Major Markets, 1960-1984
(% of Total Log Exports)

Country	1960[a]	1965	1970	1975	1980	1984
Bulgaria	0.0	0.6	2.6	2.4	2.4	2.3
Czechoslovakia	3.9	1.5	1.4	1.2	1.0	0.8
East Germany	8.4	6.8	6.0	5.7	5.2	5.5
Hungary	20.1	11.3	10.2	9.7	9.1	8.4
Poland	4.2	1.5	2.1	1.3	1.5	1.0
Eastern Europe (Total of Above)	36.6	21.7	22.3	20.3	19.3	18.0
Austria	0.3	1.0	2.1	0.1	2.7	0.8
Belgium	4.3	2.7	3.4	0.3	0.0	0.0
Finland	5.6	18.3	11.4	22.0	22.6	26.0
France	2.3	2.8	4.8	1.5	2.2	0.0
Great Britain	7.9	6.9	2.3	1.0	0.4	0.0
Italy	2.6	1.2	3.7	2.8	4.0	3.9
Netherlands	1.2	0.6	1.1	0.5	0.5	0.0
Norway	4.1	3.7	0.3	0.0	0.0	0.0
West Berlin	0.0	0.1	0.1	0.0	0.1	0.1
West Germany	12.8	3.1	1.5	0.1	0.0	0.0
Western Europe (Total of Above)	41.1	40.5	30.6	28.3	32.6	30.8
China	0.2	13.9	0.0	0.0	0.0	11.9
Japan	22.1	23.9	47.1	51.3	48.2	39.3
The West[b]	63.2	64.4	77.7	79.7	80.7	70.1
Total	100.0	100.0	100.0	100.0	100.0	100.0

[a]Category 500, the three-digit classification for timber employed in Soviet foreign trade statistics published in annual volumes of *Vneshnyaya Torgovlya SSSR*, includes logs and *shpaly* (cross-ties or sleepers). Figures for all entries except *shpaly* are volume measures (cu. m); *shpaly* are reported as number of individual items. Entries for various subcomponents of this category employ a five-digit classification 500XX (e.g., 50001 represents sawlogs). Figures in the above table include all 500XX entries except *shpaly*.

[b]The West includes Western Europe and Japan.

products shown in Chart 7.7. Over time, however, their relative importance for Western trade with the USSR has declined severely.

Actual export of roundwood from the European-Uralian RSFSR may occasionally be inhibited because of reliance on ports which can only remain open eight months (Archangel) or three to four months (Igarka). Archangel, the main port for shipping wood to Western Europe, moves up to 1.8 million cu. m annually (Eronen, 1983).

Europe plays a large role as a consumer of Soviet *lumber*; 81.4 percent (by quantity) is sold to Eastern and Western Europe (Table 7.11 and Chart 7.19). Within the total European "pie," Western Europe tends to be a larger consumer, except for the banner harvest year of 1975, when East German lumber purchases in particular took a large jump. Within Western Europe, Great Britain has remained the largest customer for Soviet lumber sales. The pattern noted above for logs is repeated in Chart 7.19: lumber plays a relatively greater (but nevertheless declining) role in Western European markets than in Eastern European markets.

Relative shares of *pulp* exports within Eastern Europe for 1984 (Chart 7.20) compared to log purchases, are more evenly divided among the CMEA members. In non-CMEA European markets (Chart 7.21), France, Yugoslavia and Great Britain play the largest roles. Europe definitely dominates international Soviet pulp consumption - it comprised 92 percent of the market (by quantity) in 1984 (Table 7.12). The split of this large market share within Europe (East versus West) (Chart 7.22) shows that the two macro regions exhibited opposite trends over the study period, and provided a complementary relationship in Soviet pulp sales. The remaining percentage of pulp sales (Chart 7.23) is mainly accounted for by India, Sri Lanka, Cuba, and Egypt. Unlike logs and lumber, however, pulp exports have not played a relatively more significant share as a proportion of total exports by value to Western Europe (Chart 7.24); their more significant share of the CMEA European market has prevailed since 1970.

Paper exports (Table 7.13) are dominated in Europe by the CMEA bloc whose share was 66 percent in 1984. This dominance has been consistent over the study period (Chart 7.25). East Germany and Hungary are the major paper purchasers within this bloc. Asian and Western-hemispheric markets have been stronger over the study period than those in Western Europe. (Cuban purchases of newsprint and other papers within CMEA present a strong share of the Western-hemispheric total.) Thus, in paper as in pulp, export to the West is fairly small.

JAPAN AND OTHER PACIFIC MARKETS

Soviet trade in forest products to Pacific markets has mainly been limited to Japan, with a few exceptions. China, which was an early trading partner for Soviet wood, recently re-entered the market with a large purchase of Soviet roundwood in 1984. The wood represented an accumulation of unsold stock in Eastern Siberia, probably larch, that the Soviet Union was unable to sell to Japan.[13] The Chinese market may prove to be good for Siberian larch because of

Table 7.11
USSR Lumber Exports, by Country and Region, 1960-1984
(Selected Years)

% of Total USSR Lumber Exports

Country	1960	1965	1970	1975	1980	1984
Bulgaria	3.1	1.4	2.4	2.9	2.5	2.5
Czechoslovakia	3.6	2.1	1.9	2.2	1.6	2.0
East Germany	14.7	16.6	18.1	24.2	19.2	19.3
Hungary	7.4	8.1	11.7	13.5	9.4	9.7
Poland	0.0	2.0	3.1	2.8	2.7	2.0
Rumania	0.0	0.0	0.0	0.0	0.0	2.9
Eastern Europe (Total of Above)	28.7	30.2	37.2	45.5	35.4	38.4
Belgium	4.0	3.0	2.9	3.0	3.4	2.9
Denmark	1.4	1.8	0.8	0.7	1.3	1.2
Finland	0.0	5.9	0.0	0.0	0.0	0.0
France	1.9	3.1	4.0	2.3	5.3	2.5
Great Britain	36.2	27.5	22.5	16.0	14.9	16.0
Greece	3.1	2.2	1.5	0.9	0.7	0.7
Iceland	0.0	0.0	0.1	0.0	0.3	0.2
Ireland	0.0	0.0	0.0	0.2	0.2	0.2
Italy	2.7	3.8	4.3	5.3	6.2	5.3
Netherlands	6.9	3.7	2.6	2.4	3.1	3.3
Spain	0.4	0.3	0.8	0.8	1.2	1.4
Switzerland	0.0	0.0	0.0	0.0	0.0	0.0
West Berlin	0.0	0.1	0.0	0.0	0.2	0.2
West Germany	5.7	6.3	5.9	6.4	7.8	7.3
Yugoslavia	0.0	0.6	1.3	0.6	1.6	1.8
Western Europe (Total of Above)	62.3	58.3	46.7	38.4	46.2	43.0
Total for Eastern and Western European Countries Above	91.1	88.5	83.9	84.0	81.7	81.4
Algeria	0.6	0.3	1.8	0.0	1.5	0.0
Cyprus	0.2	0.3	0.4	0.0	0.0	0.4
Egypt	3.8	3.7	4.2	4.8	3.1	4.6
Libya	0.0	0.1	0.1	0.0	0.1	0.0
Morocco	0.3	0.2	0.5	0.0	0.8	0.6
Somalia	0.0	0.0	0.0	0.0	0.0	0.0
Sudan	0.6	0.1	0.2	0.0	0.0	0.0
Tunisia	0.2	0.6	0.5	0.3	0.7	1.2
Africa (Total of Above)	5.8	5.2	7.8	5.2	6.2	6.9
Iran	0.7	0.4	0.6	0.8	1.0	0.0
Iraq	0.8	0.7	0.5	0.9	0.0	0.0
Japan	0.0	0.5	1.1	1.3	2.0	2.0
Jordan	0.0	0.2	0.2	0.0	0.5	0.0
Kuwait	0.0	0.1	0.1	0.0	0.1	0.1
Lebanon	0.9	0.9	1.0	0.7	0.1	1.0
Saudi Arabia	0.0	0.2	0.0	0.4	1.6	0.2
Syria	0.6	0.6	0.8	0.9	0.7	1.8
Vietnam	0.0	0.0	0.0	0.0	0.1	0.3
Yemen Democratic Republic	0.0	0.0	0.0	0.0	0.4	0.0
Asia (Total of Above)	3.0	3.4	4.4	5.1	6.4	5.5
Cuba	0.2	2.9	3.8	5.8	5.8	6.1
Total	100.0	100.0	100.0	100.0	100.0	100.0

Chart 7.19

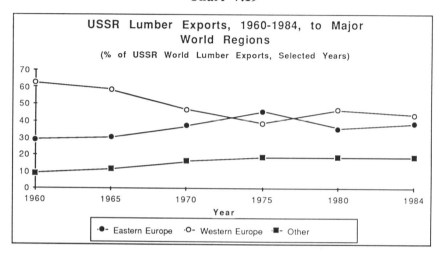

Chart 7.20

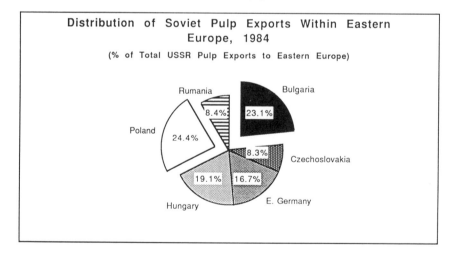

Chart 7.21

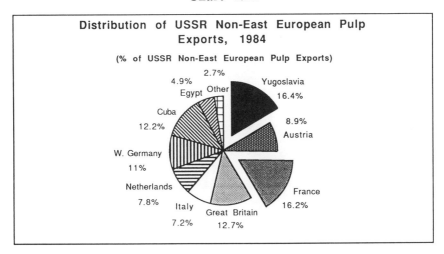

Chart 7.22

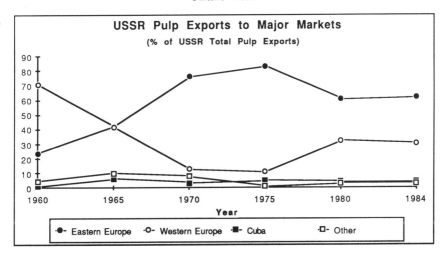

Table 7.12
USSR Pulp Exports, 1960-1984
(Selected Years)

% of Total USSR Pulp Exports

Country	1960	1965	1970	1975	1980	1984
Bulgaria	6.4	9.0	14.8	14.0	15.1	14.4
Czechoslovakia	0.0	4.5	8.9	10.9	6.5	5.1
East Germany	11.3	17.4	16.2	15.1	10.8	10.4
Hungary	6.1	11.0	20.3	19.3	10.9	11.9
Poland	0.0	0.0	13.4	23.8	15.8	15.1
Rumania	0.0	0.0	2.3	0.0	1.3	5.2
Eastern Europe (Total of Above)	23.8	42.0	76.0	83.1	60.5	62.1
Yugoslavia	0.0	0.0	0.0	1.6	9.1	6.2
Austria	0.1	0.0	0.0	0.0	4.0	3.4
Belgium	1.5	0.0	0.0	0.0	0.0	0.0
France	19.2	5.0	4.3	4.4	6.9	6.1
Great Britain	37.0	16.0	1.7	1.0	0.7	4.8
Greece	1.2	0.0	0.0	0.0	0.0	0.0
Italy	7.3	7.0	3.4	1.9	4.3	2.7
Netherlands	0.2	0.1	0.9	0.2	1.3	3.0
Sweden	0.0	6.6	0.0	0.0	0.0	0.0
West Germany	4.3	7.0	2.6	1.9	6.0	4.1
Western Europe (Total of Above)	70.7	41.7	12.9	10.9	32.3	30.4
Sri Lanka	0.5	1.0	0.5	0.3	0.0	0.0
India	1.7	7.9	0.0	0.0	0.0	0.0
Japan	0.0	0.0	5.2	0.3	0.0	0.0
Thailand	0.0	0.0	0.0	0.0	1.0	0.0
Turkey	0.0	0.0	0.0	0.0	0.0	0.5
Asia (Total of Above)	2.3	8.9	5.6	0.6	1.0	0.5
Cuba	1.1	6.2	3.3	4.9	4.2	4.6
Egypt	2.1	1.1	2.2	0.5	2.1	1.9
Morocco	0.1	0.0	0.0	0.0	0.0	0.0
Africa and Other (Total of Above)	2.2	1.1	2.2	0.5	2.1	2.4
Total	100.0	100.0	100.0	100.0	100.0	100.0

Chart 7.23

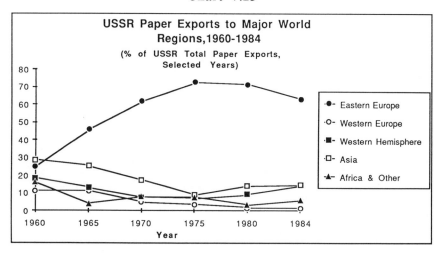

Chart 7.24

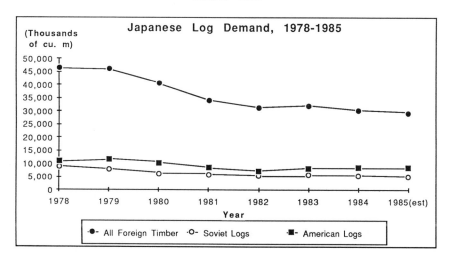

Chart 7.25

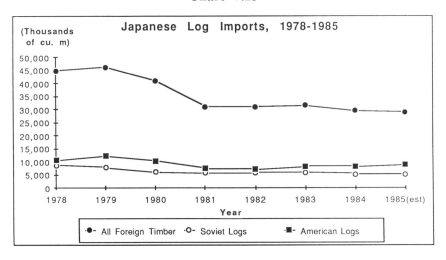

Chart 7.26

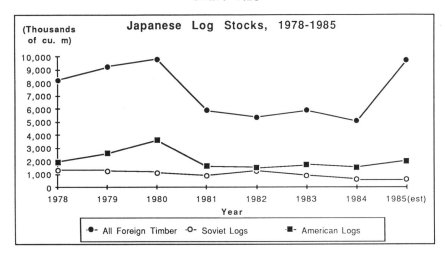

its potential complementarity and its proximity. Larch at this time is used mainly for communications infrastructure (rails and telephone poles), and Chinese economic expansion may require such Soviet timber under favorable trade conditions. On the other hand, continued trade may presuppose both a thaw in Sino-Soviet relations, lack of market expansion for larch in Japan, and lack of intervening opportunities in the Pacific. Trade statistics from South Korea suggest that Japanese firms may be reselling Soviet wood in South Korea, thereby creating an indirect additional Pacific trade pattern for the Soviet Union, one that could not be publicly acknowledged.[14]

Other opportunities for the USSR in the Pacific have not emerged, but sales of paper to some Asian markets, such as India, continue. The major Pacific market, therefore, is Japan. Soviet plans for Pacific trade in wood from Eastern Siberia and the Far East appear contingent on that country's continued participation in the Japanese market. In many senses, the USSR has been fairly successful in infiltrating the Japanese market (Table 7.13), although the same obstacles common to all sellers in Japan have been encountered: protection for home industries and strict production standards which skew imports toward primary products. The ability of the USSR to continue its foothold in Japan's market for logs, pulpwood, and chips is not certain. Constraints on Soviet maintenance or expansion of the market in Japan include: competition from North American, Southsea, and New Zealand timber; willingness of the Japanese government to continue bilateral umbrella agreements; Japanese satisfaction with quality of Soviet wood exports and prices; continued supply of desirable species from the Soviet Far East; and a technological breakthrough in the efficient use of larch.

The USSR appears to have created a role for itself as the low pricer of timber sellers to Japan; Soviet sales tend to consist of the lowest price species (Chart 7.9). A factor which might contribute to Soviet success is the decrease in wood supply from the Southseas (Philippines, Indonesia, and Malaysia) due to the deforestation of their tropical forests, and hence a decline in their forest industries (*World Wood*, February 1984). Japanese plywood manufacturers in fact have already begun a process of "delauanization" to decrease reliance on Southsea wood sources. The total decline in overall Japanese demand has apparently affected imports of Russian logs more than American, although stocks of American logs have also remained higher (Charts 7.24 to 7.26). In 1984, the USSR comprised 18 percent of the Japanese timber market, the USA 37 percent, and the Southseas 44 percent. The Soviet share had increased by 3.3 percent from 1980 but that of the United States was 9.6 percent greater (*Japan Lumber Journal*, 5 May 1982, pp. 4-5; 20 January 1985, p. 9).

Although trade is conducted under the auspices of the "K-S" agreements (the Japan-USSR Forest Resource Development Project with an acronym stemming from the first letter of the surnames of its principal negotiators), periodic meetings still determine prices and actual amounts of timber purchased within the general guidelines. As discussed in Chapter 8, the third K-S agreement, 1981-1986, provided for Soviet export of 13.3 million cu. m of timber to Japan during the period. Reports about the meetings to set purchase quotas and prices suggest that the USSR has complained of Japan's failure to purchase the required amount of timber during a market recession, although Japan has at times

Table 7.13
USSR Paper Exports, 1960-1984
(Selected Years)

% of USSR Paper Exports

Country	1960[a]	1965	1970	1975	1980	1984
Bulgaria	10.6	13.8	10.8	9.5	12.3	9.5
Czechoslovakia	1.0	0.7	9.6	6.9	5.5	4.7
East Germany	7.5	15.4	22.3	23.5	23.9	21.6
Hungary	6.0	16.1	10.4	18.0	15.2	14.6
Poland	0.0	0.0	7.0	12.8	10.4	8.8
Rumania	0.0	0.0	1.9	1.9	4.2	3.8
Eastern Europe (Total of Above)	5.0	46.1	61.9	72.6	71.5	63.1
Albania	1.2	0.0	0.0	0.0	0.0	0.0
Yugoslavia	1.1	3.7	1.8	2.5	0.1	0.0
Austria	0.0	0.0	0.0	0.2	0.0	0.0
Belgium	1.7	2.3	0.9	0.4	0.2	0.0
France	3.3	0.0	1.3	0.4	0.2	0.0
Greece	2.9	0.0	0.0	0.0	0.0	0.0
Netherlands	1.1	0.0	0.2	0.0	0.5	0.1
Sweden	0.0	5.3	0.0	0.0	0.0	0.0
W. Germany	0.0	0.0	0.7	0.2	0.5	1.4
Western Europe (Total of Above)	11.3	11.3	4.9	3.6	1.6	1.5
Cuba	16.9	12.0	7.7	6.7	9.5	13.8
Argentina	1.6	1.2	0.0	0.0	0.0	0.0
Nicaragua	0.0	0.0	0.0	0.0	0.0	0.9
Peru	0.0	0.0	0.0	0.3	0.0	0.0
Western Hemisphere (Total of Above)	18.5	13.2	7.7	7.1	9.5	14.6
Afghanistan	0.2	0.3	0.1	0.1	0.4	0.3
Cambodia	0.4	0.1	0.0	0.0	0.0	0.0
Sri Lanka	0.0	0.7	0.0	0.2	0.0	0.0
China	0.1	0.2	0.0	0.0	0.0	0.0
India	12.6	13.8	8.8	4.8	7.3	8.6
Indonesia	4.0	3.3	0.2	0.0	0.0	0.0
Iran	1.3	1.1	1.7	1.6	1.4	0.0
Iraq	0.3	0.0	0.0	0.0	0.0	0.0
Japan	0.0	0.0	0.5	0.0	0.0	0.0
Laos	0.0	0.0	0.0	0.0	0.2	0.1
Mongolia	1.5	2.5	1.1	1.1	1.3	0.9
North Korea	2.9	1.2	0.5	0.7	0.8	1.1

Pakistan	0.0	0.0	0.0	0.0	0.0	0.4
Thailand	2.7	1.2	1.5	0.0	0.6	1.8
Turkey	2.9	0.0	2.9	0.0	0.7	0.0
Vietnam	0.0	1.0	0.1	0.3	1.4	1.7
Asia (Total of Above)	28.9	25.4	17.5	9.0	14.2	14.9
Egypt	8.1	3.5	3.9	3.4	1.7	2.8
Tunisia	0.0	0.0	0.3	0.0	0.0	0.0
Africa	8.1	3.5	4.2	3.4	1.7	2.8
Other	8.2	0.6	3.8	4.3	1.5	3.0
Africa and Other (Total of Above)	16.3	4.1	8.0	7.7	3.2	5.9
Total of All Above (excluding Other)	91.8	99.4	96.2	95.7	98.5	97.0
Total	100.0	100.0	100.0	100.0	100.0	100.0

[a]Category 500, the three-digit classification for timber employed in Soviet foreign trade statistics published in annual volumes of *Vneshnyaya Torgovlya SSSR*, includes logs and *shpaly* (cross-ties or sleepers). Figures for all entries except *shpaly* are volume measures (cu. m); *shpaly* are reported as number of individual items. Entries for various subcomponents of this category employ a five-digit classification 500XX (e.g., 50001 represents sawlogs). Figures in the above table include all 500XX entries except *shpaly*.

---

increased its purchases of other foreign timber. Delegates from the Lumber Importers Association of Japan, in turn, have complained about the quality of wood being exported from the USSR (*Japan Lumber Journal,* 5 May 1982, pp. 11-12).

Such complaints about quality reflect the changing composition of Soviet timber sales to Japan, particularly the greater shares of smaller diameter wood and larch. The Japanese in 1983 requested an 18 cm minimum diameter size on logs from the USSR and asked that shipments from Soviet ports be based on species assortment, rather than on random mixtures. Shipments have often arrived with a much larger mixture of larch and a smaller share of other coniferous species than agreed upon by Japanese importers (*Japan Lumber Journal,* 15 January 1983, pp. 8-9).

When the 1965-1980 exports of logs to Japan based on species breakdown (available through Japanese, not Soviet, trade statistics) are separated into large- and small-diameter timber (Charts 7.27 and 7.28), the predominance of larch in small diameter sales is apparent. In the 1961-1965 period, fir comprised 61 percent of log exports from the USSR to Japan, and larch 21 percent. By 1981, larch bypassed fir exports to Japan: the share of fir had fallen to 30 percent, and that of larch reached 33 percent (*Japan Lumber Journal,* 28 February 1982, p. 29). Larch has been priced very low by the Soviet Union (Charts 7.29 and 7.30) but still has enjoyed some price rises between 1985 and 1986 after a decline beween 1982 and 1985.

Because ever greater amounts of larch appear to be arriving from the USSR, Japan has recently attempted to achieve technological breakthroughs in its use.

Chart 7.27

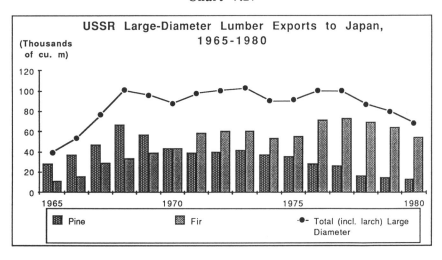

Chart 7.28

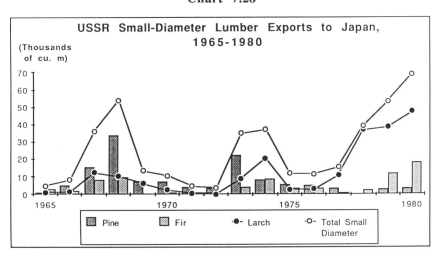

Chart 7.29

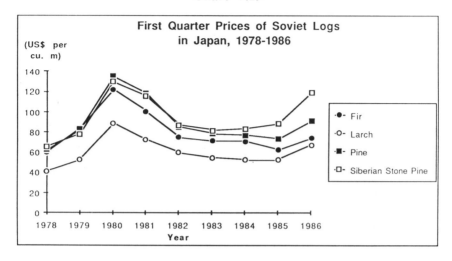

Chart 7.30

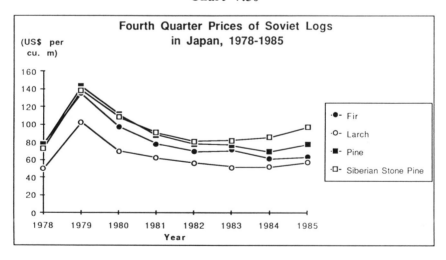

Normally, the high resin content of the wood depreciates equipment too quickly to make larch profitable for use as anything other than minimally processed items, such as poles. Akita Plywood Company in Japan began test production in 1982 of plywood made from Russian larch and lauan veneer. Hayashi Veneer Industries also began construction of a mill for manufacturing plywood from Russian larch. Hayashi reported that, once the technical difficulties were solved, 54,000 pieces of Russian larch substituted for 350,000 pieces of lauan sheets to produce the same monthly plywood volume, an attractive substitution given the low price of larch (*Japan Lumber Journal,* 11 November 1982, p. 14). By 1985, the Japan Plywood Manufacturers' Association began testing plywood made from Russian larch, as well as from some Soviet deciduous species - birch, poplar, and aspen (*Japan Lumber Journal,* 31 October 1985, p. 14). Results of the tests may determine the likelihood of continued exploitation of the Eastern Siberian larch forest (including that along the BAM railroad) for Japanese markets. Hayashi meanwhile has already begun marketing larch plywood in Japan.[15]

For some Japanese customers, the diameter of roundwood ceases to be a problem if the wood is first chipped. The USSR in 1984 exported chips worth almost 10 million FTR to Japan. The first agreement on Japanese import of Soviet chips and pulpwood expired in 1981, and a new agreement was signed to cover the 1986-1996 period (although chip and pulpwood imports has continued without the agreement being in effect). Japan promised to import 8.2 million cu. m of chips and 3 million cu. m of pulpwood during the new agreement.

The 1986 prices of woodchips from the USSR in Japan were set at US$110 per bone dry unit (BDU) for fir and pine, and US$91 for larch and Siberian stone pine. Douglas fir chips from the United States, sold in Japan at US$79, reflected the decline in chip prices in the United States (*Japan Lumber Journal,* 20 February 1986, p. 12). Although Japan may want to ensure future pulpwood supplies and to decrease the US supply share in its pulpwood purchases (*Japan Pulp and Paper,* vol. 20 [no. 1], May 1982, p. 5), reports early in 1986 suggested that Japan was not purchasing the expected amounts of pulpwood from the USSR. This may reflect Soviet inability to deliver more than 75 percent of the agreed amount for 1985. Japan expected the 1986 shortfall to be consumed by the Soviet pulp industry itself (*Japan Lumber Journal,* 31 December 1985, p. 10).

As go exports to Japan, so goes the wood resource of the Soviet Far East. But the reverse is also true, and increasing shares of small-diameter trees in more remote zones, with high proportions of larch, will come to dominate export shipments. Japanese uses for larch and the ability of the USSR to make itself available as a substitute for Southsea timber are the two key factors likely to influence the future Soviet role in the Japanese market.

CONCLUSIONS

Forest-product exports should continue to play a small role in overall sales abroad for the USSR, although key existing Western customers may continue as strong sources of hard-currency earnings (i.e., Japan and Great Britain). The USSR meanwhile has locked itself into some longer-term obligations both to

Japan and to Eastern Europe through compensation agreements, and to CMEA nations through normal intrabloc bilateral agreements.

The USSR appears to be a price-taker in international wood markets, although in the case of Japan negotiations reported between *Exportles* and Japanese representatives, it is suggested that the Soviet Union is following a distinct learning curve in its anticipation of capitalist market conditions. The main influences on future Soviet sales of wood products outside its borders appear to be competition from other sources, and its ability to cultivate new markets, such as China, much of the Third World, the newly industrialized countries (NICs) of Asia, and even North America. Thus far, except perhaps for China, the Soviet Union does not seem to be making any aggressive attempts to cultivate such new markets, particularly in the Pacific.

The main roadblock may lie within the Soviet Union itself in the form of continuing supply constraints and inefficiencies. Whether the USSR can squeeze domestic consumption to achieve relatively small gains in foreign trade probably depends on how desperate the country remains for hard currency. The downward trend in Soviet trade with the West (except for purchases of grain) may indirectly free up more forest output for home consumption.

NOTES

1. As reported in *Vneshnyaya Torgovlya SSSR v 1984 godu* (1985, various pages).
2. Council for Mutual Economic Assistance.
3. Jensen, Shabad, and Wright (1983) point out that, by 1980, the USSR ranked seventh in value of exports worldwide, and has played a limited role in the world economy since World War II. This is partly due to the drive for self-sufficiency: with an economy as large as the USSR, the need to look outside the borders for goods is lessened. A short-term change has occurred, however, with the USSR now seeking to achieve greater integration with global economies. The cost of increasing hard-currency imports has been to meet balance-of-trade problems with raw-material exports (which account for about one-half of total Soviet exports, and up to four-fifths of hard-currency earnings). The authors (Jensen, Shabad, and Wright, 1983, p. 680) conclude, "Thus, the Soviet Union has a pattern of international trade more akin to a developing country than a modern, industrial superpower."
4. Actual percentage shares are slightly smaller than those those in Table 7.2 because some miscellaneous forest-product exports (such as paperboard) are not included in the table. The total FTR value of forest-product exports for 1984, for example, is reported in Table 7.2 as 1.9 million rubles; this actually represents approximately only 93 percent of forest exports. Thus, the 26 percent share for roundwood portrayed in Chart 7.1 varies slightly from the 27.9 percent share reported for logs in Table 7.2.
5. Sleepers are often included with lumber (*pilomaterial)* and other sawn items in Soviet export statistics to comprise the category, lumber or (sawn) timber. Domestic statistics are not consistent in this category and do not always include sleepers. Thus, we exclude sleepers from lumber in our analyses.

6. Properly transliterated, it is *Eksportles*, but Japan and the USSR both use the term *Exportles* when writing in English.
7. Bozek (1979, p. 514) writes, "A number of other organizations (for example, the State Committee on Foreign Economic Relations, the State Committee on Inventions and Discoveries, the State Committee on Science and Technology), with both administrative and operational foreign trade functions, have become more involved in the Soviet foreign trade system." (Greater opportunity for direct contact between Soviet ministries and foreign firms was to commence in 1987. [*Globe and Mail*, 5 September 1986].)
8. Personal discussion with Donovan (1976).
9. Cooper (1982, pp. 454-78), however, reviewing Soviet methods of conducting trade with the West, concludes that the rate of growth in trade between the USSR and the West has tapered off.
10. We noted in Chapter 5 that Finnish specialists (Eronen, 1984, 1985) have observed recent shipments of timber by rail to Finland which originated more than 5000 km inside the USSR. By conventional accounting in the USSR and abroad, such flows would normally be totally uneconomic.
11. The "West" is defined here to include the non-CMEA countries of Europe and Japan. Western-hemispheric countries are not included in the forest-product estimates because the proportion of Soviet forest exports to capitalist countries of the Western hemisphere has been so small. The category "East Europe" includes the CMEA countries except Mongolia, Cuba, and Vietnam; the category "Other" reflects mainly trade with these countries plus underdeveloped nations.
12. Our discussion uses *Vneshnyaya Torgovlya SSSR* yearbook statistics, which are less than satisfying on two accounts. Soviet trade statistics are not always reliable or consistent (Wolf and Hewett [1982] discuss this problem), and implied prices must be computed by dividing ruble value of exports reported by the USSR by quantity to obtain a measure of rubles per physical unit. Foreign trade rubles and domestic rubles are accounted separately by the USSR, and the former do not bear a true relationship with actual prices on the world market. Conversion is laborious, and the implied ruble price is utilized because the authors desire to show long term trends among many disparate regions and commodities. Some prices for the market in Japan are presented in U.S. dollars or yen. Finally, some implied ruble prices are skewed by either small quantity of shipments to certain regions, or because products are not always differentiated in the tables (paper, for example, shows a range in quality and price).
13. Personal discussion with representatives of Timber Resources Company, Seattle, Washington. The *Japan Lumber Journal* (20 May 1983, p. 4) reported the sale at 1.0 to 1.2 million cu. m and discussed the comments by *Exportles* representatives that this sale relieved Japan of some purchase obligations.
14. Personal communication with representatives of Timber Resources Company, Seattle, Washington.
15. The larch problem is further discussed in Braden (1983, pp. 454-55) and in Rodgers (1983, pp. 204-9).

8
The Quest for Solutions

A number of problems and management dilemmas have been noted thus far in our examination of the Soviet forest-products sector. To solve these problems, Soviet planners have employed a variety of economic tools in their attempt to stimulate desired growth and improve efficiency. In addition, they have tried both to develop technology at home and to import new techniques from abroad. The efficacy of these measures is examined in Chapter 8.

TECHNOLOGY AND IMPORTS

Chapter 5 noted that, for many wood commodities, North American production exceeds that of the USSR. *VNIPIEILesprom,* the All-Union Scientific Research and Design Institute of Economics, Organization of Production Management and Information for the Forest Product Industries, published a study in 1976 which showed that, from 1000 cu. m of wood, the USSR produced substantially fewer forest products than did the USA (Table 8.1). Ten years later, an article in *Izvestiya* quoted Deputy Minister Pronin of *Minlesbumprom* that the USSR still only manufacturers 35 kg of pulp and paper per capita to the 270 produced by the USA (*Izvestiya,* 17 February 1986, p. 3).

What factors account for the poor record of efficiency in the Soviet forest industries? We have noted thus far that the resource base itself is more constrained than perhaps perceived by many Soviet and Western scholars. Geographic distribution is disadvantageous, investment capital has been scarce, and organization has been faulty. An additional problem lies within the realm of technological development, a main ingredient in the production equation for all the forest industries. Lack of adequate technological progress causes stagnation in labor productivity and hinders the achievement of production targets.

TECHNOLOGICAL DEVELOPMENT AS A BOTTLENECK

Technology, although difficult to define, is often interpreted as either *embodied* technology, represented by capital, or *disembodied*, represented by patents, technical journals, or learning accomplished by labor.[1] Technology represents the process of technical change; and, although technology is recognized as an element of the production function, econometric measurements of it have been controversial.

Technology is viewed here according to its most conventional meaning: machinery and equipment and new industrial processes. We might recognize that, to create new machinery and equipment, or embodied technology, a process should be followed in which (1) R&D leads to inventions, (2) inventions are

Table 8.1
USSR-USA Comparison of Output
from 1000 cu. m of Roundwood, 1972

	USSR	USA
Sawn Materials (cu. m)	321.1	255.3
Plywood (cu. m)	5.5	47.8
Fiberboard (sq. m)	662.0	2,508.0
Particleboard (cu. m)	6.9	15.5
Pulp (tons)	14.8	100.0
Paper (tons)	12.0	69.0
Paperboard (tons)	7.3	73.4

Source: Karpov (1976, p. 5).

Table 8.2
USSR Imports of Forest Industry Machinery and Equipment,
1960-1984
(Selected Years)

	Millions of Rubles					
Machinery Imports	1960	1965	1970	1975	1980	1984
Category 151[a]	30.3	36.7	91.4	150.0	209.2	333.1
Including -						
Paper				11.9	13.1	29.9
Paperboard				44.5	35.6	52.1
Pulp				20.3		
Category 152[b]	3.7	0.5	2.0	10.2	8.1	19.6
(1) Total Forest M & E[c]	34.0	37.3	93.3	160.3	217.2	352.7
(2) Total M & E	1,507.7	2,419.0	3,706.2	9,045.7	15,063.5	23,916.3
(1) as % of (2)	2.3%	1.5%	2.5%	1.8%	1.4%	1.5%

[a]Category 151 includes pulp and paper machinery and equipment, and some woodworking machinery and equipment not subdivided by type of machinery for years 1960, 1965, and 1970.

[b]Category 152 includes woodworking machinery and equipment.

[c] M & E = machinery (M) and equipment (E).

Source: *Vneshnyaya Torgovlya SSSR* (various years).

tested in a laboratory or by "lead" firms, (3) innovations are achieved whereby inventions are applied to the work place, and (4) a new level of technology is eventually diffused throughout an entire industry.

The USSR has long been accused by both domestic and foreign critics of being deficient in its ability to achieve technological change without significant help from abroad.[2] The status of technological developments in the forest industries tends to support that criticism, particularly in logging and sawmilling. Despite the long history of forest exploitation in the USSR, which would suggest that a stock of learning might have been built up, and despite continuous imports of technology since World War II, levels of mechanization continue to fall short of goals. In composition board, pulp, and paper industries, wholesale imports of production lines have allowed technological growth, but even these improvements are handicapped by shortfalls in material supplies.

Inadequacies in technology, particularly at the logging stage, thus contribute to the overall problems preventing forest-product industries from achieving growth targets. Technology deficits, in addition to constraining output and labor efficiency, are also damaging because they encourage the shift to more costly, distant stands of timber, which was discussed in Chapter 4. More complete use of accessible timber would require better adoption of technology and production management. The total picture of technological change in forest products, however, shows an uneven record, in which some branches have achieved (often through imports) fairly high levels of modernization, while others continue to require improvements.

TECHNOLOGY LEVELS IN THE FOREST-PRODUCTS INDUSTRY

In studying three logging firms to determine factors contributing to labor productivity, Demintsev *et al.* (1976, p. 12) concluded that "technical outfitting" was the most significant variable. Although Soviet planners appear to recognize that mechanization and quality of machinery are key elements in achieving economic growth, many sectors continue to be undermechanized.

Logging has the least developed technology of any forest industry branch, yet other processes depend on this branch for their own productivity. In 1972, the USSR planned that, by 1980, 35 percent of timber would be felled by machine; the actual level achieved was 12 percent. Forty percent of timber was to be skidded by grapple skidder, but the actual volume reached only 21 percent. Thirty percent was to be delimbed mechanically, but the actual figure was 15 percent (Blandon, 1984, p. 18).[3] The Twelfth Five-Year Plan (1986-1990) envisions a 28 percent growth in mechanization of logging, with a total growth of mechanization in the sector (including grappling and delimbing) of 45 percent (Dirks, 1986, p. 1).

In addition to low levels of mechanization, logging appears to be suffering from lack of machinery deliveries as well as problems with quality of equipment. Much machinery proves unsatisfactory in the field, and 1985 shortfalls of harvested timber have been blamed on the lower productivity of the average timber-felling machine in 1984 (Dirks, 1986, p. 2). Blandon's report that, in 1981, only 51 percent of skidding tractors were ready to be used at any one time (Blandon, 1984, p. 18), indicates a high rate of breakdown and shortage of spare parts typical of many Soviet industries. Despite complaints about equipment, however, the USSR exhibited several lines of prototype logging machinery at its Moscow international trade fair, *Lesdrevmash,* in 1984. (Previous shows for forest-product machinery were held in 1973 and 1974 [*World Wood*, June 1984, p. 5; and *Lesnaya Promyshlennost',* August 1984, pp. 16-17].)

Road construction for logging appears to suffer from problems with technology. Although from 1975 to 1984, the extent of paved logging roads in the USSR grew from 2889 km to 3766 km, the actual volume of timber that moved along paved roads shrunk from 18.1 million cu. m to 15.3 million cu. m (Dirks, 1986, pp. 1-2). Thus, a main item imported from Japan under the K-S agreements discussed below has been transportation and road-building equipment.[4]

Another technological shortcoming pertains to complete tree use. The logging industry has long been guilty of wasteful cutting practices as noted in Chapter 3; one source estimated that, in 1985, an additional 2.7 million cu. m of wood harvest could have been realized by *Minlesbumprom* (Dirks, 1986, p. 2).[5]

Sawmilling is second only to logging in the low level of overall technology. As in logging, however, this branch appears to rely on manual labor more than *Minlesbumprom* desires. The 1976 level of automation within Soviet sawmills was estimated as 35 percent for larger enterprises and 25 percent for smaller ones (Mugandin, 1977, p. 30). A basic decision for the sawmilling industry appears to be whether to construct entirely new facilities, usually in conjunction with LPK, or to update existing mills. Older sawmills in the European-Uralian region may date from World War II, when the acquisition of Karelia and war reparations from Finland brought in a rush of new sawmilling technology. Such technology continues to originate from abroad: the Ust'-Ilimsk and Novomakalakovo enterprises (Eastern Siberia) have imported debarking, drying, and materials-handling equipment, as well as computers to determine optimum log cut (Braden, 1981, Appendix 2). The USSR has also developed a chipping headrig, the LAPB, which cuts logs, produces cants, and creates chips, similar to the "Chip-n-Saw" mobile model of the West. Despite such modern facilities, however, the USSR still uses over 70,000 two-story, outdated gang mills and 65,000 one-story mills (Turushev, 1975, p. 110; *CDSP*, vol. 30 [17] 1978, p. 9).

Plywood processes are quite diverse in the USSR, and the products are less comparable with those of the West because Soviet plywood is used more for concrete forms and furniture than for interior panels or direct construction. Deciduous species are frequently used, and a technological breakthrough in the use of larch for veneer sheets in the USSR could prove to be crucial for the future utilization of Siberian forests. Materials handling does not appear to be highly mechanized in plywood production. Soviet indigenous plywood technology received a boost with the import of Raute (Finnish) peelers for smaller-diameter logs.

Composition board in the USSR is mostly consumed by the furniture industry. This branch appears to have relatively higher technologies than the logging or sawmilling sectors. One factor in favor of the composition board industry may be its relative youth; it did not really "take off" until the 1960s, and thus allowed managers to be free of the baggage of older equipment kept in use too long. The particleboard industry employs a mixture of imported and Soviet-made equipment, while the fiberboard industry is more permeated with foreign capital. In 1973, over 63 percent of capacity in fiberboard comprised non-Soviet machinery (Mel'nikov, 1974, p. 40). Older insulation board plants were constructed with Soviet indigenous technology, but recently more equipment has been imported for hardboard plants, including those utilizing dry production techniques.[6]

The pulp and paper branch also benefited from World War II. The USSR acquired Japanese pulp and paper mills on Sakhalin Island, paper mills in the Baltic republics, and Finnish pulp and paper technology. Until World War II, the Soviet Union had copied American models and did not begin manufacturing any pulp and paper equipment until 1932 (Sutton, 1973, pp. 184-89). This branch has also purchased modern technology from abroad, particularly for massive LPKs in Siberia and the European Northwest. As noted above, the USSR produces both chemical (sulphate and sulphite) and mechanical pulp. Soviet attempts to increase production of sulphate (kraft) pulp in order to diversify its paper industries have succeeded on the basis of large amounts of imported technology. Despite investments from 1975 to 1985 of 7 billion rubles worth of capital, however, the pulp and paper industry is still failing to meet quotas (*Izvestiya,* 23 June 1985, p. 2).

One important path for technological development in pulp and paper is the more efficient use of raw materials in paper production, including chips, waste paper, and hardwoods, as noted in Chapter 5. Mills producing hardwood pulp exist or are planned at 22 locations in the USSR (Eronen, 1984, p. 53).

TECHNOLOGY IMPORTS IN FOREST INDUSTRIES

The amount of indigenous technology existing in the Soviet forest industries is difficult to estimate because so much reliance has been placed in the past and at present on imports. Machinery is imported through *Prommashimport,* a foreign trade organization. Systematic measurement is difficult because data series for individual machines imported are not available for different forest industries, and the destinations of imported technology are not reported except as anecdotal literature or, occasionally, through information provided by foreign companies.[7] Total amount of forest-products machinery and equipment imports are reported yearly in *Vneshnyaya Torgovlya SSSR* (Table 8.2).

Both Western and Soviet-bloc countries export forest-product equipment to the USSR. Finland, Austria, Sweden, Japan, France, West Germany, Poland, and Czechoslovakia are major suppliers (Table 8.3). Trade data may underestimate sales of equipment from some countries because only direct trade is reported. Multinational companies funnel technology into the USSR indirectly from various Western countries. Lamb-Grays Harbor Company of the U.S. has sold pulp-cutting, conveying, and wrapping equipment to the USSR for use in Bratsk, Ust'-Ilimsk, Kotlas, and Arkhangel, but this transaction did not appear in national-level trade data between the U.S. and the USSR because the equipment was sold via Finnish firms (interview of company representative by Braden, 23 March, 1976). A more recent example of this phenomenon is the plan by Buckeye Cellulose Corporation of Tennessee to sell, via an Italian

Table 8.3
USSR Imports of Forest-Product Technology
by Country of Origin, 1975 and 1984

Country	1975[a]	%	1984	%
Austria	1,961	1.2	20,918	6.3
Bulgaria	0	0.0	2,298	0.7
Canada	1,498	0.9	0	0.0
Denmark	29	0.0	215	0.1
West Germany	22,510	14.0	42,483	12.8
Finland	58,487	36.5	147,922	44.4
France	12,291	7.7	1,810	0.5
Great Britain	1,863	1.2	10,205	3.1
Italy	6,502	4.1	16,256	4.9
Japan	1,601	1.0	33,345	10.0
Poland	25,136	15.7	34,820	10.5
Sweden	20,743	12.9	16,723	5.0
Switzerland	1,578	1.0	4,207	1.3
Other	6,078	3.8	1,904	0.6
Total	160,277	100.0	333,106	100.0

[a]Figures are in Thousands of Rubles.
Source: *Vneshnyaya Torgovlya SSSR v 1975 godu* (1976); *Vneshnyaya Torgovlya SSSR v 1984 godu* (1985).

company, a dissolving wood pulp mill valued at US$300 million to the USSR for location along the Volga River (*Pulp and Paper,* January 1986, p. 37).

Foreign technology enters the Soviet forest industries as machinery imports, as patents, as copies, by licensing agreements, and by whole-mill purchases. This last channel has become particularly useful to forest industries as *turnkey* plant sales have evolved; foreign companies take responsibility for engineering, technical design, construction, and timely start-up. An example of this approach is the Svetogorsk complex near the Finnish border. Tampella and Rauma-Repola of Finland supplied the technology for this 165,000-ton-per-year capacity pulp and paper complex, one of the most successful and modern in the USSR. The latest phase at Svetogorsk will be a 40,000-m tissue machine, valued at US$18 million and made by Valmet of Finland. The machine will make use of waste paper and pulp from the Svetogorsk mill, and operations were planned to commence in 1986 (*Pulp and Paper,* January 1986, p. 37). Syktyvkar, a giant capacity, 610,000-ton-per-year pulp and paper mill, was built in the late 1970s in the Komi ASSR with Finnish equipment. Rauma-Repola has also sold at least 11 complete particleboard mills to the USSR, each capable of producing 100,000 cu. m per year. Turnkey plants are expensive, but construction delays are minimized because of foreign involvement in management.

Another form of technology transfer to forest industries in the USSR is the *barter arrangement.* Also known as *compensatory trade agreements,* these provisions call for technology purchases by the USSR (often with credits underwritten by foreign countries) in exchange for a share of output. France, for example, sold pulp equipment for the Ust'-Ilimsk plant in exchange for pulp delivery (*Journal of the US-USSR Trade and Economic Council,* vol. 5 [5], 1979, p. 5). Perhaps the most long-lasting barter arrangements in forest products for the USSR have been with Japan. The so-called K-S agreements noted in Chapter 7, and named for the principal original negotiators on both sides, Kawai of Japan and Sedov of the USSR, began in 1969.[8] The first one ran through 1973, the second from 1975 to 1979, and the third from 1981 to 1986. Officially called the Japan-USSR Forest Resource Development Project, the latest agreement called for Soviet export of 13.24 million cu. m of timber (12 million in logs; 1.24 million in lumber) to Japan over the period of the agreement, and the import of US$1.04 million (1981: 230 billion yen) worth of equipment, including 2000 tractor-trailers, 1500 bulldozers, and 500 to 1000 forklifts and/or cranes (*Japan Lumber Journal,* 20 June 1981, p. 19). The "shopping list" for Soviet machinery purchases during the second K-S agreement is shown in Table 8.4.

In addition to the K-S agreements, the USSR and Japan also concluded a barter arrangement in pulp and paper with the General Agreement on Deliveries of Technological Chips and Pulpwood of Leaf-Bearing Trees and Deliveries from Japan of Equipment for Production of Technological Chips and Pulpwood. The agreement, in effect from 1972 through 1981, allowed the USSR credits for US$45 million worth of machinery and equipment. Japanese paper companies in turn purchased 8 million cu. m of chips and 4.7 million cu. m of pulp logs. After the first agreement expired, negotiations for a second one were delayed several years due to arguments over amounts and prices, although trade continued without a blanket agreement. Finally, in December, 1985, a second "pulpwood

Table 8.4
USSR Machinery Purchases Specified Under
Second K-S Agreement, 1975-1979

Category	Machinery	Quantity/Value
Transportation	Logging trucks	2,000-2,700
	Bulldozers	693
	Roadgraders	150-250
	Dump trucks (8-ton capacity)	1,245
	Excavators	200
	Cranes	185
	Floating cranes	4
Small vessels and marine suction dredgers		US$20-$25 million
Woodworking equipment	Plywood machinery	US$20-$25 million
	Plane-veneer machinery	
	Edging layer machinery	
	Synthetic veneer machinery	
	Band sawmill	
	Prefabricated house machinery	
	Automatic screwdrivers	
Machine-building equipment for wood industries		US25-30 million
Machine-building equipment for logging	Autoloaders	US$20-$25 million
	Foundry equipment	
	Forge-press equipment	
	Metal-cutting lathes	
	Heat-exchange equipment	
	Pipe-manufacturing machinery	
	Paper-conditioning assemblies	
	Lamination machinery	
Paper and paperboard machinery		US$20-$25 million
Spare parts for log transport, bulldozers, and woodworking equipment		US$55-$70 million
Repair factory, cables, other		US$16-$19 million

Source: Soviet order data obtained from various Japanese companies.

agreement" was signed with *Exportles*. Under the new arrangement, which will run from 1986 to 1996, Japan will import 8.2 million cu. m of chips and 3 million cu. m of hardwood pulp; the USSR will purchase US$200 million worth of equipment (*Japan Lumber Journal*, 31 January 1986, p. 15).

Rising prices for Soviet logs (Chapter 7), fluctuating demand for wood products in Japan, and depletion of desirable species in the Soviet Far East have all contributed to the difficulty of creating continued barter arrangements between the two countries. A major drawback has been the amount of larch that Japanese companies are receiving in shipments from the USSR, although recent technological breakthroughs in the use of larch for plywood by the Hayashi Veneer Company may eventually reduce resistance to this species in Japan (Chapter 7).

ASSESSING TECHNOLOGICAL NEEDS

One can demonstrate more easily that a considerable amount of foreign technology exists in the various wood industries than that such purchases have benefited the USSR over the long run. Certainly, at a time when better utilization of resources is paramount, modernization and new techniques should be essential for achieving goals. The fact remains, however, that, for a sector of the economy which has relied to a large extent on imported machinery and equipment, the forest industries do not seem to be improving in terms of productivity, particularly at the level of logging and sawmilling. Perhaps the most one can say is that the sector would be worse off without imported technology.

Why have improvements in this sector been slow? Three main factors suggest an answer.

1. Mechanization levels remain low at the essential point of origin, the logging industry; thus, more sophisticated processes further down the line suffer from lack of raw materials.

2. The Soviet economic system does not reward risk takers, despite the presence of incentive payoffs in the bonus system. The penalty for not achieving output targets is just too great to allow for experimentation. Thus, new equipment which performs well in the laboratory or at an international exhibit may be resisted by plant managers who will be responsible for its installation, start-up, and maintenance.

3. Alternatively, final users of equipment may be separated from sellers by a layer of bureaucracy in the foreign trade organization, such as *Prommashimport*, despite the fact that some foreign companies such as Valmet Sawmills even advertise directly in Soviet forest product journals.

A key factor in evaluating the effectiveness of new technology may be in the area of labor itself. When a new machine is introduced into a production process, how much does labor benefit? What sort of learning curve improves the quality of the Soviet labor force in forest industries? The USSR indeed has been interested in technical cooperation agreements which provide for direct training of personnel, often abroad.[9] Blandon, however, disputes the importance of the "learning effects" of new technology in the logging branch, and estimates that productivity increases are explained more by the type of machinery introduced than by a learning and organizational factor. Blandon (1983, pp. 114-55) notes that, while some Soviet machines developed for logging have performed well, such as the LP-19 feller buncher, reliability of new Soviet machinery may continue to be a detriment to achieving greater productivity.

Finally, our definition of technology as equipment leaves out the importance of management culture. We have seen that the mistaken perception of unlimited resource stocks may not substitute for sound administrative decisions. Similarly, reliance on imported machinery that may not transfer well across the Soviet border may also be a poor substitute for good management policy in the forest industries.[10]

ECONOMIC INDICATORS

The absence of market prices in the USSR forest industries causes allocation of harvest, production efficiency, and profit margins to be largely influenced by planners' actions. We may ask, therefore, whether optimal choices are made regarding use of the forest resource. In the absence of an econometric model, the book now provides an empirical answer to that question by examining some of the tools available to forest-product planners. While physical output targets are still paramount for decision making, the financial indicators that also have an impact on economic performance include investment, prices, costs, taxes, and profits.

Some basic indicators are reported in the USSR both for industry as a whole and for the forest industries (Table 8.5). The indicator, index of the value of output, describes the growth trend in ruble value of output, using 1960 as a base year. While industry on the whole has experienced a growth in output by value since 1960, all the forest industries have performed below average industry norms (Charts 8.1 and 8.2). Pulp, paper, and woodworking tend to do better than the logging industry. The rate of growth in value of output, which slowed down during the 1975-1980 period for all five sectors (and continued to do so for average industry), began picking up again in forest products for the latest period (Chart 8.3). Logging tended to depress the overall indicators for forest products. The forest industries are also contributing a smaller share to the overall value of industrial output, dropping from a 6.9 percent share in 1960 to 4.1 percent in 1984 (Table 8.5 and Chart 8.2).

In divisions of the industrial investment "pie," forest products have also experienced a decline since 1960. Both in terms of capital investment and basic funds (productive capital in structures and machinery available in the current period), forest industries *as a group* are receiving less from central planners (Tables 8.5 and 8.6; Charts 8.2 and 8.4).

COSTS

The most important economic trend in the entire forest industry of the USSR is the fact that trees are becoming more expensive to harvest. This trend since the

Table 8.5
Value, Investment, and Profits in USSR Forest
Industries, 1960-1984

Year	1960	1965	1970	1975	1980	1984
Indicator						
1. Index of Value of Output 1960=100						
All Industry	100	151	227	325	404	468
Forest Products	100	128	168	217	234	269
Logging	100	111	125	146	143	152
Woodworking	100	134	184	241	274	325
Pulp & Paper	100	147	222	311	349	411
2. Forest Industry Share of Value of Industrial Output[a]	6.9	5.8	5.1	4.7	4.1	4.1
3. Industry Basic Funds						
All Industry[b]	100	168	255	385	551	716
Forest-Product Share	6.8	5.6	5.1	4.8	4.5	4.3
4. Profit - All Industry[c]	14,017	22,548	55,956	65,941	73,295	96,332
Forest Products	864	696	2,587	2,216	1,565	3,935
Logging	363	202	901	512	-258	840
Pulp & Paper	80	100	484	588	410	1,094
5. Profitability[d]						
All industry	13.6	13.0	21.5	15.8	12.2	12.1
Forest Products	12.7	6.9	20.0	11.4	6.1	12.1
Logging	13.0	4.3	16.4	6.3	-2.6	7.0
Pulp & Paper	5.7	5.9	14.7	10.7	5.2	10.2

[a]1960, 1965, 1970 use 1967 prices; 1975, 1980, 1984 use 1975 prices; 1984 share would be 4.5 in 1982 prices. Discrepancy of 0.1 percent exists in shares for 1965 and 1970 depending on yearbook consulted (could be 5.9 and 5.2, respectively).

[b]In billion rubles; 1960 share estimate is based on growth in basic funds reported in 1965 yearbook.

[c]In million rubles.

[d]profitability = profit divided by basic fund and is expressed as a percentage; official series data reported except for 1960, where estimates are based on 1965 basic fund proportions for logging, pulp, and paper.

Source: *Narodnoye Khozyaystvo SSSR* (various years).

Chart 8.1

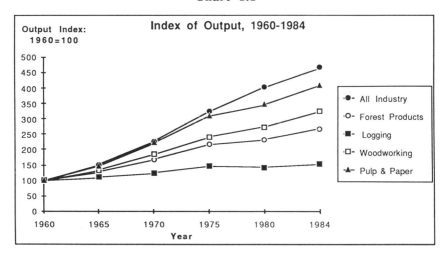

Chart 8.2

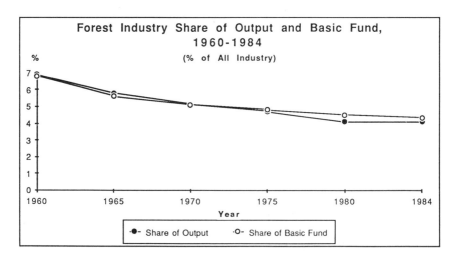

Chart 8.3

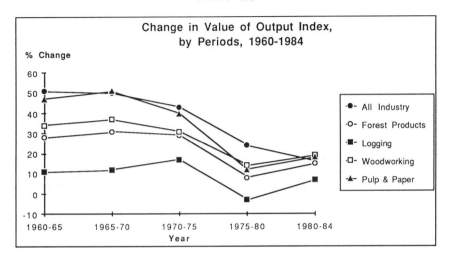

Chart 8.4

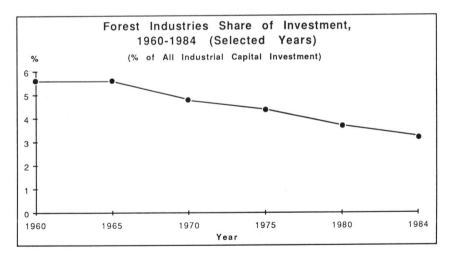

Table 8.6
Forest Industries' Share of Capital Investment*,
1950-1984 (Selected Years)

Year	% of Total Capital Investment in Industry
1950	5.5
1958	5.9
1960	5.6
1964	5.9
1965	5.6
1970	4.8
1971	5.0
1972	5.1
1973	4.9
1974	4.5
1975	4.4
1976	4.4
1977	4.6
1978	4.2
1979	3.9
1980	3.7
1981	3.8
1982	3.7
1983	3.7
1984	3.2

*Capital investment *(Kapital'nye vlozheniya)* is a smaller value than overall investment (basic funds) shown in Table 8.5. For example, in 1984 total basic funds in all Soviet industry comprised 720 billion rubles; capital invested (i.e., capital investment) in all Soviet industry during 1984 was 61.9 billion rubles *(Narodnoye Khozyaystvo SSSR v 1984 godu* [1985, pp. 59, 381]).

Source: *Narodnoye Khozyaystvo SSSR* (various years).

1950s has caused cost indicators to be on the rise, largely due to increases in cost of raw materials, as harvesting has shifted geographically toward more remote areas. Raw materials have contributed the largest share of total cost to forest industries (Table 8.7 and Chart 8.5). Their level was stable between 1972 and 1980, but had increased again by 1984. Prices were reset in 1967 and 1982 to take this spiralling materials cost curve into account. Wages, on the other hand, have decreased as a share of total costs (Chart 8.6).

These overall trends in cost structure have a considerable range among individual enterprises and regions. Kozhin and Styazhkin (1976) compared five logging-woodworking enterprises in 1974 (Table 8.8) and noted that variation in raw-materials cost depended on complexity of product. Vakhtanskiy, with only one-third of its total product in logging, had the highest cost for raw materials, while the logging enterprise, *Karellesprom*, incurred only a 4.9 percent cost share for raw materials. Estimates of regional unit production of logs (Table 8.9) suggest that costs increase more steeply northwest of the Urals than to the east. A major deficiency, as noted in Chapter 5, however, in regional unit costs of products is that they omit transport costs. Such costs may or may not be given separately. Transport charges and variations in regional cost tend to show up, however, in the structure of users' prices.

PRICES

Prices of forest products are set by planners according to formulae based on production costs. Production costs with added profit margins form the f.o.b. price (also called the *enterprise wholesale price*) to the logging firm (Chart 8.7). The cost factor (which is the heart of the price set) has three components: (1) average cost for all logging enterprises; (2) a regional cost coefficient (which is higher in forest-deficit zones); and (3) a quality factor which is set largely by end use (Blandon, 1983, pp. 196-197).[11] Stumpage fees, discussed in Chapter 4 and below, form part of the cost (Table 8.8). Profit thus ends up being the difference between the cost and the selling price.

Delivered prices for materials to intermediate users are the c.i.f. price. Logging enterprises usually do not sell wood directly, but operate through *Gossnab,* the procurement and distribution agency used by *Minlesbumprom.* Price code 07-03 is used for domestic selling, whereas prices are set for wood exports according to code 07-04 (Mugandin, 1977, p. 122). C.i.f. prices include a transport charge based not only on distance, but also on regions designated by forest cover, not contiguity.[12] A turnover tax, typical of all selling transactions in the USSR, is then added to the c.i.f. price to form the industrial wholesale price (Chart 8.7). Finally, a surcharge tax is added for sales to the end consumer (state retail price).

As extraction costs for wood began to rise in the 1960s, the profit margin apparently suffered. To bring revenues more into line with costs, prices were increased in 1967 by an average of 26 percent. Profitability (unit price per unit cost) for logging firms then rose accordingly. Blandon reports an increase in profitability from 3.7 percent in 1965 to 20 percent following the price increase (Blandon, 1983, p. 200). The official series reported in the yearbook, *Narodnoye*

Table 8.7
Cost Structure in Forest Industries, 1961-1984
(Selected Years)

% of Each Industrial Category

	1961	1965	1972	1975	1980	1984
All Forest Industries						
Raw Materials	39.5	40.9	43.9	43.3	42.1	48.4
Auxiliary Materials	6.4	6.2	5.7	5.3	5.3	5.4
Fuel	4.1	3.7	4.0	3.7	4.0	3.9
Energy	1.4	1.8	2.3	2.3	2.5	2.6
Amortization	4.1	7.9	7.9	9.2	10.7	10.6
Wages	36.1	32.6	28.9	28.1	27.1	23.7
Other	8.4	6.9	7.3	8.1	8.3	5.4
Total	100.0	100.0	100.0	100.0	100.0	100.0
Logging						
Raw Materials	14.9	16.4	18.9	19.1	18.4	29.1
Auxiliary Materials	9.4	9.3	7.8	6.9	6.8	7.1
Fuel	4.9	4.3	4.8	4.3	5.2	4.5
Energy	0.3	0.7	0.9	1.0	1.4	1.3
Amortization	5.2	11.9	11.8	13.0	14.6	14.0
Wages	50.0	45.0	41.3	39.6	37.9	33.4
Other	15.3	12.4	14.5	16.1	15.7	10.6
Total	100.0	100.0	100.0	100.0	100.0	100.0
Woodworking[a]						
Raw Materials			57.9	56.9	55.4	58.7
Auxiliary Materials			3.6	3.6	3.7	3.9
Fuel			2.1	2.1	2.3	2.5
Energy			1.8	1.9	1.9	2.0
Amortization			4.5	5.6	6.5	6.6
Wages			26.3	25.7	24.9	22.7
Other			3.8	4.2	5.3	3.6
Total			100.0	100.0	100.0	100.0
Pulp & Paper						
Raw Materials	50.9	49.8	51.8	51.5	48.0	52.5
Auxiliary Materials	5.9	6.1	7.2	6.9	6.6	6.2
Fuel	9.8	8.4	7.5	6.7	6.1	6.2
Energy	4.7	5.7	6.0	5.7	5.9	5.9
Amortization	4.9	8.6	10.1	11.7	14.7	14.6
Wages	20.5	18.7	14.3	14.3	15.2	12.9
Other	3.3	2.7	3.1	3.2	3.5	1.7
Total	100.0	100.0	100.0	100.0	100.0	100.0

[a]Woodworking not reported separately for 1961 and 1965.

Source: *Narodnoye khozyaystvo SSSR* (various years).

Chart 8.5

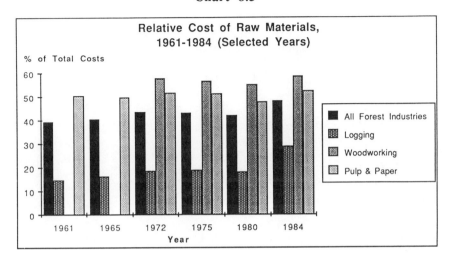

Chart 8.6

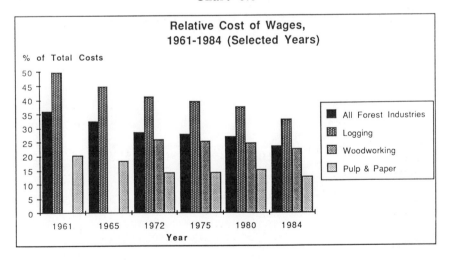

Table 8.8
Cost Structure for Five Forest-Product Enterprises, 1974
(% of Total Costs for each Enteprise)

Enterprise

Cost Elements	Karel-lesprom	Irkutsk-lesprom	Murmansk-lesprom	Gor'kles	Vakhtansk LPKh [a]
Raw Materials	4.9	21.2	24.5	30	45.4
Auxiliary Materials	8.5	7.1	5.3	8.3	6.8
Energy & Fuel	5.1	5.9	3.6	4.9	2.3
Wages & Insurance	50.4	38.6	48.4	38	30.3
Amortization	15.2	12.9	9.4	9.7	7.9
Stumpage Fee	10.7	5.8	3.2	5.5	5.8
Other	5.2	8.5	5.6	3.6	1.5
Total	100.0	100.0	100.0	100.0	100.0

[a]Part of *Gor'kles*.
Source: Compiled from Kozhin and Styazhkin (1976, p. 29).

Table 8.9
Index of Regional Production Costs for Roundwood[a]

Region	Index
Archangel	137
Karelia	127
Komi	121
Krasnoyarsk	106
Bashkir	107
Tyumen	119
Khabarovsk	113
Irkutsk	112
Buryat	114

[a]Raw material and transport costs are not included
(Sverdlovsk=100).
Source: Compiled from Voyevoda (1980, p. 79).

Chart 8.7

Structure of USSR Industrial Prices

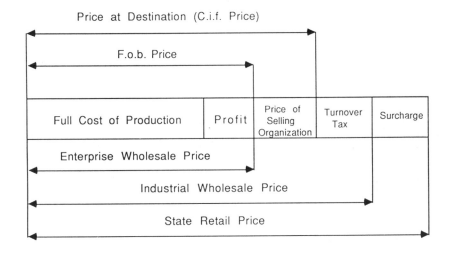

Source: Mugandin (1977, p. 121).

Chart 8.8

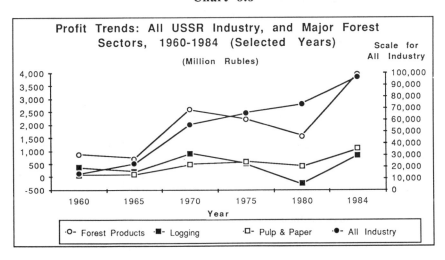

Khozyaystvo SSSR v 1975 godu (1976, p. 728) states that profitability increased in logging from 4.3 percent in 1965 to 16.4 percent in 1970.

The 1967 price reforms also attempted to achieve other goals, such as the more complete use of broadleaf species. While the f.o.b. price for deciduous species was 15 percent lower on average than that for conifers, the c.i.f. price was 30 percent lower; conifers thus were subsidizing deliveries of deciduous wood. Drozhalov (1984, pp. 202-3) has noted that this policy may not have been entirely successful because deciduous species are still insufficiently used in the European-Uralian zone. He suggests that the reason for this may be the divergent sizes in diameter between the two categories of tree. Thus, deciduous timber with smaller diameters and less wood return per unit of expenditure may still be at a disadvantage despite official price support.

Notwithstanding the 1967 price reforms, cost increases by the 1980s further reduced indicators of profitability for the forest-product industries. In 1982, therefore, prices were increased again. Timber prices rose by 40 percent on average, and prices were correspondingly adjusted for smaller-diameter trees. Profitability responded in turn by moving from -2.6 percent for logging in 1980 to 7 percent in 1984 (Table 8.5).

Pricing issues of particular note relate to (1) residual wood chips, (2) discount rates, and (3) exported forest products. The first of these issues, wood chip prices, has been a controversial topic in the USSR, and forest planners do not appear to have yet arrived at a satisfactory means of encouraging maximum use of residual chips. In 1967 a new category of industrial wood, low-quality wood for technological needs, was created. The c.i.f. price for chips was then set at twice that of firewood in the hope of reducing the amount of low-quality wood that was burned for fuel. Blandon (1983, p. 203) writes that a drawback to the policy was the fact that more residual wood did go into chips, and less into low value uses such as boxes and packing materials.

Klyeshev (1984, pp. 24-25) examined the production of residual wood chips in 1981 and 1982, and is critical of the current pricing system. Prices, he writes, should be based not only on production costs, but also on various methods through which chips are produced. Thus, chips from waste left in the cutting area should be priced differently from those derived from raw-material waste. He also feels that the quality of the wood chips varies greatly and hence can affect the quality of the end product. By Klyeshev's design, the price per cu. m of chips from cutting-area waste should be 10.3 rubles to fiberboard enterprises, while chips from sawmill waste should be 12.15 rubles. Prices also should be differentiated by species to encourage more use of broadleaf chips in particleboard production, while coniferous chips should still go into pulp production to maintain standards of paper quality. Klyeshev, however, also feels that chips from small-diameter wood should be priced higher than those from large-diameter trees, because unit production costs, especially in terms of labor consumption, are higher for small-diameter wood.

Klyeshev's discussion underscores the balancing act that forest planners must conduct in pricing issues: chips from small-diameter, broadleaf trees need to be brought into production to reduce raw-material costs. At the same time, the double factor of per unit labor consumption and quality prejudices have appeared to influence planners against better incentives for using residual wood chips.

Complaints by Soviet industrial personnel themselves indicate that an optimal pricing policy to encourage more complete use of cutting-area waste wood and residual wood has not yet been determined.

As a dynamic resource, forests require management of growing stock, but the role of time has traditionally been an interesting dilemma for planners in all Soviet industries, perhaps due to initial philosophical distaste for interest rates in Marxist-Leninist dogma. Thus, the second pricing issue is time, expressed as a discount rate applied to pricing future uses of forest resources. This factor has long been debated by forest economists in the USSR. Many have decided that time is merely part of the physical production equation (determining proper rotation cycle of a stand of trees), but some have argued that it is an economic problem (optimal time to remove trees).[13] At this point, time appears to be dealt with as a physical, technical factor. If it is eventually used to discount future revenues, then the value of the benefits stream will be reduced and may have a negative impact on costs, pricing, and indicators of profitability of forest products. On the other hand, Soviet planners would obtain a more accurate picture of the trade-offs involved in using stands of trees from various regions.

Export prices, the third controversial pricing issue, are set separately from domestic prices for timber (Table 8.10). The foreign trade organization responsible for forest products, *Exportles,* sets prices in concert with *Gosplan* and the Ministry of Foreign Trade. Soviet export prices (as noted in Chapter 7) are responsive to changing world market conditions, although they vary considerably depending on the trading partner and on whether or not long term agreements are in effect. Export prices are traditionally higher than domestic prices (Table 8.10) to encourage foreign trade.

TAXES (STUMPAGE FEES)

While turnover taxes are added to wholesale prices at each transaction, a government tax on timber, the stumpage fee, is considered part of f.o.b. production cost.

This tax is incorporated in the following formula:

$$T = (S + P/L) + S_1 + S_2$$

where

T = Tax per cu. m of timber
S = Cost of harvest
P = Net income
L = Cutting area in the zone
S_1 = Cost of harvest under full use of plot
S_2 = Cost of harvest from the actual plot

This fee was charged until 1930, abolished, and then re-established in 1949. To lower costs, the fees were cut by 50 percent in 1950, but then raised again in the 1967 price reforms. By 1971, rising costs were again diminishing the

Table 8.10
1973-1974 Regional Costs and Prices for Various Forest Products[a]
(Rubles per Unit of Output[b])

	USSR Domestic	USSR Export	North-west	Center	Volga Littoral	Volgo-Vyatka	Urals	West Siberia	East Siberia	Far East
Logs (P[c], 1964)[d]	6.8	15.7	6.49			6.5			6.1	11.6
Logs (P, 1974)	16.6	21.8	12.0	11.7	12.0	11.5	12.2	13.2	11.5	18.0
Logs (C)	11.7		11.4	11.4	11.7	10.3	11.0	12.0	10.9	15.6
Lumber (P)	32.6	57.3	48.2	35.1		33.6	36.1	45.2	47.1	48.5
Lumber (C)	39.6		41.6	32.6		29.0	32.9	41.1	46.6	50.9
Chips (P)	12.2		13.8	10.1		12.5	12.3	6.6	16.1	18.7
Chips (C)	11.5		11.1	8.9		10.8	10.4	5.7	15.9	19.5
Plywood (P)	170.2	128.0	158.2	169.7	180.0	185.5	170.8			
Plywood (C)	136.6		131.0	139.6	143.4	123.2	136.9			
Particleboard (P)	88.8	47.0	74.8	82.9	85.2		88.6	79.8		
Particleboard (C)	63.9		62.1	57.2	69.8		68.0	66.7		
Fiberboard (P)	380.0	197.3	362.0			350.0	450.0	400.0	392.0	
Fiberboard (C)	332.4		305.8			408.0	392.3	365.0	357.0	

[a]Based on representative enterprises, averages weighted by volume of output, f.o.b. prices.

[b]Rubles per cu. m except fiberboard where price refers to rubles per thousand sq. m.

[c]P = price; C = cost.

[d]USSR domestic (i.e., all-union) 1974 price for logs, lumber, and chips is obtained from Mugandin (1977, pp. 112, 120). All other prices are calculated by weighted regional averages, by profitability, or by data from Lobovikov and Petrov (1976, pp. 117, 121, 125). 1974 price for lumber may have been closer to 39 to 41 rubles. Mugandin (1977) lists 57.30 as the export price, but Ministry of Foreign Trade statistics for 1973 suggest it is 45 rubles.

Source: Barr (1970, p. 108); Mugandin (1977, pp. 112, 120); Kozhin (1976, p. 152); Lobovikov and Petrov (1976, pp. 117, 121, 125); and USSR Ministry of Foreign Trade export prices 1973 (1969 log export price).

relative value of the stumpage fee (operating costs in that year exceeded the fee by 43 percent), and the fee was reset at 10 percent of production cost (Bayzakov, 1981, pp. 92-93). *Gosplan* uses weights to set the stumpage fee (Anoshin *et al.* 1984, pp. 51-52), as follows:

1. National zones I through VII, with zone I taxed 8 to 10 times higher than zone VII to encourage a shift to peripheral areas. Pine, for example, may be taxed at 14.50 rubles per cu. m in zone I, but only 2.10 rubles in zone VII.

2. Species differentials, whereby pine is taxed at an index number of 100, other conifers at 85, birch at 50, and other deciduous species between 20 and 25.

3. Size differentials produce variations in rates: higher rates are placed on trees greater than 25 cm diameter to accommodate age factors and to encourage harvesting of small-diameter trees.

4. Transport factors are differentiated according to five zones within a cutting region based on distance to nearest loading point for timber, and also on the mode (road, rail, or raft) of transport.

5 A "complete harvest" factor, which includes a charge set as though all possible wood had been harvested, even if a plot is not completely cut (Chapter 2).

Bayzakov (1981, p. 94) has criticized this system because the stumpage fee is not fulfilling its main objectives. The most utilized regions now are zones III through VI; the first three zones, however, provided 61 percent of all fee revenue in the 1970s although they comprised only 35 percent of national logging volume. The stumpage fee, therefore, is not set high enough in those regions to offset higher costs of exploitation in more remote zones. The purpose of the tax is thus called into question. Should it reflect expenditures on logging, or should it attempt to allocate harvest in desired geographical directions? Bayzakov (1981, p. 94) feels that the stumpage fee should accomplish both tasks: it should be related to the cost of logging operations, but also should serve to smooth rent differentials among regions. As a further criticism, Blandon (1983, p. 203) has noted that the differential for species is offset by the c.i.f. prices, which are relatively less favorable to deciduous species. The tax break for using small-diameter trees also is insufficient to offset the higher unit transport costs incurred in their delivery. If stumpage fees are to influence geographical patterns of harvesting and to ensure better use of broadleaf species, they may have to be both increased and redefined to combat adverse trends in production costs.

PROFITS AND PROFITABILITY

Profit (*pribyl'*) to enterprises reflects the differential between production cost and f.o.b. price. The year 1980 represented a low point for forest industries, particularly logging, when profits which had been declining since the peak year of 1970 bottomed out at the negative rate (Table 8.5 and Chart 8.8) of -258 million rubles.

Profitability (*rentabel'nost'*), which represents a ratio of price per unit to cost per unit, likewise declined during the study period (Table 8.5 and Chart 8.9). While profit and profitability statistics are not usually reported by region in

Chart 8.9

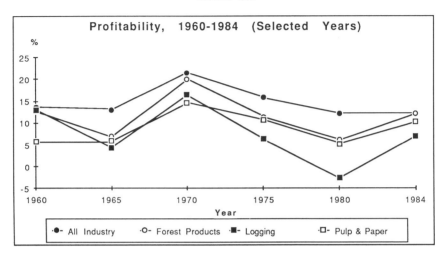

Chart 8.10

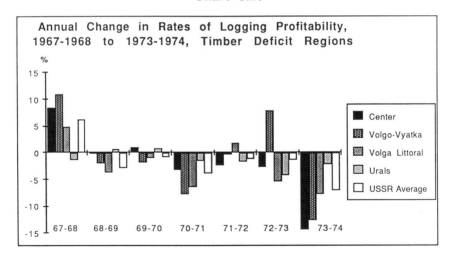

national economic yearbooks, occasional series are available. Logging profitability can be examined for eight regions of the RSFSR from 1967 to 1974 on the basis of information published in 1976 (Table 8.11). The utility of this series, however, is questionable because "sample" enterprises from regions may not always represent regional averages. Profitability ratios for the particleboard firms in Table 8.12, for example, vary largely because of differences in production costs.

Nevertheless, as production costs rose during the study period, all regions registered a downward trend in profits, but the decline was unevenly distributed (Charts 8.10 and 8.11). The Volgo-Vyatka region, for example, represented by the union *Gor'kles,* did not experience as precipitous a decline as did the Volga Littoral (Transvolga). While the regions in the European USSR along the Volga showed an increase in profitability in the 1971-1972 and 1972-1973 periods that was larger than recoveries in other regions, they also experienced the largest range in values (0.6 percent increase over the 1967-1968 period but a 0.5 to 0.8 percent decrease in the 1973-1974 period). The forest deficit regions (represented by the Center, Volgo-Vyatka, Volga Littoral, and Urals) in general experienced a sharper decline in profitability (Chart 8.12) over the 1967-74 period than did those which are forest surplus (Northwest, Western Siberia, Eastern Siberia, and the Far East). Given that these numbers are based on f.o.b. prices for logging enterprises, plus a profit margin expressed as a percentage of cost, the result is not surprising. Furthermore, delivered prices are not considered. If the exercise were repeated for a different forest product-sector (such as sawmilling or composition board) by region, then the decline of profitability would incorporate higher transport charges for the forest surplus zones.

Economic indicators, therefore, reveal several processes that have occurred in the forest industries:

1. Planners have attempted, not always successfully, to use pricing and tax mechanisms to direct harvest, material allocation, and type of raw material consumed.

2. Profitability ratios have declined over time as costs have increased.

3. Prices and stumpage fees periodically have been rescheduled upwards to reflect rising costs and to ensure "positive" profits.

4. A decline in logging indicators has affected the performance of all forest industries.

CONCLUSIONS

This chapter has examined various attempts at "repair" work by planners in the forest industries. When performance does not reach expectations, improvements are sought through enhanced allocation and movement of timber, ministerial reorganization, greater purchases of foreign technology, and revisions of the pricing and tax system. Improvements attained, however, seem largely to comprise stopgap measures offering short-term relief. The basic ills affecting timber's distribution and efficient utilization remain to be resolved.

Table 8.11
Profitability of Logging, by Region (1967-1974)
(Rubles per cu. m)[a]

Region	1967	1968	1969	1970	1971	1972	1973	1974
Northwest	20.0	21.2	19.8	17.6	14.7	12.3	8.1	5.1
Center	16.7	25.2	25.0	26.0	22.7	20.3	17.6	3.2
Volgo-Vyatka	18.3	29.2	27.1	25.3	17.6	17.3	25.2	12.5
Volga Littoral	20.0	24.8	21.1	20.1	13.7	15.5	10.1	2.3
Urals	20.4	19.1	19.8	20.6	19.1	17.4	13.1	10.9
Western Siberia	20.4	21.5	11.2	11.3	12.3	12.1	13.3	10.1
Eastern Siberia	20.0	28.4	22.5	19.8	17.6	15.4	12.2	7.8
Far East	21.8	37.5	37.1	35.7	27.3	25.2	24.5	15.3
Average	19.7	25.9	22.9	22.1	18.1	16.9	15.5	8.4

[a]Profitability is derived from ratio of price to cost, per cu. m, of logs. Data in table represent percent by which price exceeds cost.

Source: Compiled from Kozhin and Styazhkin (1976, pp. 102-3).

Table 8.12
Profitability[a] of Eight Particleboard Firms, 1970
(Rubles per cu. m of Output)

Firm	Profitability
Arkhangel LZ No. 4	10.1
Volgograd MDK	34.4
Kiev DOK	28.2
Kostroma FK	4.6
Kotlas DOK	24.8
Tyumen DOK	24.6
Cherepovets FMK	68.2
Leningrad MK	26.8

[a]Profitability is percentage by which price exceeds cost per cu. m of output.

Source: Computed from Delimov (1972).

Chart 8.11

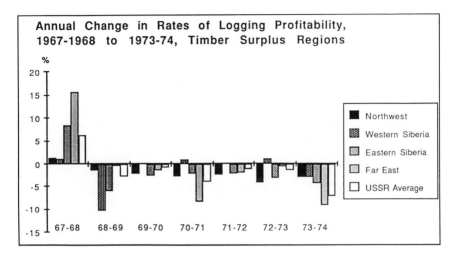

Chart 8.12

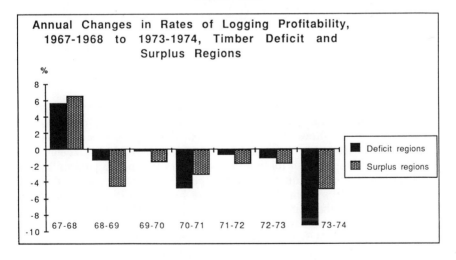

NOTES

1. The meaning of "technology" has been argued in the economics literature by scholars such as Arrow, Mansfield, and Schmookler, whose work represents a rich body of classical study, which the present authors do not attempt to review here. An extensive discussion, however, is provided by Braden (1981, Chapter 2).
2. The topic of technology in the USSR has been well-studied, particularly the aspect of technology transfer (Braden, 1981). Detailed case studies of technology transfer have been carried out by Holliday (1979) and Sutton (1973). A problem arises when we wish to go beyond anecdotal case studies and attempt to measure the true impact of technology imports on the Soviet economy, however. The debate on such econometric approaches is elaborated in Green and Levine (1977-1978), Weitzman (1979), and Toda (1979).
3. These targets represent a significant increase over the early 1970s. In 1975, the share of machinery capacity in the felling of timber was estimated to be only 0.4%; in trimming, 6.5%; and in bucking, 11.5% (Karpov, 1976, p. 14).
4. Lack of roadbuilding effort was a difficulty also cited in the Eleventh Five-Year Plan. Complaints by Soviet writers about lack of adequate logging roads were reported in *World Wood* (July 1981, p. 18). Furthermore, many tractors used for log transport were originally designed for agriculture. For skidding logs, tracked cable skidders with limited mobility are the most common; 68,000 were in use in 1978 (Holowacz, 1979, pp. 24-25).
5. Blandon (1983) provides a comprehensive discussion of technology in Soviet logging, including information on whole-tree felling (pp. 119-22) and on individual types of machinery used in felling, skidding, delimbing, and transportation.
6. Braden (1981, Chapter 6) has attempted to compare the productivity of Soviet and foreign fiberboard technology for five Swedish-made and eight Soviet-made insulation board plants, but could not prove any statistically significant differences in marginal productivity of the two types of capital.
7. A Canadian forestry specialist visited the Bratsk LPK and other timber areas of the USSR in the late 1970s and observed the amount of imported equipment in use. Rees (1977, p. 19) wrote, "There is a sober realization among the Soviet bureaucrats that it [satisfying consumer demand] cannot be done without bringing in foreign systems, as was seen in a pulp mill with Swedish and Finnish equipment, a cardboard production line from West Germany, forklifts from the USA, and a highball felling and skidding operation right in the heart of Siberia using brand new Canadian equipment."
8. The K-S agreements are further discussed by Braden (1983).
9. Finland, for example, has long-term agreements with the USSR on technical cooperation. Valmet, in the contract to supply paper machinery to Syktyvkar, agreed to work with Soviet engineers on some equipment manufacture (personal interview by Braden with representative of Rauma-Repola, 13 February 1978). The subject is also discussed by Levcik and Stankovskiy (1978).

10. Fleuron (1977) argues that machines are easier to transfer than the structure necessary for their wise use.
11. Blandon (1983, Chapter 7) provides a thorough discussion of pricing in the logging industry. The comments here are intended to complement, not replicate, his analysis.
12. An extensive discussion of the rebate and additions system of c.i.f. pricing is offered by Blandon (1983, pp. 197-98).
13. This topic is discussed by Blandon (1983, pp. 230-31) and by Bayzakov (1981, pp. 38-40).

9
Forests without Trees

The trees of the world are disappearing. In past centuries, European and North American forests have given way to grasslands, agriculture, and industrial development. The United States was estimated to have originally contained 1100 species of trees, only 647 of which remain (Dorst, 1970, p. 136). More recently, the attention of the world has shifted to the tropical moist forests which are undergoing severe disruption in South and Southeast Asia, Latin America, and Africa. Thus, the experience of the USSR is not so very different from that of other nations located in forested zones. As the wood in trees and the land that grows them are utilized, people have made choices about resource use. The choices increasingly do not favor preservation or nonconsumptive uses, and trees continue their natural cycle; sometimes harvests are managed carefully to sustain a yield over time and to allow forests a limited and managed tree stock. In many cases, however, timber has been utilized in a one-time, mining form of exploitation, and the result is a landscape devoid of trees or with forests lacking commercially viable stands. Sadly, much of the forest of the USSR appears to have gone this route.

There is another sense in which the USSR may be characterized by "forests without trees" - it is the concept that an item should not be considered a resource just because it exists in great quantity. As we have seen in this book, the forests of the USSR, particularly those in eastern regions, are burdened with so many constraints on their exploitation, that the authors question how valuable a resource they are in terms of commercial utilization.

What, then, would it take, first, to attain true resource value from the trees of the Russian forests and, second, to keep the forestlands from being severely depleted? Our examination has presented the dilemma faced by Soviet planners in trying to utilize efficiently their nation's forests. The problems are summarized in this chapter, and a broader framework is presented for viewing the forest-products industry of the USSR. Finally, we offer some suggestions which may ameliorate our discordant image of a Russian forest without trees.

A SUMMARY OF FINDINGS

The dilemma of forest utilization in the USSR seems to arise out of constraints on the forest stock itself and the response of Soviet planners. The phrases we have used, "buying time" and "muddling through," suggest the dominance of short-term solutions chosen by Soviet decision makers. When familiar paths are chosen over successive periods to avoid meaningful reforms, the demands of expediency then deepen the dilemma. In a world of management for the long term, the processes viewed as resources are efficient exploitation of accessible stocks, utilization of intermediate cut and waste products, and widespread reforestation. In a world of expediency, processes such as harvest shifts to eastern regions and unprofitable long hauls of timber may become the resources of the moment. Thus, we believe that Soviet forest-industry planners, in responding to the exigencies of the short term, only worsen their predicament and delay the day of needed changes.

The preceding chapters have identified many facets of this dilemma facing Soviet planners.

CONSTRAINTS ON FORESTS

As noted in Chapter 3, the forests of the USSR are large, amounting to 20 percent of the world's forest area, but size alone does not guarantee efficient utilization, and in fact may have been a detriment to wise planning because Soviet decision makers have apparently believed forests to be a "free good." *Location* appears to be a key element in the usefulness of the forests, and we have suggested that the more accessible stands of the European-Uralian and Siberian regions need to be better utilized. *Species mix* is also a constraint for eastern forests because of the dominance of larch, a coniferous species of limited commercial value due to technological difficulties in processing it.

CONSTRAINTS ON FOREST UTILIZATION

We have noted that past management practices have lead to wasteful overcutting of the more accessible European forests, and that the shift of harvesting toward eastern regions may be an attempt to fulfill production goals while the more centrally located stock is regenerated. At the same time, reforestation programs have apparently not yet been launched on a significant scale in Soviet forests. Other utilization problems have occurred due to waste: underemployment of European-Uralian zone deciduous species, inefficient harvesting of forest stands, incomplete use of intermediate cuts, and insufficient use of by-products in linked industrial processes.

CONSTRAINTS OF GEOGRAPHY

Anuchin's "geographic scissors" syndrome - the disadvantageous location of consumer versus virgin forests - was discussed in Chapter 4. We identified planning misperceptions and rigidity as factors which have helped shift the harvest to eastern regions, rather than promote more efficient use of less peripheral stocks. Long hauls of timber (up to 5000 km) have been the result, and rail movements still dominate timber transportation. Mix and share analysis, presented in Chapter 5, shows that wood processing is becoming increasingly polarized (Europe versus Asia) in regions of the RSFSR. Asia is developing an emphasis on lumber and plywood, while the fiber-based industries of Europe are growing. The overall shift in industry, as in harvest, however, is to the East, a disturbing trend given the dilemma of geography.

CONSTRAINTS ON FOREIGN MARKETS FOR SOVIET FOREST PRODUCTS

We have noted that forest-product exports do contribute to hard-currency earnings, CMEA bloc trade, and trade with the Third World, but are not proportionate to the apparent size of the Soviet timber resource. Forest-product exports, in terms of share of all exports from the USSR, peaked in 1975, and then declined before registering a small upswing in 1985. In addition, lower-value products, such as roundwood, dominate exports. Japan plays an important role in the utilization of eastern output, and the USSR has entered into some long-term arrangements with Japan for export of eastern roundwood and chips. Two key factors, however, continue to have significance for Pacific markets (and, therefore, to continued profits from Soviet Far Eastern forests): (1) technological advance in the use of larch, and (2) limitations in Soviet ability to expand in other Pacific and Asian markets. We suggest in addition that imports of wood products *into* the USSR itself may eventually play a greater role in satisfying domestic needs for certain products and in helping to satisfy some regional needs.

CONSTRAINTS OF TECHNOLOGY

Many processes within the forest-product industries of the USSR, particularly logging and lumber, still rely on outmoded technologies. While plans call for more efficient utilization and a higher level of mechanization, evidence suggests that technology still needs much improvement. Gains have apparently been achieved in the composition board, pulp, and paper industries, partly through the importation of machinery, equipment, and entire plants.

CONSTRAINTS OF PRESSURES FROM COMPETING USERS

Growing demands are placed on Soviet forests for multipurpose utilization. To the use of forests for commercial exploitation must now be added the uses for environmental conservation, recreation, and even food. In Chapter 6, we reviewed the cultural importance of the forests to the people of the USSR and the increasing requirements by urbanites for access to recreational forest zones.

CONSTRAINTS ON ECONOMIC PLANNING TOOLS

As seen in this book, planners in Soviet forest industries have largely attempted stopgap measures to meet output targets which often lead to poor results in the longer term. Chapter 8 demonstrated that increasing depletion of accessible stocks and the eastward shift of harvesting have helped create an overall downward trend in profits for the industry, particularly in logging, lumber, and plywood. Only the periodic rise in prices has overcome the adverse effect of increased raw-material costs and driven profits back up. Desperate attempts to halt these trends in the industry have led to short-term, usually ineffective, solutions, such as reorganization of industrial ministries, reassignment of personnel, tolerance of harvesting levels beyond those specified as allowable cut, and further shifts toward peripheral forests.

Meanwhile, investment in forest industries remains low (4.3 percent of all industrial basic funds in 1984) and has declined since 1960. In addition, the system of rail transportation tariffs apparently has sent mixed signals to industrial enterprises and has not appropriately reflected the greater expenses incurred by logging in peripheral forests.

VIEWING SOVIET FORESTS IN A LARGER FRAMEWORK

In terms of domestic trends in the USSR, constraints which form the dilemma for planners in the Soviet forest sector are similar to those for all the nation's industries. The avoidance of needed economic reform and the conservative nature of decision making have long been noted as basic features of the Soviet economy. Whether General Secretary Gorbachev will indeed achieve any radical departures from past policies has yet to be determined. Two signs, however, may portend significant changes to come: (1) the recent questioning of massive shifts of investment capital toward eastern regions, and (2) the empowering of some individual enterprises to deal directly with foreign traders. As noted several times in this book, the problems we have identified have not gone unnoticed by Soviet planners themselves, who have indeed recommended plans for improvements. But the gap between the Twelfth Five-Year Plan's insights (examined in Chapter 5 above) and the reality of enterprise management may yet prove too wide for desired changes to occur.

The fortunes of the forest industries to some extent will also depend on the overall health of the Soviet economy and the level of spending undertaken by the armed forces. The wood products sector has traditionally been the "poor cousin" of the Soviet economy, receiving a small share of investment attention overall, although individual industries such as composition board, pulp, and paper have been given occasional boosts of capital investment. An increasingly strained Soviet economy cannot be expected to reverse this trend by showing greater generosity to a lagging and "nonstrategic" sector. Instead, continued squeezing of domestic consumption and constraints on the growth of exports may be expected.

In addition to these facets of the domestic framework affecting how we view the USSR's forest industries, international events will surely also have an impact. Trade relations with the West will affect the amount of machinery received and the speed with which Soviet sectors may substitute foreign for domestic technology in the forest industries. We suggest that, in terms of improving technology in the forest industries, the ability to form long-term barter arrangements and to send Soviet personnel abroad for direct training may be as important over the long run as importing individual machines.

Surprisingly, we have suggested that imports of forest products into the USSR may occur on a larger scale, particularly in the absence of more effective utilization of accessible wood and increasingly expensive long hauls by rail from peripheral regions. Scandinavia appears to be the most likely candidate for such imports, but the eastern Canadian forests and the American southern pine resource cannot be ruled out as possible foreign sources. Third World trade partners may provide specialized wood-product imports for the USSR.

Soviet forests may receive increasing attention from the world's conservation community. As deforestation comes to be viewed as a hazard for global climatic patterns, the taiga of Soviet eastern regions may come under greater scrutiny like the degradation of the world's tropical forests. With such a substantial share of the world's remaining forests, Soviet exploitation of eastern timber on a huge scale may come under criticism, not only from those who regard it as poor economic policy, but also from those who are concerned with the health of the world's ecosystems.

DOES THE DILEMMA HAVE A SOLUTION?

We believe that Soviet planners and scholars themselves have already identified changes which are needed to achieve better utilization of the Russian forests. If the Twelfth Five-Year Plan is successful in its goals for the forest sector, it will attain greater efficiency in the use of each tree felled and in the achievement of a higher level of reforestation. Waste, recovered materials, and deciduous wood will all contribute much more substantially to raw material needs.

Unfortunately, insufficient attention to actual regeneration of supply in the European-Uralian zone may persist, and eastward shifts of harvesting may continue to be an attractive interim solution. Many indications suggest, however, that planners are beginning to form differential regional strategies for development of forest industries.

To attain long-term managerial objectives, solutions must proceed within a context of overall reform in the Soviet economy. Incentives for planners and enterprise managers should take longer-term goals into account and deemphasize the dominant influence of yearly plan fulfillment. The short time horizon that discounts the value of reforestation must be overcome, and Soviet planners must finally reconcile themselves to the incorporation of a meaningful time variable into their forest accounts.

A vital element in achieving long-term stability in forest utilization will continue to be the formation of sound regional policy with respect to logging and to the location of industry. The eastern regions cannot continue to be regarded as a costless alternative to good management of accessible stands in Europe-Uralia and Central Siberia. On the other hand, the more peripheral forests will have a selective role to play in the future, depending on transportation linkages, labor supply, overall growth in local industry and population, and development of markets in the Pacific.

We stated at the beginning of this book that we did not seek to compare the performance of the forest industries of the USSR with that of other nations, but rather sought to evaluate the industries against the objectives which Soviet leaders have set for themselves. We have seen that, while the utility of the forest resource in the USSR cannot be determined by its size alone, a great potential for achieving domestic consumption and export goals may be unrealized due to institutional constraints. As noted in Chapter 3, we believe that a sustained yield of 400 million cu. m per year could be achieved from Soviet commercial forests with proper management. But as yet, such improvements in administration of forests appear to be still only on the drawing board, and a tragedy of resource waste is in the making whose cost to the Soviet economy will continue to grow and whose damage to the Russian environment will accelerate. Soviet planners may be facing a crucial choice: to remain on the path of expediency and conservatism, which will surely continue to strip the timber from the Russian forest, or to incorporate the wisdom of the long view and the need to bravely undertake changes in order to provide both wood for current needs and trees for the future.

Bibliography

Alekseyev, D. I, *et al.* (1983), *Slovar' Sokrashcheniy Russkogo Yazyka*: Moscow: Russkiy Yazyk.

Amman, R.,*et al.*, eds. (1977), *The Technological Level of Soviet Industry*, New Haven, Conn.: Yale University Press.

Anoshin, R. M.,*et al.* (1984), *Ekonomika Organizatsiya i Planirovaniye Proizvodstva v Leskhozakh*, Moscow: Lesnaya Promyshlennost'.

Anuchin, N. P. (1986), *Problemy Lesopol'zovaniya*. Moscow: Lesnaya Promyshlennost'.

Anuchin, N. P., *et al.* (1985), *Lesnaya Entsiklopediya*, 2 vols. Moscow: Sovetskaya Entsiklopediya.

Atrokhin, V. G., *et al.* (1982), *Drevesnye Porody SSSR.* Vol. 3 of *Drevesnye Porody Mira.* Moscow: Lesnaya Promyshlennost'.

Ayzenberg, E. B., and Sobolev,Yu. A. (1982), *Kompleksnye Programmy Razvitiya Vostochnykh Raionov SSSR.* Moscow: Ekonomika.

Barr, B. M. (1970), *The Soviet Wood-Processing Industry: A Linear Programming Analysis of the Role of Transportation Costs in Location and Flow Patterns.* Toronto: Univ. of Toronto Press.

Barr, B. M. (1971), "Regional Variation in Soviet Pulp and Paper Production." *Annals of the Association of American Geographers,* vol. 61 (1), pp. 45-64.

Barr, B. M. (1982), "Soviet Forest Resources: A Review and Summary." *Soviet Geography: Review and Translation,* vol. 22 (6) June, pp. 452-62.

Barr, B. M. (1983), "Regional Dilemmas and International Prospects in the Soviet Timber Industry." In *Soviet Natural Resources in the World Economy,* eds. R. G. Jensen, T. Shabad, and A. W. Wright, pp. 411-441. Chicago: Univ. of Chicago Press.

Barr, B. M. (1984), "The Soviet Forest in the 1980s: Changing Geographical Perspectives." In *Geographical Studies on the Soviet Union: Essays in Honor of Chauncy D. Harris,* eds. G. J. Demko and R. J. Fuchs, pp. 235-55. Dept. of Geography Research paper no. 211. Chicago: Univ. of Chicago.

Barr, B. M. (Forthcoming), "Perspectives on Deforestation in the USSR." In *World Forests and the Global Economy in the Twentieth Century,* eds. J. F. Richards and R. P. Tucker. Durham, N.C.: Duke Univ. Press.

Barr, B. M., and Smillie, K. (1972), "Some Spatial Interpretations of Alternative Optimal Solutions to the Transportation Problem." *The Canadian Geographer,* vol. 16 (4), pp. 356-64.

Bayzakov, S. B. (1981), *Ekonomicheskaya Otsenka Lesnykh Resursov.* Alma-Ata, USSR: Kaynar.

Bekh, I. A. (1985), "Ob Organizatsii Rekreationnogo Ispol'zovaniya Lesov," *Lesnoye Khozyaystvo,* no. 5, pp. 31-33.

Belov, S. V. (1983), *Lesovodstvo.* Moscow:Lesnaya Promyshlennost'.

Bendavid, A. (1974), *Regional Economic Analysis for Practitioners.* Rev. ed. New York: Praeger.

Blam, Yu. Sh., Babenko, T. I. and Arzymanyan, E. A. (1982), "Ekonomicheskaya Otsenka Lesnykh Resursov v Modelyakh Optimizatsii Plana Razvitiya Lesnoy i Lesopererabatyvayushchey Promyshlennosti," in *Prirodnye Resursy v Modeliakh Territorial'no-proizvodstvennykh Sistem,* eds.G. M. Mkrtchyan and S. A. Suspitsyn pp. 128-49. Novosibirsk, USSR: Nauka, Siberian Division.

Blandon, P. (1983), *Soviet Forest Industries.* Boulder, Colo.: Westview Press.

Blandon, P. (1984), "Mechanization Essential to Soviet Forest Goals," *World Wood,* August, pp. 18-19.

Bobrov, A. I. *et al.* (1984), *Proizvodstvo Voloknistykh Polufabrikatov iz Listvennoy Drevesiny.* Moscow: Lesnaya Promyshlennost'.

Bokshchanin, Yu. R. (1982), *Obrabotka i Primeneniye Drevesiny Listvennitsy.* Moscow: Lesnaya Promyshlennost'.

Borisovets, Yu. P. (1985), "Vodnym Perevozkam Lesa - Ratsional'nye Transportnye Skhemy," *Lesnaya Promyshlennost',* no. 4, pp. 3-4.

Borisovets, Yu. P. (1986), "Vodnyy Transport Lesa: Sostoyaniye i Perspektivy," *Lesnaya Promyshlennost',* no. 3, pp. 8-9.

Bozek, S. (1979), "Intensifying the Development of the USSR: Its Foreign Trade Structure." U.S. Congress, Joint Economic Committee, *Soviet Economy in a Time of Change,* vol. 2, pp. 506-25. Washington, D.C.: U.S. Govt. Printing Office.

Braden, K. (1981), *Technology Transfer to the USSR Forest Products Sector.* Unpublished doctoral dissertation. Seattle: Univ. of Washington, Department of Geography.

Braden, K. (1983), "The Role of Imported Technology in the Export Potential of Soviet Forest Products." In *Soviet Natural Resources in the World Economy,* eds. R. G. Jensen, T. Shabad, and A. W. Wright, pp. 442-63. Chicago: Univ. of Chicago Press.

Braden, K. (1986a), "Regional Shifts in Timber Harvest and Profitability in the USSR." Paper presented at Western Slavic Association Meeting, 27 March. Portland, Oregon.

Braden, K. (1986b), "Wildlife Reserves in the USSR." *Oryx,* vol. 20 (3), pp. 165-69.

Bradshaw, M. J. (1986), "Japan-USSR Trade Relations - The Implications for Western Canada." Paper presented at the Annual Meeting of the Canadian Association of Geographers, 20 June. Calgary, Canada.

Burdin, N. A., *et al.* (1980), *Spravochnik Ekonomista Lesnoy Promyshlennosti.* Moscow: Lesnaya Promyshlennost'.

Burdin, N. A. and V. M. Evdokimov (1985), *Sotsial'no-Ekonomicheskaya Effektivnost' Novoy Tekhniki v Lesnoy Promyshlennosti.* Moscow: Lesnaya Promyshlennost'.

Busygin, M. I. (1986), "Pyatiletke - Energichnyy Start," *Lesnaya Promyshlennost',* no. 1, pp. 1-3.

Buzykin, A. I., ed. (1984), *Ekologo-geograficheskiye Terminy v Lesovedenii. Slovar'-Spravochnik.* Novosibirsk: Nauka, Siberian Division.

Chernovol, A. P. (1984), "Perspektivy Razvitiya Tsellyulozno-Bumazhnoy Promyshlennosti." *Bumazhnaya Promyshlennost'*, no. 6, pp. 1-3.

Chichkanov, V. P., and Minakur, P. A. (1984), *Analiz i Prognozirovaniye Ekonomiki Regiona*. Moscow: Nauka.

Conway, S. (1982), *Logging Practices: Principles of Timber Harvesting Systems*. San Francisco: Miller Freeman Publications, Inc.

Cooper, W. (1982), "Soviet-Western Trade." U.S. Congress, Joint Economic Committee. *Soviet Economy in the 1980's: Problems and Prospects*, vol. 2, pp. 454-78. Washington, D. C.: U.S. Govt. Printing Office.

Current Digest of the Soviet Press (CDSP). (Various dates and years), weekly publication. Columbus, Ohio.

Delimov, A. I. (1972), *Ekonomika i Planirovaniye Proizvodstva Drevesno-voloknistykh i Struzhechnykh Plit*. Moscow: Lesnaya Promyshlennost'.

Demintsev, Yu. I., *et al.* (1976), *Sravnitel'nyy Analiz Rezervov Rosta Proizvoditel'nosti Truda v Lesopromkhozakh*. Moscow: VNIPIEIlesprom.

de Souza, P. (1985), "On the 'Price' of a Siberian Development." Draft for Research Paper. Gothenburg, Sweden: Univ. of Gothenburg, Department of Human and Economic Geography.

Dienes, L. (1982), "The Development of Siberian Regions: Economic Profiles, Income Flows and Strategies for Growth." *Soviet Geography: Review and Translation*, vol. 23 (4), pp. 205-44.

Dienes, L. (1983),"Regional Economic Development." In *The Soviet Economy: Toward the Year 2000*, eds. A. Bergson and H. S. Levine, pp. 218-68. London: Allen & Unwin.

Dienes, L., and Shabad, T. (1979), *The Soviet Energy System*. New York: John Wiley.

Dirks, A. Ya. (1986), "Pyatiletka Lesozagotoviteley: God Pervyy." *Lesnaya Promyshlennost'*, no. 3, pp. 1-2.

Donovan, C. W. (1976), Personal Communication. Seattle, Wash.: Bank of California, International Department.

Dorst, J. (1970), *Before Nature Dies*. Boston: Houghton Mifflin.

Drozhalov, M. M. (1979), "Postoyanno Uluchshat' Lesnoy Fond SSSR." *Lesnoye Khozyaystvo*, no. 9, pp. 41-43.

Drozhalov, M. M. (1984), "Lesnaya Niva 80-x Godov." *Lesnoye Khozyaystvo*, no. 10, pp. 59-63.

Dyrenkov, S. A. (1983), "Izmeneniye Lesnykh Biogeotsenozov pod Vliyaniyem Rekreatsionnykh Nagruzok i Vozmozhnosti ikh Regulirovaniya." In *Rekreatsionnoye lesopol'zovaniye v SSSR*, eds. L. P. Rysin and M. M. Margus, pp. 20-34. Moscow: Nauka.

United Nations (Economic Commission for Europe - Timber Committee/Food and Agriculture Organization - European Forestry Commission). 1984. *Country Fact Sheets*. Mimeo Report of International Labour Organization, Joint Committee on Forest Working Techniques and Training of Forest Workers: Fifteenth Session, 22-25 May 1984. Izmir-Cesme, Turkey.

Edel', N. S. (1986), "Kursom Intensifikatsii i Progressa." *Bumazhnaya Promyshlennost'*, no. 4, pp. 1-3.

Elanov, A. (1985), "Vsesoyuznoye Soveshchaniye po Rekreatsionnomy Ispol'zovaniyu lesov." *Lesnoye Khozyaystvo*, no. 8, pp. 76-78.

Eronen, J. (1977), "Experience in East-West Cooperation: Finland's Trade with COMECON Countries." *Geojournal,* vol. 1 (3), pp. 37–40.

Eronen, J. (1981), *Neuvostoliiton Massa- Ja Paperiteollisuuden Alueellinen Ekspansio.* Helsinki: Helsingin Kauppakorkeakoulun Julkaisuja B 50.

Eronen, J. (1982a), "Les Forêts de l'Industrie du Bois en Mongolie." *Le Courrier des Pays de l'Est,* no. 266 (Octobre), pp. 59-62.

Eronen, J. (1982b), "Soviet Pulp and Paper Industry: Factors Explaining Its Areal Expansion." *Silva Fennica,* vol. 16 (3), pp. 267-85.

Eronen, J. (1983), "Routes of Soviet Timber to World Markets." *Geoforum,* vol. 14 (2), pp. 205-10.

Eronen, J. (1984), *Location Strategy and Patterns: An Empirical Investigation of the Soviet Pulp and Paper Industry,* Series A:42. Helsinki: The Helsinki School of Economics, Acta Academiae Oeconomicae Helsingies.

Eronen, J. (1984, 1985), Personal Communications.

FAO (Food and Agriculture Organization of the United Nations). 1986. *1984 Yearbook of Forest Products, 1973-1984.* Rome: Food and Agriculture Organization of the United Nations.

Fenton, R. T., and Maplesden, F. M. (1986), *The Eastern USSR: Forest Resources and Forest Products Exports to Japan.* Forest Research Institute Bulletin no. 23. Rotorua, New Zealand: New Zealand Forest Service.

Fischer, D. (1981), "Nature Reserves of the USSR: An Inventory." *Soviet Geography, Review and Translation,* vol. 22 (8), pp. 500-22.

Fleuron, F. (1977), *Technology and Communist Culture.* New York: Praeger.

Gendel', I. M. (1982), *Vodnyy Transport Lesa Karelii.* Petrozavodsk, USSR: Kareliya.

Globe and Mail (Various issues and years), Toronto.

Glotov, V. V. (1977), *Razmeshcheniye Lesopromyshlennogo Proizvodstva.* Moscow: Lesnaya Promyshlennost'.

Goldman, M. I. (1983), "The Changing Role of Raw Material Exports and Soviet Foreign Trade." In *Soviet Natural Resources in the World Economy,* eds. R. G. Jensen, T. Shabad, and A. W. Wright, pp. 623-38. Chicago: Univ. of Chicago Press.

Green, D. and Levine, H. (1977-1978), "Soviet Machinery Imports." *Survey,* vol. 23 (2), pp. 112-25.

Gusev, N. N., *et al.* (1981), *Lesoustroystvo v SSSR.* Moscow: Lesnaya Promyshlennost'.

Haygreen, J. G., and Bowyer, J. L. (1982), *Forest Products and Wood Science: An Introduction.* Ames: Iowa State Univ. Press.

Hewett, E. A. (1983), "Soviet Primary Product Exports to CMEA and the West." In *Soviet Natural Resources in the World Economy,* eds. R. G. Jensen, T. Shabad, and A. W. Wright, pp. 639-58. Chicago: Univ. of Chicago Press.

Holliday, G. D. (1979), *Technology Transfer to the USSR, 1928-1937 and 1966-1975: The Role of Western Technology in Soviet Economic Development.* Boulder, Colo.: Westview Press.

Holowacz, J. (1968), "Forestry in the USSR: Resources, Industry and Production." *Pulp & Paper Magazine of Canada,* 6 September, pp. 2–11.

Holowacz, J. (1979), "1979 World Wood Review. USSR." *World Wood,* vol. 20 (7), pp. 23-24, 26.

Holowacz, J. (various years), Personal Communications.

Honer, T. G., and Bickerstaff, A. (1985), *Canada's Forest Area and Wood Volume Balance 1977-1981: An Appraisal of Change Under Present Levels of Management.* Victoria, B.C.: Canadian Forestry Service, Pacific Forestry Centre.

Honer, T. G.; Hegyi, F.; and Bonnor, G. M. (1985), *Forest Inventory in the USSR, l982: A report on the visit of Canadian Forest Inventory Specialists to the Soviet Union.* Forestry Technical Report 34. Ottawa: Government of Canada, Canadian Forestry Service.

Ivanyuta, V. M.; Kozhukhov, N. I.; and Moiseyev, N. A.(1983), *Ekonomika Lesnogo Khozyaystva.* Moscow: Lesnaya Promyshlennost'.

Izvestiya (Various issues and years), Moscow.

Japan Lumber Journal (Various issues and years), Tokyo, Japan: Central PO Box 1945, Tokyo 100-91.

Japan Pulp and Paper (Various issues and years), Tokyo, Japan: Tec Times Co. Ltd.

Jensen, R. G.; Shabad, T.; and Wright, A. W. eds. (1983), *Soviet Natural Resources in the World Economy.* Chicago: University of Chicago Press.

Jensen, R. G.; Shabad, T.; and Wright, A. W. (1983), "The Implications of Soviet Raw Materials for the World Economy." In *Soviet Natural Resources in the World Economy,* eds. R. G. Jensen, T. Shabad, and A. W. Wright, pp. 679-86. Chicago: Univ. of Chicago Press.

Journal of the US-USSR Trade and Economic Council (Various issues and years), New York City, U.S.A.

Kalinkin, V. N. (1984), *Gigant na Angare.* Moscow: Lesnaya Promyshlennost'.

Kanevskiy M. V., and Shaytanov, G. Ya. (1975), *Lesnoy Eksport SSSR.* Moscow: Lesnaya Promyshlennost'.

Karpov, B. M. (1976), *Analiz Raboty Lesnoy Promyshlennosti.* Moscow: VNIPIEILesprom.

Kazakov, S. V. (1984), *Leso-pererabatyvayushchiye Kompleksy.* Moscow: Stroyizdat.

Klyeshev, L. S. (1984), "Tsena na Shchepy iz Otkhodov." *Lesnaya Promyshlennost',* no. 6, pp. 24-25.

Kolesnichenko, M. V. (1981), *Lesomelioratsiya s Osnovami Lesovodstva.* Moscow: Kolos.

Kozhin, V. M., and Styazhkin, V. P. (1976), *Sebestoimost', Tseni i Rentabelnost' na Lesozagotovkakh.* Moscow: Lesnaya Promyshlennost'.

Kozhukhov, N. I. (1984), *Osnovy Upravleniya v Lesnom Khozyaystve i Lesnoy Promyshlennosti.* Moscow: Lesnaya Promyshlennost'.

Kuchko, A. A., and Krutov, V. I. (1986), "Vliyaniye Rekreatsii na Sostoyaniye Nasazhdeniy Valaama." *Lesnoye Khozyaystvo,* no. 3, pp. 44-46.

Lamb-Grays Harbor Company (1976), Interview by Braden, 23 March.

Lesnoye Khozyaystvo SSSR (1977), Moscow: Lesnaya Promyshlennost'.

Lesnoye Khozyaystvo SSSR za 50 let (1917-1967 gg.) (1967), Moscow: Lesnaya Promyshlennost'.

"Less Forestry Investment in USSR's Eleventh Plan." (1981), *World Wood*, July, pp. 18-19.

Levcik, F., and Stankovskiy, J. (1978), "Industrial Cooperation Between East and West," *Soviet and East European Foreign Trade*, vol. 14, (1-2), pp. 32-72.

Livanov, A. P. (1983), *Ekspluatatsiya Gornykh Lesov*. Moscow: Lesnaya Promyshlennost'.

Livanov, A. P., *et al.* (1980), *Perevozka Shchepy*. Moscow: Lesnaya Promyshlennost'.

Lobovikov, T. S., and Petrov, A. P. (1976), *Ekonomika Kompleksnogo Ispol'zovaniya Drevesiny*. Moscow: Lesnaya Promyshlennost'.

Margus, M. M. (1983), "Nauchnye Osnovy Ratsional'nogo Ispol'zovaniya i Okhrany Rekreatsionnykh Lesov Estonskoy SSR." In *Rekreatsionnoye Lesopol'zovaniye v SSSR*, eds. L. P. Rysin and M. M. Margus pp. 35-43. Moscow: Nauka.

Martens, J., and Young, J. (1979), "Soviet Implementation of Domestic Inventions: First Results." U.S. Congress, Joint Economic Committee, *Soviet Economy in a Time of Change*, vol. 1, pp. 472-523. Washington, D.C.: U.S. Govt. Printing Office.

Medvedev, N. A. (1986), "Yedinyy Lesnoy Kompleks." *Lesnaya Promyshlennost'*, no. 1, pp. 3-5.

Mel'nikov, V. I. (1974), "Prommashimport Celebrates Its Tenth Anniversary." *Foreign Trade*, December, pp. 38-43.

Mel'nikov, V. I. *et al.*, (1977), *Transportnye Zatraty pri Perevozke Lesnykh Gruzov Zheleznodorozhnym Transportom*. Moscow: VNIPIEIlesprom.

Mikhaylov, L. E., and Bronina, A. B. (1984), *Sbornik Normativnykh Materialov po Lesnomu Khozyaystvu*. Moscow: Lesnaya Promyshlennost'.

Mikhaylov, L. E.; Mikhalin, I. Ya.; and Tolokonnikov, V. B. (1983), *Planirovaniye Lesnogo Khozyaystva*. Moscow: Lesnaya Promyshlennost'.

Miller, J. W., Jr. (1972), "Forest Fighting on the Eastern Front in World War II." *The Geographical Review*, April, pp. 186-202.

Morozova, T. G. (1983), *Territorial'no-proizvodstvennye Kompleksy SSSR*. Moscow: Prosveshcheniye.

Mozhayev, *et al.* (1983), *Anglo-Russkiy Lesotekhnicheskiy Slovar'*. Moscow: Russkiy Yazyk.

Mugandin, S. I. (1977), *Povysheniye Effektivnosti Lesopil'nogo Proizvodstva*. Moscow: Lesnaya Promyshlennost'.

Narodnoye Khozyaystvo Estonskoy SSR v 1984 godu. Statisticheskiy Yezhegodnik (1985). Tallin, USSR: Eesti Raamat.

Narodnoye Khozyaystvo Litovskoy SSR v 1984 godu. Statisticheskiy Yezhegodnik (1985). Vil'nyus, USSR: Mintis.

Narodnoye Khozyaystvo RSFSR. Statisticheskiy Yezhegodnik (Various years), Moscow: Statistika (after 1980: Finansy i Statistika).

Narodnoye Khozyaystvo SSSR. Statisticheskiy Yezhegodnik (Various years), Moscow: Statistika (after 1980: Finansy i Statistika).

Narodnoye Khozyaystvo SSSR, 1922-1982: Yubileynyy Statisticheskiy Yezhegodnik (1982). Moscow: Finansy i Statistika.

Narodnoye Khozyaystvo Ukrainskoy SSR v 1983 godu. Statisticheskiy Yezhegodnik (1984). Kiev: Tekhnika.

Nikolayuk, V. A. (1975), "Izmeneniya v Lesnom Fonde v Resul'tate Khozyaystvennoy Deyatel'nosti." *Lesnoye Khozyaystvo,* no. 7, pp. 2-6.

Nikolayuk, V. A., *et al.* (1982), *Razmeshcheniye Lesokhozyaystvennogo Proizvodstva.* Moscow: Lesnaya Promyshlennost'.

Nikol'skiy, N. G. (1986), "Zadachi Nauchno-Tekhnicheskoy Obshchestvennosti v Novoy Pyatiletke." *Bumazhnaya Promyshlennost',* no. 3, pp. 1-3.

North, R. N., and Solecki, J. J.(1977), "The Soviet Forest Products Industry: Its Present and Potential Exports." *Canadian Slavonic Papers,* vol. 19 (3), pp. 281-311.

"Osnovnye Napravleniya Ekonomicheskogo i Sotsial'nogo Razvitiya SSSR na 1986-1990 Gody i na Period do 2000 Goda" (1986), *Ekonomicheskaya Gazeta,* no. 12, pp. 7-18.

Pankratov, A. A. (1985), "Pod'em Zatonyvshey Drevesiny," *Lesnaya Promyshlennost',* no. 8, p. 28.

Pavlov, B. I. (1972), *Tekhniko-ekonomicheskoye Proektirovaniye Predpriyatiy Lesnoy i Lesoobrabatyvayushchey Promyshlennosti.* Leningrad: LLTA (Leningradskaya Lesotekhnicheskaya Akademiya imeni Kirova).

Petrov, A. P. (1977), Personal Communication. Leningrad: LLTA (Leningradskaya Lesotekhnicheskaya Akademiya imeni Kirova).

Petrov, A. P., and Morozov, F. N., (1984), *Ekonomika Lesnoy Promyshlennosti: Uchebnik dlya Vuzov.* Moscow: Lesnaya Promyshlennost'.

Petrov, A. P., *et al.* (1986), *Lesnoy Kompleks. Voprosy Teorii i Praktiki.* Moscow: Lesnaya Promyshlennost'.

Podkovyrin, A. I. (1984), "Printsipial'no Novye Zadachi." *Bumazhnaya Promyshlennost',* no. 6, pp. 4-5.

Ponomarenko, Yu. I. (1985), "Vedeniye Khozyaystva v Rekreatsionnykh Lesakh Moskvy." *Lesnoye Khozyaystvo,* no. 7, pp. 28-30.

Ponomarev, A. D. (1963), "Lesnoy Fond SSSR." *Lesnoye Khozyaystvo,* no. 6, pp. 48-55.

Pravda (Various dates and years), Moscow.

"Proizvodstvo Tovarov Narodnogo Potrebleniya. Opyt. Problemy. Perspektivy." (1984), *Bumazhnaya Promyshlennost',* no. 6, pp. 6-7.

Prokhorchuk, I. S., *et al.* (1981), *Ekonomika Leso-obrabatyvayushchey Promyshlennosti.* Moscow: Lesnaya Promyshlennost'.

Prokhorenko, A. G. (1986), "Uluchshat' Perevozki Lesnykh Gruzov." *Lesnaya Promyshlennost',* no. 1, pp. 5-6.

Promyshlennost' SSSR, Statisticheskiy Sbornik (1957), Moscow: Statistika.

Pryde, P. R. (1972), *Conservation in the Soviet Union.* New York: Cambridge Univ. Press.

Pryde, P. R. (1977), "Recent Trends in Preserved Natural Areas in the USSR." *Environmental Conservation,* vol. 4, (3), pp. 173-77.

Pryde, P. R. (1983), "The 'Decade of the Environment' in the USSR." *Science,* vol. 220, pp. 274-79.

Pulp & Paper (Various issues and years), San Francisco: Miller Freeman Publications, Inc.

Rauma-Repola Company. 1978. Interview by Braden, 13 February. Helsinki, Finland

Rees, G. (1977), "Soviet Competition No Real Threat - Yet." *British Columbia Lumberman,* vol. 61 (6), pp. 18-19, 54-55.

Reymers, N. F., and Shtil'mark, F. R. (1978), *Osobo Okhranyemye Prirodnye Territorii.* Moscow: Mysl'.

Rodgers, A. (1955), "Changing Locational Patterns in the Soviet Pulp and Paper Industry." *Annals of the Association of American Geographers,* vol.45 (1), pp. 85-104.

Rodgers, A. (1983), "Commodity Flows, Resource Potential and Regional Economic Development: The Example of the Soviet Far East." In *Soviet Natural Resources in the World Economy,* eds. R. G. Jensen, T. Shabad, and A. W. Wright, pp. 188-213. Chicago: Univ. of Chicago Press).

"Razvitiye Otrasli. Puti Uskoreniya." (1986), *Bumazhnaya Promyshlennost',* no. 4, pp. 4-5.

Rysin, L. P. (1983), "Rekreatsionnye Lesa i Problema Optimizatsii Rekreatsionnogo Lesopol'zovaniya." In *Rekreatsionnoye Lesopol'zovaniye v SSSR,* eds. L. P. Rysin and M. M. Margus, pp. 5-20. Moscow: Nauka.

Rysin, L. P., and Margus, M. M. eds. (1983), *Rekreatsionnoye Lesopol'zovaniye v SSSR.* Moscow: Nauka.

Sagers, M. J. and M. B. Green (1985), "The Freight Rate Structure on Soviet Railroads." Economic Geography, vol. 61 (4), pp. 305-22.

Sankin, I. N., and Simakov, A. A. (1985), "V Aktivnom Poiske." *Lesnaya Promyshlennost',* no. 10, pp. 6-7.

Sapozhnikov, A. P. (1983), "Rekreatsionniye Lesopol'zovaniye v Vostochnoy Chasti Zony BAM." In *Rekreatsionnoye Lesopol'zovaniye v SSSR,* eds. L. P. Rysin and M. M. Margus, pp. 112-24. Moscow: Nauka.

Scherer, J. L., ed. (1981), *USSR Facts and Figures Annual,* vol. 5. Gulf Breeze, Fl.: Academic International Press.

Sennov, S. N. (1984), *Ukhod za Lesom: Ekologicheskiye Osnovy.* Moscow: Lesnaya Promyshlennost'.

Shabad, T. (1986), "Geographic Aspects of the New Soviet Five-year Plan, 1986-90," *Soviet Geography,* vol. 27 (1), pp. 1-16.

Shafirkin, G. I., ed. (1978), *Ekonomicheskiy Spravochnik Zheleznodorozhnika, Chast' II.* Moscow: Transport.

Sharpe, G. W.; Hendee, C. W.; and Sharpe, W. F. (1986), *Introduction to Forestry.* 5th ed. New York: McGraw-Hill.

Shcheglov, V. F.,*et al.* (1984), *Spravochnik Mastera Lesopil'nogo Proizvodstva.* Moscow: Lesnaya Promyshlennost'.

Shchukin, G. S. (1984), "Na Osnove Shirokogo Sotrudnichestva" *Bumazhnaya Promyshlennost',* no. 6, pp. 7-8.

Shiyanskaya, K. F. (1985), "The Geography of Soviet Water Transportation by Combined River-Sea-Going Vessels." *Soviet Geography,* vol. 26 (10), pp. 721-27.

Shutov, I. V., *et al.,* eds. (1984), *Lesnye Plantatsii (Uskorennoye Vyrashchivaniye Yeli i Sosny).* Moscow: Lesnaya Promyshlennost'.

Sinitsyn, S. G. (1976), *Lesnoy Fond i Organizatsiya Ispol'zovaniya Lesnykh Resursov SSSR.* Moscow: Lesnaya Promyshlennost'.

Sinitsyn, S. G., and Ssorin, V. A. (1967), "Materialy Ucheta Lesnogo Fonda pri Prognozakh Lesopol'zovaniya." *Lesnoye Khozyaystvo,* no. 12, pp. 51-55.

Smith, H. (1976), *The Russians.* New York: New York Times Book Co..

Sotsialisticheskaya Industriya (Various dates and years), Moscow.

"Sotsialisticheskiye Obyazatel'stva Kollektivov Predpriyatiy i Organizatsiy Lesnogo Khozyaystva na 1986 godu." (1986), *Lesnoye Khozyaztvo,* no. 3, pp. 3-4.

Soule, M. H., and Taaffe, R. N. (1985), "Mathematical Programming Approaches to the Planning of Siberian Regional Economic Development: A Nonmathematical Survey." *Soviet Economy,* vol. 1 (1) (January-March), pp. 75-98.

Sovetskiy Entsiklopedicheskiy Slovar' (1982), Moscow: Sovetskaya Entsiklopediya.

Sovetskiy Soyuz: Politiko-ekonomicheskiy Spravochnik (1975), Moscow: Politizdat.

Soviet Geography, Washington, D.C.: V. H. Winston & Sons, Inc.

Spravochnik Lesnichego (1965), Moscow: Lesnaya Promyshlennost'.

SSSR v Tsifrakh v 1982 godu (1983), Moscow: Finansy i Statistika.

Stepin, V. V. (1982), *Ekonomicheskiye Osnovy Prirodo-pol'zovaniya.* Moscow: Lesnaya Promyshlennost'.

Sutton, A. C. (1973), *Western Technology and Soviet Economic Development 1945 to 1965.* Palo Alto, Calif.: Stanford Univ., Hoover Institution Press.

Sutton, W. R. J. (1975), "The Forest Resources of the USSR; Their Exploitation and Their Potential." *Commonwealth Forestry Review,* no. 160 (June), pp. 110-38.

Tarasov, A. I. (1986), *Rekreatsionnoye Lesopol'zovaniye.* Moscow: Agropromizdat .

Thornton, J. (1980), *Soviet Resource Valuation and the Efficiency of Resource Use.* Discussion Paper no. 26. Washington, D. C.: Association of American Geographers Project on Soviet Natural Resources in the World Economy.

Timofeyev, N. V. (1979), *Osvoyeniye Lesnykh Bogatstv.* Moscow: Lesnaya Promyshlennost'.

Timofeyev, N. V., ed. (1980), *Lesnaya Industriya SSSR.* Moscow: Lesnaya Promyshlennost'.

Timofeyev, N. V., et al. eds. (1967), *Les - Natsional'noye Bogatstvo Sovetskogo Naroda.* Moscow: Lesnaya Promyshlennost'.

Toda, Y. (1979), "Technology Transfer to the USSR: The Marginal Productivity Differential and the Elasticity of Intra-Capital Substitution." *Journal of Comparative Economics,* no. 3, pp. 181–94.

Tonyayev, V. I. (1984), *Geografiya Vnutrennikh Vodnykh Putey SSSR.* 3rd ed. Moscow: Transport.

Tseplyayev, V. P. (1965), *Lesnoye Khozyaystvo SSSR.* Moscow: Lesnaya Promyshlennost'.

Tseplyayev, V. P., and Gusev, N. N. (1967), "Lesnye Resursy Sovetskogo Soyuza," *Lesnoye Khozyaystvo,* no. 12, pp. 45-51.

Turushev, V. G. (1975), *Teknologicheskiye Osnovy Avtomatizirovannogo Proizvodstva Pilomaterialov.* Moscow: Lesnaya Promyshlennost'.

UNIDO (United Nations Industrial Development Organization) (1983), *The USSR Forest and Woodworking Industries. Sectoral Working Paper Series,* no. 7, UNIDO/IS.406. Mimeo. Vienna: Sectoral Studies Branch, Division for Industrial Studies.

United Nations (United Nations Economic Commission for Europe/Food and Agriculture Organization of the United Nations) (1982), *Conversion Factors for Forest Products.* Supplement 12 to vol. 34 of the *Timber Bulletin for Europe.* Geneva, Switzerland.

U.S. Congress, Joint Economic Committee (1979), *Soviet Economy in a Time of Change,* 2 vols. Washington, D.C.: U.S. Govt. Printing Office.

U.S. Congress, Joint Economic Committee (1982), *Soviet Economy in the 1980's: Problems and Prospects,* 2 vols. Washington, D.C.: U.S. Govt. Printing Office.

USDA (U.S. Department of Agriculture, Foreign Agricultural Service) (1983), Mimeo. *USSR: Annual Forestry Report - 1983.* Moscow.

"Uskorennoye Razvitiye Ekonomiki Sibiri i Dal'nego Vostoka" (1985), *Ekonomicheskaya Gazeta,* no. 37 (September), p. 1.

Veselov, L. I. (1985), "Povysheniye Effektivnosti Ispol'zovaniya Makulatury v Narodnom Khozyaystve." *Bumazhnaya Promyshlennost',* no. 7, pp. 1-3.

Vneshnyaya Torgovlya SSSR. Statisticheskiy Sbornik (Various years), Moscow: Statistika (after 1980: Finansy i Statistika).

Vneshnyaya Torgovlya SSSR. 1922-1981: Yubileynyy Statisticheskiy Sbornik (1982). Moscow: Finansy i Statistika.

Vorob'yev, G. I. (1982), *Effektivnost' Lesnogo Khozyaystva SSSR.* Moscow: Lesnaya Promyshlennost'.

Vorob'yev, G. I.,*et al.* (1979), *Ekonomicheskaya Geografiya Lesnykh Resursov SSSR.* Moscow: Lesnaya Promyshlennost'.

Vorob'yev, G. I., *et al.* (1980), *Ekonomika Lesnogo Khozyaystva SSSR.* Moscow: Vysshaya Shkola.

Vorob'yev, G. I., *et al.* (1984), *Lesnoye Khozyaystvo Mira.* Moscow: Lesnaya Promyshlennost'.

Voyevoda, I. N. (1980), *Lesnaya i Lesopererabatyvayushchaya Promyshlennost' Sibiri.* Novosibirsk: Nauka, Siberian Division.

Weck, J. (1966), *Dictionary of Forestry in Five Languages - German - English - French - Spanish - Russian.* Amsterdam: Elsevier Scientific Publishing Co.

Weitzman, M. (1979), "Soviet Postwar Economic Growth and Capital-Labor Subsitution." *American Economic Review,* vol. 60 (4), pp. 676-92.

Williston, E. M. (1976), *Lumber Manufacturing: The Design and Operation of Sawmills and Planer Mills.* San Francisco: Miller Freeman Publications, Inc.

Wolf, T. and Hewett, E. A.(1982), "A Puzzle in Soviet Foreign Trade Statistics." U.S. Congress, Joint Economic Committee, *Soviet Economy in the 1980's: Problems and Prospects,* vol. 2, pp. 575-87. Washington, D.C.: U.S. Govt. Printing Office.

World Wood (Various issues and years), San Francisco: Miller Freeman Publications, Inc.

Wright, A. W. (1983), "Soviet Natural Resource Exports and the World Market." In *Soviet Natural Resources in the World Economy,* eds. R. G.

Jensen, T. Shabad, and A. W. Wright, pp. 617-22. Chicago: Univ. of Chicago Press.

Yakunin, A. G. (1985), "Luchshye Ispol'zovat' Lesa Evropeyskoy Chasti SSSR." *Lesnaya Promyshlennost'*, no. 6, pp. 1-2.

"Za Povysheniye Effektivnosti Ispol'zovaniya Drevesiny i yeye Otkhodov v Tsellyulozno-Bumazhnoy Promyshlennosti" (1985), *Bumazhnaya Promyshlennost'*, no. 1, pp. 1-3.

Index